"This Long Disease,
My Life"

"This Long Disease, My Life"

Alexander Pope and the Sciences

By MARJORIE NICOLSON
AND
G.S. ROUSSEAU

Princeton University Press
Princeton, New Jersey
1968

Preface

DURING the Restoration years laymen had been more "science conscious" than at any time since Galileo's *Sidereus Nuncius* in 1610 had revealed a new cosmic universe. By the time Pope came to write, some of the excitement aroused by the establishment of the Royal Society of London and the discovery of another universe of the small through the microscopic observations of such men as Robert Hooke and Antony van Leeuwenhoek had subsided, settling to an intelligent interest on the part of laymen in the scientific world around them. Pope was not a "scientific poet" to the extent we find a number of self-conscious writers after the death of Sir Isaac Newton in 1727, but, as we have pointed out, a study of his scientific interests is more legitimate than might be the case among some of his contemporaries, because of his membership in the Scriblerus Club and the amount of time he devoted to editing *The Memoirs of Martinus Scriblerus* and various *Miscellanies* in which other Scriblerian fragments appeared, some concerned with scientific satire.

Of the various sciences, medicine was the one to which Pope referred most frequently, since he was a chronic invalid all his life. Every student of his works knows that Pope was a hunchback, and the reader of his letters quickly becomes aware of his numerous allusions to ill health of various sorts. It seems strange that, while literary and medical historians have written widely on the physical and psychological vagaries of many other men of letters, almost nothing has been said about Pope's health and the extent to which it affected his work. We have prefaced our study of his scientific interests with a medical "case history." Evidence for his symptoms is drawn largely from the *Correspondence*.

In preparing the "case history" we have had the assistance of various medical advisers, to all of whom we extend our warm thanks. Three of them—Dr. Herman Tarnower of the Scarsdale Medical Group, Dr. Marian Ropes, Associate Clinical Professor of Medicine in the Harvard University Medical School, and Dr. Victor A. McKusick of the Moore Clinic, Johns Hopkins Hospital—have read the entire "case history" and advised us on the interpretation of various of Pope's symptoms. Dr. Guy Leadbetter and Dr. T. Fiumara of the Department of Urology, Massachusetts General Hospital, considered particularly the operation William Cheselden performed on Pope, with Pope's descriptions of his urinary troubles both before and after the operation. Dr. Gilbert Daniels of the Massachusetts General Hospital assisted us in several ways. Dr. McKusick, a leading authority on dwarfism of all types and author of *Cardiovascular Sound in Health and Disease*, a widely used text on heart sounds and murmurs, as well as a paper on the "illness of the great and near-great" (*Bull. Hist. Med.* [1955], 29.377), made himself particularly responsible for the relationship of kyphoscoliosis to Pope's illnesses, and has permitted us to quote his diagnosis in our text.

In addition to an analysis of Pope's various symptoms, we have discussed his chief physician and surgeon, Richard Mead and William Cheselden, and have attempted to throw more light on the supposed "quack," Dr. Thomas Thompson, who attended Pope on his deathbed while the doctor was still comparatively unknown in England. Although Thompson's treatment was technically correct at the period for the condition he diagnosed, there seems little question that he somewhat hastened Pope's death, since that frail physique was incapable of tolerating the violent purgation to which it was subjected.

The "case history" is followed by "Pope and Medicine," a study of five medical themes or episodes in his work, ranging from the circulation and transfusion of blood, through his interest in animalitarianism and the case of Mary Toft, "the rabbit woman," to the disputed "Mummius" episode in *The Dunciad*. The central and most extensive section is concerned with "Pope and Astronomy," of all the sciences the most important to his imagination. This was first treated in 1951 by Professor George Sherburn in a paper, "Pope and 'The Great Shew of Nature.' " Various materials on the subject have come to light since that time. We have gone into much more detail than was possible for Professor Sherburn in 1951, treating Whiston at length, and suggesting that Pope attended more than one Whiston lecture— indeed was apparently preparing under his tutelage for the eclipse of April 22, 1715, the first total solar eclipse over England in 575 years, as Edmund Halley pointed out to the Royal Society. In "Pope and Astronomy" and also in "The Mary Toft Case," we have added some details to what has been known about the Scriblerus papers, sometimes shifting the attribution to a particular author, and mentioning a few hitherto unrecognized fragments. The final section deals with Pope's interest in other sciences than medicine and astronomy. Here limitations in those interests become apparent. With the exception of medicine, the biological sciences are seldom reflected in his works. Physics is limited to certain aspects Pope drew from Newton. He shows some of the interest of his age in microscopy, but his eyesight was so defective that he could have done little in observing the minute in Nature. As we have suggested, geology might have become as engrossing to him as astronomy, had he discovered it earlier.

The writing of this volume has been the work of Marjorie Nicolson. Much of the research was done by G. S. Rousseau, first in libraries on our eastern seaboard, then in London at the British Museum, the Royal Society of London, the Royal College of Physicians, the Royal College of Surgeons, and the Wellcome Medical Historical Library and Museum. To the staffs of all these libraries, as well as those of Cambridge and Oxford, we express our appreciation, and mention for special assistance Philip Wade, Esq., Librarian, Royal Society of Medicine; Dr. A. Wright, the

Wellcome Medical Historical Library; W. Le Fanu, Esq., Librarian of the Royal College of Surgeons; L. M. Payne, Esq., Librarian of the Royal College of Physicians; Ian Willison, Esq., Superintendent of the North Library, the British Museum; Miss Marjorie G. Wynne, Librarian, the Beinecke Library, Yale University; Dr. William H. Bond, Librarian, the Houghton Library, Harvard University. We offer particular thanks to the staff of the Firestone Library, Princeton University, and to various Princeton graduate students, particularly Herbert Williams.

We are very appreciative of the fact that Sir Zachary Cope, F.R.C.S. sent us information and materials. Professor Robert Halsband of Columbia University was good enough to answer a number of questions, particularly about Lady Mary Wortley Montagu. Professor Louis Landa of Princeton University assisted with answers to questions and the loan of some of his books. Particular gratitude is due Professor James L. Clifford, Columbia University, who during a sabbatical year loaned his admirable Pope library to Marjorie Nicolson, where it became so much a part of her office at the Institute for Advanced Study that she almost resented its return after fifteen months of daily use. Wandering scholars who have officially retired cannot carry their libraries from pillar to post.

In this volume all references to Pope's letters, unless otherwise noted, are to *The Correspondence of Alexander Pope*, edited by George Sherburn (Oxford: Clarendon Press, 1956). References to his poetry, unless otherwise noted, are to the Twickenham edition (London: Methuen, New Haven: Yale University Press, 1939-61, some volumes reprinted or reset, 1958-65).

G. S. ROUSSEAU
Cambridge, Mass.
August 1967

MARJORIE NICOLSON
The Institute for Advanced Study, Princeton, N.J.
August 1967

Contents

Introduction

"Satire on scientific topics," wrote Professor George Sherburn in 1934,[1] discussing the origin of the Scriblerus Club, "had been a commonplace of the time since the founding of the Royal Society; and satire on pedantry with regard to classical literature had existed long before the *Battle of the Books*, which 'battle' the Scriblerus Club more or less inherited. But Pope knew nothing of science." Professor Sherburn had changed his mind by 1951, when he concluded his essay on "Pope and 'The Great Shew of Nature'":

Pope shows a reverence for Universal Nature that is both inspiring and noble. The "scarlet-circled eyes" of the pheasant and other particular details appear in his verse largely by accident, and not much would be lost if they did not appear at all. One cannot, however, make that remark concerning his glimpses of the millennium, and his symbolic use of astronomical images, which open wide visions in a spirit of lofty cosmic reverence.[2]

A study of the effect of science on poetic imagination is even more legitimate in Pope's case than it might be with some of his contemporaries, though it would be difficult to find a poet in the late seventeenth or early eighteenth centuries who was not to some extent "science conscious." Pope's great-grandfather, who died in 1633, might have shared in the popular excitement caused by Galileo's discovery of a new cosmos, his father in the interest aroused

[1] *The Early Career of Alexander Pope* (Oxford: Clarendon Press, 1934), p. 80.
[2] In *The Seventeenth Century: Studies in the History of English Thought and Literature from Bacon to Pope, in honor of Richard Foster Jones* (Stanford: Stanford University Press, 1951), p. 315.

1

by Robert Hooke and other microscopists during the early Restoration years and in that occasioned by the foundation of the Royal Society of London and its publication of the *Philosophical Transactions,* frequently read by laymen as well as by scientists. Seriously, satirically, fancifully, literary imagination caught fire from the then New Science. By the time Pope began to write, some of the first fine careless rapture of the Restoration years had died down and much of the novelty had given way to quieter acceptance of scientific theories and ideas.

In Pope's case we have more specific and certain knowledge of his acquaintance with such theories and discoveries than we have of that of some of his contemporaries. We know of his close association, early in his literary career, with the Scriblerus Club and with the genesis and development of *The Memoirs of Martinus Scriblerus.* Even though it is impossible to determine with certainty what sections of the *Memoirs* Pope may originally have written, the venture had originated in a suggestion made by him. We know too that the youthful Pope and John Gay were involved in the Club with Jonathan Swift and Dr. John Arbuthnot, twenty years their seniors, and that Pope collaborated to some extent with Gay and Arbuthnot in the farce *Three Hours after Marriage,* which paralleled the kind of satire they had practiced in the *Memoirs.* The influence of Swift on Pope was great. The younger man knew the satires on philosophy and science in *The Battle of the Books* and *A Tale of a Tub,* and was better aware than anyone, with the possible exception of Dr. Arbuthnot, of the extent to which *Gulliver's Travels* was an outgrowth of the *Memoirs.* Even if we can never determine Pope's contributions to the first version of the *Memoirs,* we know that he mulled over them for long hours during a period of years and that it was he who finally prepared them for publication in the form in which we have known them, he too who devoted periods of time to the editing and publishing of various *Miscellanies* that were developed from them.

On the other hand, we must remember that Alexander

Pope was largely self-educated. By the time he might have attended a university, some aspects of "science" as we understand it were being taught in institutions of higher learning. Had it not been for his health, on the one hand, his religion on the other, Pope might have fallen under the influence of an undergraduate teacher who would have inflamed his imagination as William Whiston was to do. It is remarkable, indeed, that Pope drew as much as he did from Newton's *Opticks*, from which he coined a number of figures well before other English poets and before he came in contact with the Scriblerians. Had he followed other courses as assiduously as he seems to have followed Whiston's, he might well have written other poems as great as the first Epistle of *An Essay on Man*. Popular courses were springing up in London, in part thanks to the attention Whiston had attracted, but the death of Pope's father in 1717 and increasing attendance upon his bereaved mother put an end to London courses on popular science.

Because of his semi-invalidism, medicine was naturally the science that most affected Pope throughout his life. We begin our study with a medical "case history," in which we attempt to give an account of his various ills, the most important of which was, of course, spinal curvature. This is followed by "Pope and Medicine," a study of various medical themes or figures which appear in his works. The central part of this study is devoted to "Pope and Astronomy," the effect of Whiston's lectures on Pope's imagination and the recurrence of various astronomical themes in the works of some other Scriblerians. This is followed by "Pope and Other Sciences," a study of the recurrence in his works of themes drawn from sciences other than medicine and astronomy. Less pervasive than medical or astronomical themes, these show nevertheless that Pope took a highly intelligent interest in various scientific developments of his time.

Part One
A Medical Case History
of Alexander Pope

A Medical Case History of
Alexander Pope

I

PROBLEMS of Milton's blindness have been considered in detail by literary and medical historians. Eighteenth-century scholars have concerned themselves with Swift's physical and mental condition in his later years. Samuel Johnson's "King Evil" has been discussed, while amateur—and occasionally professional—psychiatrists have spent ink on his possible masochism and other aberrations. The apparently ironic contrast between the supposed "Age of Reason" and frequent cases of insanity among eighteenth-century writers has led to studies of William Cowper, Christopher Smart, and others.

Curiously enough, little attention has been devoted to the physical vagaries of Alexander Pope,[1] in spite of the fact that students know he was a hunchback, and readers of his letters can hardly charge him with gross exaggeration

---

[1] Separate studies, usually brief, include: W.R. Bett, *The Infirmities of Genius* (London: Christopher Johnson, 1952), pp. 161-69, a slight and superficial treatment; a still more negligible derivative from this, *Famous People in Their Illnesses* (London: Roche Products, Ltd., 1964), pp. 9-11; a more authoritative though still brief treatment, "Alexander Pope: Poet and Cripple," by Sir Arthur Salusbury Mac-Nalty, K.C.B., M.D. Oxon., F.R.C.P., F.R.C.S., *Proceedings of the Royal Society of Medicine*, Vol. 51 (May 7, 1958), 601-604. Philip Wade, Esq., Librarian of the Royal Society of Medicine, was good enough to send us copies of these. "Famous People and their Illnesses" has been reprinted in *Brit. Rheum. Arth. Rev.*, Vol. V (June 1960). An article that has so far eluded us is "Alexander the Little." Our reference is *Clinical Excerpts*, XII, No. 9 (1939), 3-12. It is not in the British journal of that name, copies of which we have examined in

when he spoke of "this long Disease, my Life."[2] Realizing his sensitivity, we should not expect to find an extended account, in his own words, of his deformity and puny stature, as we find a full history of other illnesses. Modern biographers have paid so little attention to the first[3] that we shall attempt, so far as possible, to develop a "case history" of his basic problem of curvature of the spine, the result of tuberculosis of the bone.

The most frequently quoted description of Pope's mature physical appearance is that of Sir Joshua Reynolds,[4] reflecting the artist's observant eye:

> He was about four feet, six inches high, very humpbacked and deformed. He wore a black coat, and, according to the fashion of the time, had on a little sword. He had a large and very fine eye, and a long handsome nose; his mouth had those peculiar marks which are always found in the mouths of crooked persons; and the muscles which ran across the cheek were so strongly marked that they seemed like little chords.

---

the British Museum. There was an American house journal of that name, which we have not been able to see.

[2] The phrase is usually quoted from *An Epistle to Dr. Arbuthnot*, line 132. Pope had also used it earlier in a letter to Aaron Hill, March 14, 1731 (*Correspondence*, III. 182), although since he had written sections of the *Epistle* still earlier, it is impossible to determine priority. He wrote to Hill: "But a series of Infirmities (for my whole Life has been but one long Disease) has hinder'd me from following your Advices."

[3] Professor Sherburn, for instance, in *The Early Career of Alexander Pope* (Oxford: Clarendon Press, 1934), pp. 42-43, says only this of Pope's deformity: "Too much study was the usual explanation of the increasing fragility, recurrent headaches, *and final curvature of the spine* that ruined the poet's physique. . . . This picture of the young Pope calmly sitting down to inform 'some of his more particular friends' of his 'full expectation of death in a short time' *may be the result of the tubercular infection (Pott's disease) that eventually deformed him, or the result of some particular illness.*" (The italics are ours.)

[4] Quoted G.B. Hill, *Lives of the English Poets* (Oxford: Clarendon Press, 1905), III. 197 from Prior's *Malone*, p. 429.

One of the few occasions on which Pope entered into description of his physical infirmities was in *An Epistle to Dr. Arbuthnot*:[5]

> There are, who to my Person pay their court,
> *I cough like Horace, and tho' lean, am short,*
> *Ammon's great Son one shoulder had too high,*
> Such O*vid's* nose, and 'Sir! you have an *Eye*—'
> Go on, obliging Creatures, make me see
> All that disgrac'd my Betters, met in me.

In the same *Epistle* (line 103) occurs a momentary bitter reminiscence of the contrast between his own physical insignificance and the statuesque carriage of the once admired, now detested, Lady Mary Wortley Montagu, when "Sapho" says: "I too could write, and I am twice as tall." In his *Imitations of Horace*[6] Pope wrote:

> *Weak tho' I am of limb*, and short of sight,
> Far from a Lynx, *and not a Giant quite,*
> I'll do what Mead and Cheselden advise,
> To keep these limbs, and to preserve these eyes.

In much less caustic vein were Pope's allusions to his physique in two early papers on "The Club of Little Men," published in the *Guardian*.[7] Here Pope reported that "a

---

[5] *Imitations of Horace*, in *Works*, IV, 104, lines 115 ff. (The italics are ours.)

[6] *Epistle* I.i. lines 49-52, ed. cit., p. 283. One of Pope's few references to his physique was, curiously enough, made to a woman. Pope seldom mentioned his physical conditions to women, though other letters teem with them. Writing to Judith Cowper, October 18, 1722 (*Correspondence*, II. 138), he said: "I challenge a kind of Relation to you on the *Soul's* side . . . and if you can Overlook an ugly *Body* (that stands much in the way of any Friendship, when it is between different Sexes) I shall hope to find you a True & Constant Kinswoman in Apollo."

[7] *Guardian* Nos. 91, 92 (June 25, 26, 1713), in Ault, *Prose Works*, I. 121-29. (Italics here are as in Ault.) In a mood somewhat similar to this was Pope's reference in the spring of 1710 (*Correspondence*, I. 89-90) to the recent deaths of "Mr. Litton" and William Viscount Lumley, both apparently undersized. Dr. Victor McKusick, who is mentioned in the Preface as having read this "case history," wrote us that he was delighted to read of "The Club of Little Men." He

Sett of us have formed a Society, who are sworn to *Dare to be Short,* and boldly bear out the Dignity of Littleness under the Noses of those Enormous Engrossers of Manhood, those Hyperbolical Monsters of the Species, the tall Fellows that overlook us." Invitations were sent "to those of a Stature not exceeding *five Foot,*" several of whom declined, insisting that they were over-tall. Light though these little papers are in tone, they reflect problems experienced by any abnormally small human being, and sometimes, to an interesting degree, anticipate experiences of Gulliver. One wonders, indeed, what details Swift might have picked up for his Lilliputians and Brobdingnagians from watching actual experiences of his "little friend." The first action of the Club was to replace chairs, stools and tables designed for the *"gross of Mankind,"* and to lower the doors to the club rooms, "so as to admit no Man of above five Foot high, without brushing his Foretop." Among the "most eminent Persons of our Assembly . . . a little Poet, a little Lover, a little Politician, and a little Heroe," we readily identify Pope as the poet, Dick Distick, whom the Club elected President. Before the new furniture arrived, we see Pope, as he must often have felt himself, in normal surroundings: "The President's whole Body was sunk in the Elbow-Chair, and when his Arms were spread over it, he appeared (to the great lessening of his Dignity) like a *Child* in a *Go-cart*: It was also so wide in the Seat, as to give a Wag Occasion of saying, that notwithstanding the President sate in it, there was a *Sede Vacante.*"

The most reminiscent passage is one in the second essay, describing Dick Distick's election to the presidency: ". . . not only as he is the shortest of us all, but because he has entertain'd so just a Sense of the Stature, as to go generally in Black that he may appear yet Less. Nay, to that Perfection is he arrived, that he *stoops* as he walks. The Figure

---

continued: "In the course of study of dwarfism of all types, I have had many dealings with a similar present-day organization, Little People of America, Inc. The psychologic reactions of those who join and of those who decline invitations are precisely those found with Pope's organization."

of the Man is odd enough; he is a lively little Creature, with long Arms and Legs: A Spider is no ill Emblem of him. He has been taken at a distance for a *small Windmill*."

The Club of Little Men prided itself on ancestors of old: "Little *David* that conquered the mighty *Goliah*, and little *Luxembourg* that made *Lewis* XIV. a *Grand Monarque*, never forgetting Little *Alexander the Great*." The Club's philosophy of history sounds like that of John Donne in the *Anniversaries*:

mankinde decayes so soone,
We' are scarce our Fathers shadowes cast at noone,

but the Little Men were optimists:

It is the unanimous Opinion of our whole Society, that since the Race of Mankind is granted to have de-creas'd in Stature from the beginning to this present, it is the Intent of Nature it self, that Men should be little; and we believe, that all Human Kind shall at last *grow down* to *Perfection*, that is to say, be reduced to our own Measure.

Even passing descriptions of Pope's physical infirmities by others are proof enough that the poet's appearance was grotesque. Satirists naturally did not hesitate to emphasize deficiencies in his physique, as shown by the anonymous author of a *Martiniad*:[8]

At Twickenham, chronicles remark,
There dwelt a little parish clerk,
A peevish wight, full fond of fame,
And Martin Scribbler was his name.
Meagre and wan and steeple-crown'd,
His visage long and shoulders round;
His crippled corpse two spindle-pegs
Support, instead of human legs;
His shrivelled skin's of dusky grain,
A cricket's voice and monkey's brain.

[8] Quoted MacNalty, p. 603.

11

In spite of James Thomson's obvious admiration for Pope, lines in the *Castle of Indolence* emphasize the grotesquerie:

> He came, the bard, a little Druidwight,
> Of wither'd aspect; but his eye was keen,
> With sweetness mix'd. In russet brown bedight,
> As is his sister of the copses green,
> He crept along, unpromising of mien,
> Gross he who judges so.[9]

Most cruel of all, considering the source, were "Verses addressed to the Imitator of Horace. By a Lady," in a manuscript in the British Museum, supposedly written by Lady Mary Wortley Montagu and Lord Hervey in March 1733:

> But as thou [Pope] hat'st, be hated by mankind,
> And with the emblem of thy crooked mind
> Marked on thy back, like Cain, by God's own hand,
> Wander like him, accursed through the land.

Other familiar details of Pope's physique are largely drawn from Samuel Johnson, who paraphrased earlier biographers, but since they describe the mature man, we shall leave them for later discussion and concern ourselves at present with the condition that crippled Pope in early youth. Of this we have no contemporary account. W. R. Bett, in "The Infirmities of Genius," speaks of "Alexander's indulgent parents, both of whom were forty-six years of age when their puny child was born."[10] The mother, formerly Editha Turner, was in her forty-sixth year. The father was probably forty-two. As the family tomb demonstrates, the poet himself was responsible for the confusion about the ages of his parents.[11] Sir Arthur Salusbury Mac-

---

[9] *Castle of Indolence*, Canto II, xxxii, in *Complete Poetical Works*, ed. J.L. Robertson (Oxford: Clarendon Press, 1908), p. 290.

[10] Bett, *Infirmities of Genius*, p. 161.

[11] On Pope's confusion about his mother's age, see *Correspondence*, III. 117, 278. The age of the father on the family tombstone was given as 75, while he was actually 71 when he died. The poet dated his mother's birth as 1640 rather than 1642 and spoke of her age at

Nalty repeats a passing remark made by Owen Ruffhead in his eighteenth-century *Life of Pope,* and repeated in modern times by "George Paston," to the effect that his father was also a hunchback, for which there is no contemporary evidence, so far as we have been able to learn. On these matters Dr. Victor McKusick writes us: "My interests in hereditary diseases made me focus on the comment that the father was also hunchbacked but I know of no hereditary disease that accounts satisfactorily for the severe affliction in Pope. I also tried to make something of the advanced parental ages but could not attach any specific genetic significance to them."

There is no shred of evidence for Bett's statement that a "puny child" was born to Alexander Pope's middle-aged parents. Indeed Pope's first portrait—a charming anonymous one at an early age—is a clear refutation, since here was an obviously handsome, unusually bright and lively child.[12] His mother was quoted as saying that "he was exactly like that picture."

---

death as 93 rather than 91. For the inscription on the tombstone see *An Epistle to Dr. Arbuthnot,* line 381, *Imitations of Horace,* p. 125. Sherburn says (*Early Career,* p. 30) : "One wonders if, when he married his second wife, the father added four years to his age so that Editha Turner might seem to take an elder to herself as husband."

12 Joseph Spence, *Observations, Anecdotes, and Characters of Books and Men,* ed. James M. Osborn, 2 vols. (Oxford: Clarendon Press, 1966) , I, 5-6: "He was a child of particularly sweet temper and had a great deal of sweetness in his look when he was a boy. This is very evident in the picture drawn for him when he was about ten years old, in which his face is round, plump, pretty, and of a fresh complexion. I have often heard Mrs. Pope say that he was then exactly like that picture, as I have been told by himself that it was the perpetual application he fell into, about two years afterwards, that changed his form and ruined his constitution. The laurel branch in that picture was not inserted originally, but was added long after by Jervas." William Kurtz Wimsatt, *The Portraits of Alexander Pope* (New Haven and London: Yale University Press, 1965) uses the portrait as a frontispiece, dating it "*ca.* 1695." He says, p. 5: "An inscription in orange paint in the upper left corner, 'A. Pope. Anno Aetatis, 7' is presumably not original, but is nevertheless early. Mannock's reference to 'a picture drawn for him when about ten years old' may indicate that the inscription is later than 1730. The face, plump and

Presumably about his twelfth year occurred the changes in his physique that led his elderly correspondent, William Wycherley, to speak affectionately of his "little, tender, crazy Carcase."[13] Of the first appearance and early progress of curvature of the spine we have no contemporary evidence. Pope and various contemporaries attributed the change in his physical condition to incessant study. Spence reported Father William Mannock as saying: "I have been told that it was the perpetual application he fell into, about two years afterwards [i.e., the painting of the early portrait] that changed his form and ruined his constitution." Pope was reported as telling Spence that "his perpetual application (after he set to study of himself) " reduced him in four years' time to so bad a state of health, "that after trying physicians for a good while in vain, he resolved to give way to his distemper." With characteristic adolescent sense of drama he wrote letters to take a last farewell of his more particular friends; and among the rest, one to the Abbé Southcote.[14] The Abbé went immediately to Dr. Radcliffe, who ordered that Pope "apply less and to ride every day, and the following his advice soon restored him to his health."

Although Professor Sherburn defined Pope's affliction as "Pott's disease," he did so only in passing, with no detail other than the adjective "tubercular." A more technical

---

fair, while yet so manifestly Popean, is one good indication that it is indeed the picture described by Mannock. The laurel branch is another. It would hardly have been put in the hand of a seven-year-old boy. No doubt it *was* added by Jervas. . . ." All references to Spence's *Anecdotes* are to Osborn's edition.

13 *Correspondence*, I. 55, February 19, 1708/9. One reason for our suggesting the age of twelve is that Pope had attained the height of four feet, six inches, which, according to modern pediatric charts, would be about the height of a normal twelve-year-old. After the onset of "Pott's disease," he did not grow taller. In addition are the comments we mention below about a severe illness from his twelfth to sixteenth year, which was not the result of overstudy but marked the beginning of the spinal curvature.

14 Spence, *Anecdotes*, I, pp. 29-30. Although Thomas Southcote's name appears occasionally in Pope's letters from June 25, 1711 on, and although Pope mentioned letters that passed between them, none seems to be extant.

term may be found in the article by Sir Arthur Salusbury MacNalty:[15] "In childhood he suffered severely from rickets, being humpbacked through spinal curvature. . . . As one of his sides was also contracted . . . the condition seems to have been a kyphoscoliosis."[16] It will be well at this point to stop over some of the terms used in discussing Pope's case. "Kyphoscoliosis" in its root forms implies a "double crookedness." It is defined by *OED* as "backward and lateral curvature of the spine." One of Pope's sides was affected, as was the spine, with the result that Pope was "one-sided." The condition, as we have already said, was the result of tuberculosis of the bone. To most laymen, tuberculosis is an affection of the lung, its origin usually from direct contact or sputum. Tuberculosis of the bone is a different condition, coming from milk. It was widespread in Europe and America down to the early years of this century, when pasteurization began to be practiced, though almost unknown in tropical countries where milk was boiled for preservation. The older generation among us may recall various hunchbacked children they knew in youth, though younger generations have seldom seen a hunchback.

None of Pope's many physicians would have understood Professor Sherburn's reference to "Pott's disease," although

[15] *Proceedings of the Royal Society of Medicine, loc. cit.,* p. 603.
[16] Pope's side was affected, as was the spine. The author of "Famous Persons and their Illnesses," mentioned above, p. 9, picked up the vocabulary, presumably from MacNalty: "As a child, Pope suffered from rickets, he was humpbacked and had a kyphoscoliosis." W.R. Bett, *The Infirmities of Genius,* p. 162, says Pope inherited his tendency to headache from his mother, "while his father passed on to him a tendency to curvature of the spine." Both MacNalty and Bett seem to have followed a statement by "George Paston" (Emily Morse Symonds) in *Mr. Pope: His Life and Times,* 2 vols. (New York and London: Hutchinson and Co., 1909), I. 4: "Pope's physical heritage was inferior to his moral heritage. His parents were both middle-aged at the time of his birth. His father was afflicted with a slight spinal curvature, while his mother suffered from nervous head-aches, though both must have had strong constitutions, since they lived to advanced old age." Both these legends, however, go as far back as Owen Ruffhead, *Life of Alexander Pope* (London, 1769), where both may be found mentioned briefly in passing.

the condition itself had been recognized for centuries, and the name is still standard in medical nomenclature today for tuberculosis of the bone. The condition was named for Dr. Percival Pott (1714-88), whose most accurate clinical analysis was of "Pott's fracture," which may also have been named for him. Although Pott's diagnosis and treatment of spinal curvature was famous in his own time, he failed to recognize the tubercular origin of the disease. A Frenchman, Jean-Pierre David,[17] suggested it in the very year in which Percival Pott published his first findings. The modern reprint of Pott's work in *Medical Classics*[18] is prefaced by a note from which we borrow: "Tuberculosis of the spine is one of the oldest diseases known to medicine because it produces changes in the skeleton which lead to a correct diagnosis centuries after a patient has died. Eliot Smith has found many examples in Egyptian mummies and Sudhoff and Sticker describes a case in a mummy of the 21st Dynasty in *Zur historischen Biologie der Krankheitserreger*, Giessen, 1910. . . . Hippocrates guessed the tuberculous nature of gibbous spine (*On the Articulations*, Par. 41). Galen confirmed Hippocrates. A study of the condition was revived by J.Z. Platner in 1774 [marginal correction to 1744], and advanced by Delpech in 1816. . . . Not until 1882 when Robert Koch discovered the tubercle bacillus was the true etiology of Pott's disease of the spine established."

Percival Pott was the kind of medical man in whom historical scholars delight. He not only published papers but kept a notebook. In the library of the Royal College of

[17] Jean-Pierre David (1737-84) published a prize-winning essay, *Dissertation sur les effets du mouvement et du repos dans les maladies chirurgicales, 1779*.

[18] "Remarks on That Kind of Palsy of the Lower Limbs, Which is Frequently Found to Accompany a Curvature of the Spine, and is Supposed to be Caused by It, Together with its Method of Cure, To Which are Added Observations on the Necessity and Propriety of Amputation in Certain Cases and under Certain Circumstances." *Medical Classics*, I (December 1936), 281-97. "Further Research on the Useless State of the Lower Limbs in Consequence of a Curvature of the Spine." *Ibid.*, pp. 298-321.

Surgeons are three unpublished case books, dated and written in his own legible hand, filled with lectures and observations of patients in St. Bartholomew's Hospital, to which Pott had been appointed assistant surgeon in 1744, the year of Pope's death. That hospital, as Pott noted elsewhere, had seldom been without cases of spinal curvature, in which he became increasingly interested. In one notebook we found a series of observations[19] on curvature of the spine in a boy of sixteen, whom Pott first saw in 1765. Six months after the appearance of "a small projection of the ninth dorsal vertebra from the neck," the boy "caught cold, and all his former symptoms were much encreased, and every function greatly disturbed . . . he was also troubled with a short hacking cough and loss of appetite." We shall see that, like Pott's young patient, Pope's "symptoms were much encreased and every function greatly disturbed" whenever he caught a cold. He too coughed like Horace and became increasingly lame. Elsewhere Pott pointed out that both sexes and various ages are liable to this distemper, though it is most common in childhood; Pott remembered only one case in which it developed as late as in the thirties. When the condition occurs in infancy, said Pott, parents and nurses at first usually think of the child as merely backward, or suspect a birth injury. When it occurs later, "recourse is almost always had to some previous violence to account for it, some pulling, lifting, carrying or drawing a heavy body, which is supposed to have hurt the back."

We have no record of any explanation offered by Pope's family or nurses for his curvature or the gradual weakening of his lower limbs. Yet it is possible that they too attributed this to an early accident, which Alexander himself did not remember, but which was described to Spence by his older half-sister, Magdalen, later Mrs. Charles Rackett:

[19] The fullest contemporary account of Pott is that of Sir James Earle, *The Life of Percival Pott*, in *Works* (London, 1790). This case of "Curvature of the Spine" occupies pp. 317-21 of an unpublished manuscript notebook for 1767; it is labeled "Case B." Under Pott's treatment the boy improved markedly for a time, but died of another ailment.

17

"Mr. Pope's life . . . was in danger several times, and the first so early as when he was a child in coats. A wild cow that was driven by the place where he was at play struck at him with her horns, tore off his hat, which was tied under his chin, wounded him in the throat, beat him down, and trampled over him."[20] Pott's description of the extreme effect of the condition on older children suggests what might have happened to Alexander Pope around his twelfth year:

> When it affects a child who is old enough to have already walked, and who has been able to walk, the loss of the use of his limbs is gradual, though in general not very slow. He at first complains of being very soon tired, is languid, listless, and unwilling to move much, or at all briskly; in no great length of time after this he may be observed frequently to trip, and stumble, although there be no impediment in his way; and whenever he attempts to move briskly, he finds that his legs involuntarily cross each other, by which he is frequently thrown down, and that without stumbling; upon endeavouring to stand still and erect, without support, even for a few minutes, his knees give way and bend forward. When the distemper is a little farther advanced, it will be found that he cannot, without much difficulty and deliberation, direct either of his feet precisely to any exact point; and very soon after this, both thighs and legs lose a great deal of their natural sensibility, and become perfectly useless for all the purposes of locomotion.

Even though Pope's loss of the power of locomotion was more gradual than some cases of curvature Pott had observed in adolescents, the condition explains the four-year illness from which Pope suffered between the ages of twelve and sixteen.

[20] *Anecdotes*, I. p. 3. It is conceivable that they might have blamed Alexander's first teacher, by whom, according to the same half-sister, he was "whipped and ill-used."

Pott's two tracts on "Palsy in the Lower Limbs," published in 1779, are filled with details of various cases of spinal curvature, many of which parallel symptoms we find in Pope. Adults who could remember the onset of the disease would recall a sense of weakness, a heavy dull kind of pain, lassitude and coldness in the limbs. Later there came "involuntary twitchings, particularly troublesome in the night." The adult suffers from "laborious respiration, hard cough, quick pulse, hectical heat and flushing, pain and tightness of the stomach, &c." Such patients were usually treated by relatives and physicians with "warm liniments, embrocations, and blisters to the parts affected." The trouble, Pott says, was not infrequently diagnosed as rheumatism. Were Dr. Arbuthnot and others of Pope's physicians mistaken in their diagnosis of rheumatism in his case? When it is recognized that the symptoms are the result of curvature, Pott continues, "recourse is always had to steel stays, the swing, the screw chair, and other pieces of machinery . . . but to no real or permanent good purpose." Pope's wearing of stays was attested by the Twickenham boatman long before Samuel Johnson mentioned it. We know from Pope's passing remarks that he felt the cold severely, and wore three pairs of hose and heavy undergarments, sometimes of fur.

It is difficult to determine when Pope began to be helpless. Certainly his comments and those of others prove that for some years he could ride horseback and walk with apparent pleasure in city and country, often playing with his dogs. During the year and a half he lived in London with Jervas, studying painting—this when he was twenty-five and twenty-six—he was in and out of Jervas's residence, spending many of his evenings in coffee-houses. During one of his favorite "rambles" in September 1717 (to Hampton Court, Stonor, and Oxford) he "rid" his horse, and he also mentioned walking at Hampton Court "all alone with [Mrs. Lepell] three or 4 hours, by moonlight."[21] Lack of allusions to riding in later letters and some comments of Swift's indi-

21 *Correspondence*, I. 427.

cate Pope could no longer ride when he entered the thirties.

There is no question that he gradually lost some of the power of locomotion and became dependent on maid-servants for assistance in rising, dressing, and going to bed. Unfortunately the one detailed eighteenth-century account of such infirmities (familiar to most modern readers through Johnson's *Life*) was not published until long after Pope's death, an anonymous paper, "Particulars concerning the Person of Mr. Pope," in the *Gentleman's Magazine* for 1775.[22] If the author, still identified only as "D", based his description on first-hand information, as he implies, it would seem to have come to him from maidservants in the employ of the Earl of Oxford, who knew Pope in late middle life: "He was unable to dress or undress himself, or get into bed without help; nor could he stand upright till a kind of stays, made of stiff linen, were laced on him, one of his first [sic] sides being contracted almost to the back-bone. He wanted much waiting on, but was very liberal to the maid-servants about him, so that he had never reason to complain of being neglected. These females attended him at night, and, in the morning, brought him his writing-desk to bed, lighted his fire, drew on his stockings, etc., which offices he often summoned them to perform at very early hours, so that, when any part of their business was left undone, their common excuse was, that they had been employed with Mr. Pope, and then no further reprehension was to be dreaded."

Most of these details Johnson also used, adding, from other secondary sources, a few phrases: "extremely sensible of cold, so that he wore a kind of fur doublet under a shirt of very coarse warm linen with fine sleeves. . . . His legs were so slender that he enlarged their bulk with three pairs

---

[22] *Gentleman's Magazine*, Vol. 45 (September 1775), 435. Johnson repeated much of this in his "Life of Pope" (*Lives of the English Poets*, ed. G.B. Hill [Oxford: Clarendon Press, 1905], III. 196-97). These particular passages were not discussed by F. W. Hilles, "The Making of the Life of Pope," *New Light on Dr. Johnson* (New Haven: Yale University Press, 1959). Johnson's sources here remain the *Gentleman's Magazine*, Ruffhead, and oral tradition.

of stockings, which were drawn on and off by the maid." Both the anonymous biographer and Johnson were describing Pope in middle age, but the slenderness of his legs is attested by the full-length portrait painted by Jervas, probably when Pope was living in his home.

II

We turn from the preliminary discussion of Pope's curvature of the spine to some of the illnesses he suffered in early years, which are reported in letters to friends. An adviser suggested that an illness mentioned in this section might have been rheumatic fever, which would also account for a heart condition from which Pope suffered in later life. Dr. McKusick, however, says: "Tuberculosis adequately accounts for the prolonged febrile illnesses of youth. The cardiac complications in the last years are commonplace with severe kyphoscoliosis. . . . Thus, a single process can have produced the entire clinical picture without rheumatic fever and rheumatic heart disease. I would strongly favor the unitary hypothesis."

Pope suffered what he called "a dangerous illness" just before his twenty-second birthday. He first mentioned it in a letter to Henry Cromwell, May 17, 1710, in which he said that it had been "contracted in Town about a fortnight after my coming hither." He twitted Cromwell for his not having finished an epitaph he was writing, "when I was sick in London," and declares that in his present "living, dead Condition," he will be forced to write his own epitaph. His illness apparently continued for some time, since as late as October 12 of that year he wrote Cromwell, apologizing for not meeting him in town, "But my almost continual Illnesses prevent that, as well as most other Satisfactions of my Life." He seems to have made a good recovery from this particular attack, since his letters are singularly free from any reference to illness during the year

1711, the latter part of which he spent in Windsor Forest. A large part of 1712 was likewise a period of activity, comparatively free from illness. In May 1711 had appeared the *Essay on Criticism* though that, as Pope constantly insisted, had been written earlier. In the earlier part of 1712 the *Messiah* and the first version of *The Rape of the Lock* were published, both of which Pope wrote rapidly during a period when he seems to have been enjoying good health. In March 1713 appeared *Windsor Forest*, which Pope may have begun during his residence in the Forest in 1711 and completed in 1712. At the end of 1712, however, according particularly to letters written to John Caryll, Pope suffered a long period of physical inactivity. Evidence of his condition is given in two letters to Caryll, December 5 and December 21, 1712:[23] "I am just in the reverse of all this Spirit & Life, confin'd to a narrow Closet, lolling on an Arm Chair, nodding away my Days over a Fire, like the picture of January in an old Salisbury Primer. I believe no mortal ever liv'd in such Indolence & Inactivity of Body, tho my Mind be perpetually rambling. . . . I seem to sleep in the midst of the Hurry, even as you would swear a Top stands still, when tis in the Whirle of its giddy motion. . . . This will shew you how little I feel in this State either of Pleasure or Pain: I am fixt in a Stupid settled Medium between both."

Two weeks later he wrote again to Caryll, who had apparently invited him to spend part of the Christmas season at Ladyholt: "My ill state of health ever since the cold weather began renders vain any such pleasing thoughts as of the enjoyment of your fireside: I cannot express how thoroughly I'm penetrated by the sharpness of it. I feel no thing alive but my heart and head; and my spirits, like those in a thermometer mount and fall thro' my thin delicate contexture just as the temper of air is more benign or inclement."

This illness of Pope's seems to have been chronic, rather than the result of an acute infection, presumably part of

23 *Correspondence*, I. 163-64, 165.

the growing languor described by Pott, experienced by sufferers from tuberculous spinal curvature. It was the earlier illness, in which Pope seems actually to have faced death, rather than this period of inactivity, we think, that lay behind two papers published in the *Guardian* for August 12 and September 24, 1713.[24] Indeed these essays—emotion recollected in tranquillity—may well have begun in Pope's mind in a "disquisition" he wrote to Cromwell on October 12, 1710,[25] after describing his "serious illness." "However I may say one good thing of Sickness, that it is the best Cure in the world for Ambition, & Designs upon the World or Fortune; It makes a Man pretty Indifferent for the future, provided he can but be Easie, by Intervals, for the present. He will be content to compound for his Quiet only, & leave all the Circumstantial Part & Pomp of Life to those, who have a health vigorous enough to injoy all the Mistresses of their Desires."

As published, the first *Guardian* essay was preceded by an introduction, whether written by Steele or Pope: "Mr. Ironside: The following Letter was really written by a young Gentleman in a languishing Illness, which both himself, and those who attended him, thought it impossible for him to outlive." The paper is a composite of Pope's letter to Cromwell in 1710 and two letters to Caryll in 1712. As in the Cromwell letter he develops the idea that illness is the best cure for ambition and designs upon the world or fortune. Young though Pope was, he had had far more op-

24 The two *Guardian* papers, Nos. 132, 169 (August 12 and September 24, 1713) were attributed to Pope by Norman Ault, *Prose Works*, I. lvi-lxx, 134-40. Ault called the first "On Sickness," the other "On Nature and Death." Another reason for our dating the inception of the *Guardian* papers much earlier than their appearance was the fact that when Pope published his correspondence in 1735, he included, as a letter to Steele, dated July 15, 1712, more than a year before the papers, an almost verbatim copy of the first paper, apparently wishing to give the impression that Steele had been so impressed by the letter that he had published it, with or without the author's consent. Sherburn says of the letter (*Correspondence*, I. 147n.): "First printed in *The Guardian*, No. 132, for Aug. 12, 1713. Differences in the texts are negligibly slight."

25 *Correspondence*, I. 98.

portunity than normal young men to know suffering and inanition.

Pope finally made a good recovery from his long period of inaction and went on to spend what proved the most rewarding and exciting period of his youth in 1713-14. During the early spring of 1713 he began seriously to study painting with Charles Jervas,[26] in whose house he resided happily for some time, spending many of his evenings at coffee-houses where he came into contact with various writers of the period. In August 1713 occurred the great stimulus to his imagination of Whiston's lectures on astronomy at Button's coffee-house, an experience we consider in detail in "Pope and Astronomy." Thanks in part to his engrossment in these new enthusiasms, Pope's health seems never to have been better, since he first experienced the curvature of his spine, than during this period,[27] which reached a climax in his first visit to Bath, where he went for relaxation and pleasure, not—as on various later occasions—painfully conveying a sick and weary body for possible alleviation of his ills in spa waters. We pause over letters describing his first experience at Bath, in part because they show Pope in one of the happiest periods of his life, and in part because they offer so great a contrast to later accounts of the spa we shall consider.

On September 25, 1714 he wrote Caryll: "I am this evening arrived extremely weary." Even in this period of good health Pope felt more than ordinary fatigue on a journey,

26 On October 30, 1713, he wrote Caryll (*Correspondence*, I. 174-76), offering as excuse for a long silence, "I've been almost every day employed in following your advice in learning to paint, in which I am most particularly obliged to Mr Gervase, who gives me daily instructions and examples. As to poeticall affairs I am content at present to be a bare looker on." Norman Ault has treated this period of Pope's life in "Mr Alexander Pope: Painter," *New Light on Pope* (London: Methuen, 1949), pp. 68-100. He dates the period with Jervas as continuing from twelve to eighteen months.

27 Here we agree with Professor Sherburn in his original desire to antedate a letter of Pope's to Gay, which Sherburn finally reluctantly published as of October 23 (1713). Sherburn says (*Correspondence*, I. 195n.): "This letter was not reprinted by Pope after 1735. The present editor has elsewhere argued for 1712, but ineffectually."

which he had made by coach, his companion Thomas Parnell, riding alongside on horseback.[28] However, "new to all
the wonders of the place," as he was, he seems to have made
a rapid recovery, and although he went through the routine
of the Bath, his letters were those of an amused sightseer
rather than patient. "I have stared at the Bath, and sneaked
along the walks, with that astonished and diffident air which
is natural to a modest and ignorant Foreigner." He slid, "I
cant tell how, into all the Amusements of this Place: My
whole Day is shar'd by the Pump-Assemblies, the Walkes,
the Chocolate houses, Raffling Shops, Plays, Medleys, &c."[29]
Within a week he was so very well that his letter of October
6, 1714, to Martha Blount, was filled with exuberance, and
even sly insinuations of amours. "I am so much a Rake,"
he wrote, "as to be ashamed of being seen with Dr. Par-
nelle. I ask people abroad who that Parson is? . . . If you
ask how the Waters agree with me, I must tell you, so very
well, that I question how you and I should agree, if we
were in a roome by ourselves? But I apprehend you have
some notions of the next life that may hinder your happiness in this."

The period from early 1713, when Pope first began his
study with Jervas, through at least 1717 (his twenty-fifth
to twenty-ninth years), was one of the healthiest and happiest he was ever to know, productive also so far as his career
was concerned. In 1713 *Windsor Forest* was published, and
in October his proposals for a translation of the *Iliad*.
March 1714 saw the publication of the expanded *Rape of
the Lock*, which largely received acclaim. In 1713-14 Pope
began his close acquaintance with Swift and Arbuthnot, and
watched his proposal for *The Works of the Unlearned*
transformed in their hands to the *Memoirs of Martinus
Scriblerus*. Gradually weaned from Addison and Steele and
from Button's coffee-house to Will's, Pope and John Gay

[28] See his account of Parnell in a letter to Teresa Blount, I. 257-58.
That Pope travelled by public coach is indicated in his letter to
Martha Blount, I. 260, when he mentioned the "prettiest lady" at
Bath as "one I had the luck to travell with."
[29] The details here are from letters to the Blount sisters, I. 256-60.

became Scriblerians, a close relationship with older men, sharply interrupted by the death of Queen Anne in August 1714. That event had no such effect upon the young Pope as upon his elders. "As for myself," he wrote Caryll on August 16, 1714,[30] "I am below all the accidents of state-changes by my circumstances." Dr. Arbuthnot, who had been Physician in Ordinary to Queen Anne, was forced to return to private practice, while Swift, at the height of his political influence, sadly left England to return to Ireland.

In February 1715 Pope's *Temple of Fame* was published, followed in June by the first volume of the Homer translation, in March 1716 by Volume II, in June 1717 by Volume III. During the latter year appeared also *Eloisa to Abelard* and *To the Memory of an Unfortunate Lady*. So happy and healthy had these few years been that we find ourselves wondering what other major creative works Pope might have produced had he not settled to long hours of translation. It is entirely conceivable that he might have developed the "romantic" mood of *Eloisa to Abelard,* a possibility we shall discuss again in "Pope and Astronomy." This period of tranquillity was interrupted by the death of Pope's father, which occurred during the night of October 23, 1717. Sudden and completely unexpected—"His death was the happiest to himself, imaginable," Pope wrote to Caryll—the death naturally came as a great shock to Pope and his mother. It marked the beginning of a new period in Pope's life, presaged by his comment in a letter to Caryll, October 28, 1717: "My poor mother is so afflicted that it would be barbarity to leave this winter." Under pressure very different from the effect of the Queen's death on Swift, Pope too became a gradual exile from the carefree days in London. Pope's mother was to live another sixteen years, dying on June 7, 1733 at the age of ninety-one. Not for some time was Pope completely incarcerated by the many alarms and excursions of her increasing illness—and of

[30] In his long letter to Caryll on the Queen's death (I. 240-42), he said: "The greatest fear I have under the circumstances of a poor papist is the loss of my poor horse" (a gift from Caryll).

his own—yet in a way October 1717 marked the end of the most carefree, fortunate period of his early maturity. He wrote to John Caryll in February 1720:[31] "Your desire that I should tell you some news of the *beau monde* or from Parnassus, could not be expressed at a time when I am less capable to comply with it. I have not the least knowledge of any poetical affairs; I have not seen a play these twelve months, been at no assembly, opera, or public place whatever. I am infamously celebrated as an inoffensive unenvied writer, even by Curll himself. My friends have given me over, as to all wit & pleasure. I am the comick topick of ridicule as a country putt; and if (once a month) I trudge to town in a horseman's coat, I am stard at, every question I ask, as the most ignorant of all rustics."

There is no question that Pope's health took a turn for the worse in 1719-20. He apologized for silence to John Hughes on January 22, 1720: "Your letter found me, as I have long been, in a state of health almost as bad as that you complain of;[32] and indeed what makes me utterly incapable of attending to any poetical task, even that of Homer. This minute too I can scarce return you the civility of an answer, being in the full operation of a vomit I have taken." To Caryll he wrote in February: "I have lain under an impediment to all amusement and pleasure these many months, namely very great indispositions and such an alteration in my constitution as rather deserves to be called a ruin than a revolution."[33]

It is easy for a modern reader of Pope's correspondence to become bored and irritated by the extensiveness of Pope's references to illness, and to believe, as Professor Sherburn sometimes implies in his notes, that Pope was exaggerating

[31] *Correspondence*, II. 31.

[32] II. 28. Hughes died on February 17, less than a month later, during the night on which his play, *The Siege of Damascus*, was being produced.

[33] II. 31. He mentioned digestive troubles, "perpetual vomiting and nervous distempers," together with "a dejection of spirits that has totally taken away everything (if I ever had anything) which could be called vivacity or cheerfulness." References to the illness continue in letters through July of that year.

his condition. But we should sympathetically realize that, even during periods like those exuberant years 1713-17, the crooked body of Alexander Pope was often in severe pain from kyphoscoliosis. An interesting illustration of this appears in a letter to Martha Blount, dated 30 October (1719?),[34] but which, as Professor Sherburn suggests, might have been written earlier or later. Pope wrote with a humor that must have been difficult for any patient in his condition: "As to my health, I'm in a very odd course for the pain in my side: I mean a course of brickbats and tiles, which they apply to me piping hot, morning and night; and sure it is very satisfactory to one who loves architecture at his heart, to be built around in his very bed. My body may properly at this time be called a human structure."

III

The death of Pope's father—as the much later death of his mother—may be said to have opened a new chapter in Pope's life, continuing through the decade roughly coinciding with his thirties. This was in part because he no longer felt free to leave his mother for indefinite periods of carefree life in London, in part because of increasing ill health. The headaches about which he persistently complains were not new, as early correspondence between Pope and William Wycherley shows. Pope was only nineteen when the elderly dramatist began to write the young poet about his headaches.[35]

The motif continued throughout the Wycherley-Pope correspondence, the older man frequently mentioning "your wonted Indisposition," and commenting sympathetically

[34] *Correspondence*, II. 16n.
[35] *Correspondence*, I. 28-30. Wycherley continues the theme somewhat tediously, stressing the compensation of inward sight for "weakness of your outward sight," and reminding the young man of his "Poetic Forefathers, down from Homer to Milton."

that it was hard for Pope to realize "that the part of you (your Head) which gives others so much pleasure, should cause you so much pain." During the decade under consideration Pope was also becoming increasingly nearsighted, as he suggested in a letter of apology written in April 1722 to Viscount Harcourt:[36] "You will too naturally allow the misfortune of Want of Sight to be a very great one, but I assure your Lordship I never more found it so, than when I met your Coach & family on the Road to the Country, without knowing who you were, till you was past call." The letters of this decade are increasingly filled with references to fevers and severe colds. Had Pope been a man of normal physique, we might impatiently dismiss such reiterated references as complaints of a valetudinarian, but we may sympathetically understand that they were results of the increasing symptoms of his tubercular condition.[37]

In September 1726 Pope's maladies were compounded by an accident that might have proved more serious than it did, which may well have aggravated the symptoms from curvature of the spine. We quote from an account Gay sent to Swift, September 16, 1726:[38] "I saw Mr Pope on Sunday, who hath lately escap'd a very great danger, but is very much wounded across his right hand; Coming home in the dark about a week ago alone in my Lord Bolingbroke's coach from Dawley, he was overturn'd where a bridge had

[36] II. 114. The earliest reference to his myopia that we have noticed was in a letter to Henry Cromwell, July 11, 1709.

[37] In June 1726 Pope's troubles began to be further complicated by "a long and troublesome disorder of the piles, which has put me more out of humour than out of health," as he wrote to Broome (II. 378). In later years he mentioned this complaint frequently, particularly in connection with the difficulties he found in travelling by coach on his "rambles."

[38] II. 399-400. The accident has been discussed so fully that we shall not treat it in detail. See particularly George Sherburn, "An Accident in 1726," *Harvard Library Bulletin*, II (1948) 121-23. C.F. Burgess, "The Footman and Mr. Pope's Trial by Water," *Cithara*, III (1963), 80-81, adds nothing, and indeed the author does not seem to be aware of Sherburn's article. In his paper Sherburn quoted from the letter of Bolingbroke to Swift, which he later included in the *Correspondence*, II. 402-403, as he included Gay's letter to Swift, II. 399-400 and Arbuthnot's to Swift, II. 401-402.

been broken down near Whitton about a mile from his own house, he was thrown into the river with the glasses of the coach up, & was up to the knots of his perriwig in water; The footman broke the glass to draw him out, by which he thinks he receiv'd the cut across his hand. He was afraid he should have lost the use of his little finger & the next to it; but the surgeon whom he sent for last Sunday from London to examine it, told him, that his fingers were safe, that there were two nerves cut, but no tendon."

Dr. Arbuthnot added that "by the cutting of a Large vessel [Pope] lost a great dale of blood." Bolingbroke, also writing to Swift, added: "The surgeon thinks him in no danger of losing the use of his fingers. however he had lately had very great pains in that arm from the shoulder downwards, which might create a Suspicion that some of the glass remain'd still in the flesh. St André[39] says there is none. if so, these pains are owing to a cold he took in a fit of gallantry which carry'd him across the water to see Mrs Howard, who has been extremely ill, but is much better. just as I am writing I hear that Dr Arbuthnot says that Popes pains are Rheumatick, & have no relation to his wound. he suffers very much." The accident kept Pope from writing with his own hand for several weeks.

During the year 1727-28, in spite of increasing physical problems, Pope had been busy writing, though most of his work had still been that of translator or editor. He had added to his translation of the *Iliad* some parts of the *Odyssey*, three books of which appeared in 1725, as did his edition of Shakespeare. Under the stimulus of Swift's first visit to England he and Pope had returned to earlier Scriblerian plans, with the result that the first volumes of *Miscellanies*—including Pope's *Peri Bathous*—appeared in 1727 and 1728. Before Swift's arrival Pope had been doing some work on the first version of *The Dunciad*, but it had

[39] Sherburn, *Correspondence*, II. 403n., identifies the physician as Nathaniel St André, a Swiss physician patronized by the Court. He lost his reputation when in November of this year he upheld the contention of Mary Toft of Godalming. See below, p. 111.

gone slowly, perhaps because of the same "want of health and humour" of which Swift had complained at about the same time in connection with the progress of *Gulliver's Travels* in Ireland. Whatever the truth or exaggeration of Pope's tale that "the first sketch of this poem was snatch'd from the fire by Dr. Swift,"[40] there is little question that Swift's visit was largely responsible for making the original *Dunciad* into what it was when it appeared in three books in May 1728.

Pope's much later memories of Swift's visits in 1726 and 1727 were happy ones of "rambles" with Swift and Gay. He wrote Swift, May 17-19, 1739, when the word "rambles" had taken on painful connotations:[41] "In all those Rambles, my Mind is full of the Images of you and poor Gay, with whom I travell'd so delightfully two Summers." We hear, however, of a "lame thigh" that incapacitated Pope for some time during Swift's stay in 1726, and Swift's own letters indicate that he had hardly enjoyed his visits at Twickenham in 1727. Pope wrote to Fortescue on May 16, 1727:[42] "(I wonder my Communicative Waterman never told your people) my Mother has been & is Extremely ill, & dangerously so, of an Intermitting Fever, which requires my Constant attendance." He added: "Here is nobody with me but the *Dean of St Patricks*, who would hardly be here if he were not the Best-natur'd & indulgent man I know; it is so melancholy a way of passing his time." During his next visit in August, Swift reported to Thomas Sheridan[43] that his old deafness had seized him and he was very ill, then added: "I am very uneasy here, because so many of our Acquaintance come to see us, and I cannot be seen; besides Mr. *Pope* is too sickly and complaisant; therefore I resolve to go somewhere else."

By midsummer 1728 Pope's various symptoms had grown so troublesome that he acceded to the advice of his physi-

---

[40] "Preface to the five first imperfect Editions of the *DUNCIAD*," in *The Dunciad*, ed. James Sutherland (London and New Haven: Yale University Press, 1943, rev. edn., 1963), p. 410.
[41] IV. 179.　　[42] II. 435.　　[43] II. 442 (August 12, 1727).

cians that he spend some time at Bath. His mood was different from the elation of his first visit there. He was not unnaturally greatly concerned about leaving his mother for an extended period, as he said to Martha Blount, presumably in September 1728:[44] "I feel my being forc'd to this Bath-journey as a misfortune; and to follow my own welfare preferably to those I love, is indeed a new thing to me: my health has not usually got the better of my tenderness and affections. I set out with a heavy heart, wishing I had done this thing the last season; for every day I defer it, the more I am in danger of that accident which I dread the most, my Mother's death (especially shou'd it happen while I am away.)"

Pope made the journey alone, probably in a hired coach, not, as on the first expedition, in a public vehicle with a pretty lady among his companions. But in spite of ill health and worry, his humor had not deserted him, as may be seen in his account[45] of "taking physick"—a preliminary step prescribed by spa doctors—not at the Bath but in advance of his arrival. He had called on Sir William Codrington, Hugh Bethel's brother-in-law, intending only a brief visit, but had found it impossible "without more violence than ought ever to be offered to good nature" to get away for some time: "All his sisters . . . insisted I should take physic, preparatory to the waters, and truly I made use of the time, place, and persons, to that end. My Lady Cox, the first night I lay there, mixed my electuary, Lady Codrington pounded sulphur, Mrs. Bridget Bethel ordered broth. Lady Cox marched first up-stairs with the physic in a gallipot; Lady Codrington next, with the vial of oyle; Mrs. Bridget third, with pills; the fourth sister, with spoons and tea-cups. It would have rejoiced the ghost of Dr. Wood-

[44] II. 511. Sherburn says that this, characteristically without date and address, "is a most troublesome letter." On September 4 he wrote Martha Blount (II. 513): "I thank you for many things, and particularly for your Letters. That which gave me an account of my mother's tolerable health, told me no more than three others told me; yet it satisfied me much more, as being from you."

[45] II. 513-14.

ward to have beheld this procession;[46] and I should be inclined to think it might bring Mr. Bethel this way two
hundred miles about, if I would promise but to do the same
thing on my return home. By this means I have an opportunity of astonishing Dr. Arbuthnot, to see me begin the
waters without any physic, and to set him and Mr. Gay in
an uproar about me, and my wilfulness." Pope was greatly
intrigued by the account he heard of "Mr. B's sisters all
taking physic some days together," and the remark of "a
country wench in the house [who] thanked God heartily,
that she was not born a gentlewoman, and declared she
would not be one for the world."

Pope's letters during the period at Bath are practically
nonexistent. In one of the few, written to William
Fortescue, Master of the Rolls, he implies the difference
he felt between the lighthearted jollity and occasional
mild scandal of his earlier visit and the denizens of the spa
on this occasion: he said that he loved "above all things,
a most happy union of Truth and Scandal. I assure you
the Bath affords nothing equal to it: It is on the contrary
full of grave and sad men."[47] Pope's punnings on Fortescue's
"rambles" in riding the circuit in his judicial capacity and
his own limitations at Bath, suggest the extent to which
Pope's activities were curtailed by this time. "What an ad-
vantageous circumstance is it, for one that loves rambling
so well, to be a grave and reputable rambler? while (like
your fellower Circuiteer, the Sun) you travel the round of
the earth and behold all the iniquities under the heav'ns?
You are much a superior genius to me in rambling; you,
like a Pigeon (to which I would sooner compare a Lawyer
than to a Hawk) can fly some hundred leagues at a pitch;
I, like a poor squirrel, am continually in motion indeed,
but it is about a cage of three foot."

The expedition to Bath proved as ineffectual as various
other medical remedies, so far as improvement in Pope's

---

[46] The reference is to the satire of Gay, Pope, and Arbuthnot upon
Dr. John Woodward, "Dr. Fossile," in *Three Hours after Marriage.*
[47] II 521.

health was concerned. "I have past six weeks in quest of health, and found it not," he wrote Swift on October 12, 1728, presumably at the end of his stay.[48] In a letter to Thomas Sheridan, written immediately after that to Swift, he said: "My Eyesight is bad, my Head often in pain, my Time strangely taken up." And to Baron Bathurst on November 7,[49] he said: "I do not think I ever shall enjoy any health four days together, for the remaining Sand I have to run. The Bath was tryed after all other remedies, as a last remedy, and that has proved totally ineffectuall. I never had more long or violent Headakes, &c. than three fits since my return . . . [Planting my garden] passes away half my day; the rest I eat & sleep; for read I cannot, my eyes (since I was at Bath) being worse than ordinary." Despondently he wrote to Fortescue late in 1728: "I am in the condition of an old fellow of Threescore, with a Complication of Diseases upon me; A constant Headake; ruind Tone of the Stomach; the Piles; a Vomiting & Looseness; & an Excess of Wind. Some of these succeed, the moment I get quit of the others: & upon the whole, indeed I am in a very uncomfortable way."[50]

IV

The years 1729-33 (the forty-first to forty-fifth of Pope's life) were the most difficult he had yet experienced, thanks

[48] II. 521.

[49] In an earlier letter to Bathurst, September 15, 1728 (II. 518), Pope had said that he was to leave on the last day of September, and would dine with Bathurst "on the first of October punctually." Although Pope's superscription is "Bath, Nov. 12, 1728" this is obviously impossible. Sherburn (II. 521) dates Pope's letter to Swift as 12 [October] 1728, as he dates the next one to Sheridan. The succeeding one to Fortescue, in which Pope announces his return to Twickenham two days earlier is dated [17 or 24 October 1728]. Here Pope says: "I came from the Bath 2 days since hither; & find my mother tolerably well." The letter to Bathurst includes no year, but the date "7 November" seems clear.

[50] II. 530.

in part to his own health, still more to the general failure in his mother's condition. As he wrote Caryll on October 19, 1729: "My mother and I have both been ill . . . old age in the first, a crazy constitution in the second." Pope's mother was dead before he published the *Epistle to Dr. Arbuthnot* but the lines written earlier are an epitome of these years (lines 408-413) :

> Me, let the tender Office long engage
> To rock the Cradle of reposing Age,
> With lenient Arts extend a Mother's breath,
> Make Languor smile, and smooth the Bed of Death,
> Explore the Thought, explain the asking Eye,
> And keep a while one Parent from the Sky!

A reader of the repetitive letters of these long three and a half years would readily forgive Pope if he had indicated that he felt his was a cradle endlessly rocking, but at no time was there the slightest suggestion of self-pity, so far as his almost constant attendance upon his mother was concerned. In the earlier part of the period he occasionally left Twickenham, but the trips grew shorter and shorter, later ones limited to a maximum of three days. Throughout his mother's last year he was almost constantly at Twickenham. During this period, Pope's chronic illnesses (and one more acute) continued, and, with one exception, his periods of composition were sporadic. The *Dunciad Variorum*, published in April 1729, had been prepared well before the publication. In December 1731 appeared the *Epistle to Burlington*, in October 1732 the last volume of the *Miscellanies*, in January 1733 the *Epistle to Bathurst*, in February the first *Imitation of Horace*. Perhaps a more detailed study than has been made of Pope's illnesses and that of his mother may throw some light on the composition of *An Essay on Man*, the major work of the period, three epistles of which appeared from February to May 1733.

The year 1729 opened with an alarming illness of John Gay, who—as Pope had written Bathurst in December

1728[51]—"has just been in the jaws of Death . . . he was grown so lean that Death thought him not worth swallowing. In earnest, he is in danger of a Consumption." Pope wrote Gay early in 1729[52] that he would have taken a room in Hampstead to be with him daily, had it not been for the "immediate apprehension I have now every day lain under of losing my Mother." Undoubtedly because of his close confinement at Twickenham with its tedium,[53] Pope was even more conscious than usual of his own physical symptoms. "I have been ill," he noted on February 14, and again on May 15. On July 8 he wrote Caryll: "My head aches. I have very ill health, and 'tis one of the causes that makes me so bad a correspondent." Such attacks would seem to have been part of his chronic indispositions. In August he experienced "Such a violent Fit of the Headache & Cholick as held me three days & nights." Early in October he and his mother were acutely ill at the same time, and later in the month, on one of his rare visits to London, he was "seiz'd with a Fever, knockd down to my Bed some days in London, & carryd very closely boxed & glass'd up to this place [Twickenham] three days since, from which time I have never quitted my Room."[54]

The first half of 1730 was a comparatively placid period from the point of view of Pope's health and that of his mother, indeed a period during which he may have been working on An Essay on Man, about which he wrote Swift:[55] "Yet am I just now writing, (or rather planning) a book, to make mankind look upon this life with comfort

[51] II. 531.
[52] III. 1, 2.
[53] He wrote Gay on his own forty-first birthday, May 21, 1729 (III.3): "I have now past five weeks without once going from home, and without any company but for three or four of the days. Friends rarely stretch their kindness so far as ten miles."
[54] III. 62.
[55] [C. 19 June 1730] III. 117. Indeed with the exception of Mrs. Pope's accident, the correspondence of the whole year—until December—is peculiarly free from comments upon Pope's indispositions. He wrote Gay in October 1730 (III. 138): "I find my life ebbing apace, and my affections strengthening as my age encreases: not that I am worse, but better, in my health than last winter."

and pleasure, and put morality in good humour." Undoubtedly the improvement in Pope's health was the result of
the more even tenor of his mother's condition which had
reached still another plateau. In the letter in which he referred to *An Essay on Man*, he said to Swift—with his usual
misdating of his mother's age: "Yesterday was her birth-day,
now entering on the ninety-first year of her age; her memory much diminish'd, but her senses very little hurt; her
sight and hearing, good; she sleeps not ill, eats moderately,
drinks water, says her prayers; this is all she does."

Ironically, just about this time she suffered what might
have proved a fatal accident, which Pope mentioned in
several letters. We quote the account to John Caryll, October 22: "My own poor mother is yet a partaker of her
reason, which renders all other decays less grievous; but
her memory is very near gone. She had within this month
a very extraordinary escape from a terrible accident: She
fell into the fire without touching her body, tho' it con-
sum'd the clothes she had on, at least a yard about. Her
back lay on the grate, but her head (tho' dressed in Mus-
selin) reclining sideways was not burnt. The shock of the
fall and blow has much hurt her, but after a week or
two she recovered of all but her feebleness."[56]

In a letter to Oxford[57] he indicated that he was paying
some attention to the *Essay on Man*: "You are busie about
your New Room to lodge Books in, and I am as busy about
a Book to lodge in it." We shall hear another allusion to
the *Essay* in January, but the poem was put aside for some
time, since Pope's health took a turn for the worse and by
February 1731, he was under treatment for various disorders and forbidden to work for a time. He wrote Swift
on March 20:[58] "The Doctor puts me into Asses Milk." We
shall presently discuss the relation of this diet to Pope's
poetical work. For the present, it is enough that his health
improved, and his mother's continued for some time on
another plateau.

[56] III. 142.
[57] [C. 2 December 1730]; III. 153.
[58] III. 183-84.

That year must have seemed to Pope the longest and most monotonous he had ever known. As he wrote to Hugh Bethel on May 5:[59] "My poor old Woman is hardly able to be hearty, now, in anything. She is weak to such a degree as not to speak, even to me, thrice in 24 hours, & lyes almost wholly in bed, without any appetite." "As to your question, what I am doing?" said Pope to Jonathan Richardson in a letter written in February or March 1732,[60] "I answer, just what I have been doing some years: first, my duty; secondly, relieving myself with necessary amusements or exercises which shall serve me instead of physic as long as they can; thirdly, reading till I am tired; and lastly, writing when I have no other thing in the world to do, or no friend to entertain in company." But writing went slowly. "I know you'll desire some account of my health," he wrote Swift in March.[61] "It is as usual, but my spirits rather worse. I write little or nothing."

In December 1732 his melancholy was deepened by the sudden and unexpected death of John Gay, about which Pope and Dr. Arbuthnot wrote a joint letter on December 5.[62] Pope said: "An inflammatory fever hurried him out of this life in three days." Arbuthnot added: "Poor Mr. Gay dy'd of an inflammation, and I believe at last a mortification of the bowels; it was the most precipitate case I ever knew, having cut him off in three days."

The first three epistles of *An Essay on Man* were published February-May 1733, shortly before the death of Mrs. Pope (July 7th). Her life had been protracted seventeen years after the death of her husband, but her final passing was as peaceful as his had been. "I thank God," Pope wrote to Jonathan Richardson,[63] whom he asked to make a death portrait, "her death was as easy, as her life was innocent; and as it cost her not a groan, or even a sigh, there is yet upon her countenance such an expression of Tranquillity, nay almost of pleasure, that far from horrid, it is even amiable to behold it. It wou'd afford the finest Image

[59] III. 288.   [60] III. 269-70.   [61] III. 274-76.
[62] III. 334-35.   [63] III. 374.

Plate 1. Pope at eight

[*By kind permission of James M. Osborn of Yale University*]

Plate 2. From the Painting by C. Jervas

Plate 3. Pope in his grotto

[*The Chatsworth Collection, the Duke of Devonshire, Chatsworth, by kind permission of the Trustees of the Chatsworth Collections*]

Plate 4. Frontispage of *The Martiniad*

[*By kind permission of the Trustees of the British Museum*]

Plate 5. Frontispage of *The Memoirs of William Whiston* [*London:* 1753]

REV. WILLIAM WHISTON, M.A.

Born at Norton 1667 Died 1752.

Plate 6. Richardus Mead, M.D. painted by Ramsey

[*By kind permission of the National Portrait Gallery, London*]

of a Saint expir'd, that ever Painting drew." After years of almost continuous attention and concern, Pope was at last free to live his own life. Yet, like many who have lost parents in old age after years of devotion, his habit-patterns had become such that he felt no sense of release. "My attendance upon her living," he wrote Caryll on June 25, 1733,[64] "was not virtue, but only duty, and my Melancholy for her dead, is not virtue but weakness. . . . As it is a great and new Æra of my life, and upon which the whole course of it will in a manner change, I must pause awhile to look about me."

V

Pope's attendance on his mother for more than three years had been interrupted during only one period of several weeks, into which we enter in some detail, hoping to be able to throw light on a problem in Pope scholarship: when did Pope settle to the final composition of the first three epistles of *An Essay on Man?* Professor Maynard Mack, in the Introduction to his edition of the *Essay*,[65] says that the history of its composition is almost as obscure as that of the longer project for which it had originally been designed. He quotes Pope's reference to the book he was planning for Oxford's library, then continues: "Except for some allusions in the following February and March which suggest that Pope had lately been engaged with Epistle II, we learn nothing further till 2 August 1731," when Bolingbroke wrote Swift that the three epistles were complete. Neither Professor Mack nor Professor Sherburn pays attention to the fact that during the spring of 1731 Pope was actually residing with Bolingbroke at Dawley, follow-

[64] III. 375.
[65] See also Professor Mack's edition of *An Essay on Man: Reproductions of the Manuscripts in the Pierpont Morgan Library and the Houghton Library with the Printed Text of the Original Edition* (privately printed for the Roxburghe Club, 1962).

ing the regimen of asses' milk. If we did not know the chronology of Pope's works and were to hazard a guess as to the literary result of such a diet, we would inevitably think of the *Dunciad Variorum*, with its frontispiece of a jackass, rather than of Pope's poem of "optimism"—whatever one may mean by that disputed term. We are persuaded that the first three epistles of *An Essay on Man* were brought into publishable form under Bolingbroke's roof, during a period in which Pope's health improved markedly, in part perhaps because of his restricted diet, undoubtedly in part because he was free from the pervasive daily melancholy of his mother's chamber. Indeed he was away from his mother longer than during any one period of her latter years, writing William Broome on May 19, 1731: "I have been drinking asses' milk these three weeks at a friend's country house some miles from hence, *and never lay at home one night, making only a few day visits to my mother.*"[66]

It is impossible to date accurately the beginning of the Dawley period because of inconsistencies in Pope's letters and his irritating failure to date letters in full, if at all. In March 1731 Bolingbroke and Pope wrote the joint letter to Swift,[67] in which Pope said: "I can write nothing, not even so much as good Scraps, for I'm become but a Scrap of my self, and quite exhausted by a long Pain and Confinement[.] The Doctor puts me into Asses Milk, and I must neither use Study nor Exercise, I'm too weak." The immediate cause for the doctor's prescription may well have been a severe attack of illness suffered by Pope in London at Lord Oxford's home, which had become his London headquarters. We gain some impression of the symptoms from

[66] III. 199. (The italics are ours.)
[67] III. 183-85. The letter was dated by neither Bolingbroke nor Pope. Sherburn says: "The date is in the hand of Lord Oxford. In all Pope's texts (1740-42) it is printed March 29." Both this and the date Sherburn assigns it—March 20—seem contradicted by statements in other letters. On March 20 Gay wrote Swift (III. 185) that Pope was "at present in town. Lord Oxford, Lord Bathurst, He and I din'd yesterday at Barnes with old Jacob Tonson."

40

a letter Pope wrote to Oxford, presumably on April 3,[68] on his return to Twickenham: "I arrived better than I expected; and am much less in pain, by day, but in the nights, a little Fever, & great Headake returns. I am taking Sweats, which I fear weaken too much, but there's no help for't. . . . It vexes me to have Better Days without You; reflecting how uneasy I made Your Lordship, as well as felt myself." The attack at Oxford's house would seem to have been a climax rather than the beginning of this particular illness, since in February Pope had written Aaron Hill[69] that he had been in "almost roaring Pain, with a violent Rheumatism in my Shoulder," and to Oxford had said:[70] "Till this day, the violent pain of the Rheumatism in my left arm was such, that I could not bring it near enough to a Table, to write with my other hand. I am like to be confined many days. . . . Lord Bathurst was here yesterday and found me not fit to be seen. . . . I've felt so much that Pain is an Evil." Pope's "rheumatism," as we know, was attended by many other symptoms.

Our best evidence that Pope's protracted stay at Dawley began in April is the letter to Broome and one to John Caryll, April 15,[71] in which Pope used the present tense: "I am going into a course of asses' milk." This is the fullest account of his many recent infirmities. Apologizing for his long silence he summarized the "continued succession of accidents" which had made him incapable of writing: "First, a violent rheumatic pain settled in the shoulder joint, which was a distemper quite new to me: that kept me sleepless so long till a fever succeeded. A constant course of evacuations and plasters and phlebotomy and blisters, &c., &c., &c. Lastly, another fever from a cold taken after I went out. In the whole, nine weeks pain, confinement, and sickness; from all which I am just now free, whilst God pleases . . . I am going into a course of asses' milk to repair the weakness left behind by these disorders."

[68] III. 186-87. Again, the date is in Oxford's hand.
[69] February 15, III. 176.
[70] [11 Feb. 1731], III. 175.
[71] III.189-90.

Only two letters superscribed "Dawley" are extant, dated merely "Friday" and "Saturday,"[72] both to David Mallet, offering to meet him at Twickenham though making clear that Pope would be there only for the purpose of seeing Mallet, "& would chuse not to lye from hence, if possible, in order to continue some Medicines which I take every morning." His most specific description of his routine was in a letter to Lord Oxford on April 22: "I am daily drinking Asses Milk, which will confine me from rambling farther than betwixt this place & my Dam's Pasture, which is 4 miles off. I lye there & come hither daily, then go to Suck at night again."[73]

A "diet of Asses' milk" sounds strange to sophisticated modern ears, but it was as staple a "cure" in Pope's time as spa-waters, its virtues commonplace and praised by physicians and laymen. The diet was enthusiastically approved by Swift who wrote in reply to Pope's news:[74] "I am glad you are got into Asses milk. It is a remedy I have a great opinion of, and wish you had taken it sooner." He added: "My old Presbyterian Housekeeper tells me, that if you could bring your Stomach to woman's Milk, it would be far better than Asses." Dr. Arbuthnot made the same com-

---

[72] III. 189. During his Dawley stay, Pope combined his infrequent visits to his mother with entertaining an occasional friend at dinner. Cf. for example a note to Oxford (27 April 1731), III. 193, asking him to "dine at Twitnam next Sunday, or fix any day after it."

[73] III. 193. The last sentence is most perplexing. Pope consistently uses the word "lye" to mean "spend the night"; "come hither daily" would seem to indicate the place from which he was writing, presumably Bolingbroke's house at Dawley. He could hardly have "spent the night" outdoors in the "Dam's Pasture," particularly in an English April. It is conceivable that he slept in a cottage on the estate, nearer his "Dam's Pasture" than the main house. Since Pope probably would have been carried the four miles in his sedan chair or other conveyance, such an arrangement would save the bearers eight miles a day. Does "go to Suck" indicate that Pope took his asses' milk by the direct method? The reason for his going to the dam rather than having the milk brought to him at Bolingbroke's residence will become clear below.

[74] 20 April 1731, III. 190-92. This was not Pope's first experience with asses' milk; he wrote to Caryll, June 30, 1717 (I. 414): "I also drink asses' milk, upon which I will make no jokes tho' it be a fertile subject."

parative rating in one of his medical treatises:[75] "Women's milk is the sweetest as to the nutritious quality, the next to it is that of Asses." In the British Museum is a sixty-page *Treatise of the Extraordinary Virtues and Effects of Asses Milk In the Cure of various Diseases* translated from the Latin version of "the celebrated Frederick Hoffman, M.D., Principal Physician to his present Majesty, the King of Prussia, and Member of the Royal Societies of London and Berlin," published at London in 1754. This is probably the most extended treatment of the subject in the eighteenth century. In his Preface the anonymous translator quotes various English physicians—including Arbuthnot—in praise of the curative effects of asses' milk, apparently the universal panacea. "Mr. Lemery" is quoted as saying: "Asses milk, as to its consistence and virtues, is much like that of a woman; it is much used as a remedy against the phthisick and other disorders of the lungs, and being like woman's milk, is of a qualifying nature, is beneficial in the cure of pimples, the defluxions of the eyes, and to ease the pains of the gout." Dr. Moffet,[76] also quoted in the Preface, explains the reason that Pope went daily to his "Dam" in the pasture:

A middle age Ass's milk is the best. Having got such a one, shut her from her foal four or five hours before you use her milk, let her be well curried. . . . Feed her

---

[75] *Essay Concerning the Nature of Aliments*, London, 1731, p. 85. Swift and Pope might have been amused at tavern-talk among members of the Royal Society many years earlier, on the occasion of the first English experiments on human blood transfusion, as reported by Samuel Pepys. The discussion led Dr. Daniel Whistler to tell "a pretty story" of Dr. Caius "that built Keys College; that, being very old, and living only . . . upon the milk of an angry, fretful woman, was so himself; and then, being advised to take it of a good-natured, patient woman, he did become so, beyond the common temper of his age. Thus much nutriment, they observed, might do." *The Diary of Samuel Pepys*, ed. H.B. Wheatley (London and New York, 1897-99), XIII. 196, entry for November 21, 1667.

[76] Thomas Moffet (Muffet), a well-known sixteenth-century English physician, was the author of several literary works. The editor here quotes from *Health's Improvement*, published posthumously in 1655.

43

with grinded malt-straw dried, mingled with a little sweet fennel-seed, annis, or carraway-seeds, which she will eat with great pleasure, and digest into a sweet and wholesome blood. An hour after that milk her as near the patient as you can, that it may be drank before the air hath alter'd it; for if it be once cold it is not wholesome. This may be done twice a day, morning and evening, upon an empty stomach, neither eating or drinking after it for two hours. You may sweeten it with sugar-candy, sugar of roses, or fine honey, and it will be more effectual.

We can only surmise when Pope's stay at Dawley began in April, but we know that he was there on May 1, when he reported to Bethel[77] "an increase of strength" from the regimen. On May 19, after interrupting his diet by a brief business trip to London, he was at Twickenham, but apparently only to visit his mother, since he wrote Oxford from Dawley on May 21. That he continued to make Dawley his home for some time is implied in a letter sent him by the Earl of Burlington on June 1, apologizing because an accident had prohibited his sending his coach to Dawley for Pope. The Dawley visit would seem to have ended about this time,[78] since Pope replied to Burlington that he was about to go to London, but Bolingbroke's house had been his home from some time in April until June 2, 1731. His health had greatly improved, whether from asses' milk, restrictions on his diet, or his temporary escape from the gloom of Twickenham.

We believe that during this period, in Bolingbroke's library and with his encouragement, Pope completed the first three epistles of *An Essay on Man* that were published shortly before his mother's death. Swift had known from both Bolingbroke and Pope, at least as early as Novem-

77 III. 196-97.
78 If Sherburn is correct in attributing to 1731 a letter dated only "June 15," Pope was briefly at Dawley two weeks after he left for London. This letter to Oxford reads: "I've been once more at Dawley, where my Lameness left me in 2 days, & am now returned home."

ber 1729, of Pope's project of "a system of Ethics in the Horatian way."[79] Pope had gone into a little more detail for Swift in June 1730: "Yet am I just now writing, (or rather planning) a book to make mankind look upon this life with comfort and pleasure, and put morality in good humour."[80] The phrase "writing, (or rather planning)" is significant. In illuminating fashion, Professor Sherburn[81] has reconstructed the various steps involved in "how Pope put his work on paper," even though, as he says, "The results of our examination can concern only humble mechanics of composition and not imaginative processes." Here is the gist of his conclusions: "There might seem to be four stages of mental and manual labor involved in this procedure: (1) Making notes for the poem, sometimes detailed, in prose; (2) the composition of verse paragraphs; (3) the arrangement of these fragments in an effective structure; and (4) the polishing and perfecting of lines. This last type of activity naturally went on in all the other steps of composition."

In May 1730 Joseph Spence, "who already aspired to be Pope's biographer," spent a week at Twickenham listening to Pope and later jotting down the memories that were to form the *Anecdotes*. Some of these notes preserved in manuscript concern the *Essay on Man*, presumably then in the "planning" stage, probably in prose with fragments of verse. The *Essay*—as was customary with Pope—was at this time involved in his mind with other future poems, particularly epistles to Bathurst and to Burlington. In October all work must have been abruptly put aside during the period of anxiety following Mrs. Pope's accident. It is interesting to note in Pope's letter to Caryll about that occurrence a

[79] Bolingbroke to Swift, November 19, 1729; Pope to Swift, November 28, 1729; III. 70-72, 79-81.

[80] III. 117-18.

[81] "Pope at Work," in *Essays on the Eighteenth Century Presented to David Nichol Smith* (Oxford, 1945; reprinted New York, 1963), pp. 49-64. The passage quoted here is on p. 52. See also John Butt, "Pope's Poetical Manuscripts" in *Essential Articles for the Study of Alexander Pope*, ed. Maynard Mack (Hamden, Conn.: The Shoe String Press, 1964), pp. 507-27; see also Mack's edition of the manuscripts.

sentence indicating that Pope's mind was running upon one of the basic themes of the *Essay*: "I am willing to think it a preservation of God, whose providence is surely sometimes particular, as 'tis always general." In December 1731 we have Pope's comment to Oxford that he was busy about a book to "lodge" in the new library. But his reply to a letter of Caryll on December 6, 1730[82] indicates that the *Essay* had not yet passed beyond the first two stages: "As to your question, if I am writing, I really very rarely dip my pen. The vanity is over: and unless I could hope to do it with some good end, or to a better pitch than I've hitherto done, I would never return to the lists. But the truth is, it is now in my hopes (God knows whether it may prove in my power) to contribute to some honest and moral purposes in writing on human life and manners, not exclusive of religious regards, and I have many fragments which I am beginning to put together, but nothing perfect, nor finished: nor in any condition to be shown, except to a friend at a fire side: I wish you would have so much curiosity to come and pass a few days to see them here."

We are inclined to think that the process of making his fragments into an effective structure had begun at Dawley in January 1731, at the time Bolingbroke wrote Swift:[83] "Pope is now in my library with me, and writes to the world, to the present and to future ages, while I begin this letter." But again the *Essay* was put aside during the protracted period of bouts of ill health which led to the prescription of asses' milk. He recovered at Dawley where he was living a more normal life than he had known for several years. Swift had said in his letter commenting on the new diet: "Descend in the name of God to some other amusements, as common Mortals do. . . . Sweeten your milk with mirth and motion." At Dawley Pope found "some other amusements." He could also spend long hours in Bolingbroke's study, with his Lordship as auditor and encourager. Here, we think, the three first epistles took on

82 III. 155.   83 III. 163.

the organic form that makes them the finest of Pope's poetical work. Returning to Twickenham, he found his mother in a comfortable condition that lasted until September. In June and early July Pope could devote himself to the final step of polishing and perfecting individual lines and couplets, so that he wrote to Hugh Bethel on July 28:[84] "I have just finished an Epistle in Verse, upon the Nature & Extent of Good nature and Social affection; & am going upon another whose subject is, The True Happiness of Man." The completed "Epistle in Verse" constituted the first three epistles of *An Essay on Man*; the one on which he was still engaged was the fourth epistle, to be put aside and further delayed by Mrs. Pope's illness and death. Four or five days later, on August 2, Bolingbroke sent Swift the lengthy and frequently quoted *précis* of the *Essay on Man*, beginning: "does Pope talk to you of the noble work which, att my instigation, he has begun, in such a manner that He must be convinced by this time I judged better of his tallents than He did?"

There seems little reason to doubt that the major work of making into a coherent, logical, and poetical whole such "fragments" as he had shown Spence and mentioned to Caryll was completed by Pope during the spring of 1731, during comfortable and placid hours in Bolingbroke's home and in his library, interrupted only by morning or evening "rambles" to the "Dam's Pasture" where Pope sucked asses' milk.

VI

As Pope wrote to Caryll, his mother's death marked the beginning of "a new Æra in my life." Inevitably that era was at first not a happy one. "My mother's loss has turned my frame of thinking," he wrote Swift.[85] "The habit of a whole life is a stronger thing than all the reason in the

[84] III. 209.   [85] 1 September 1733, III. 384.

world. I know I ought to be easy, and to be free; but I am dejected, I am confined." Othello's occupation was indeed gone. Twickenham was too filled with memories for him to remain there. During the summer following his mother's death, he wrote Bethel that he had been there only four days. "I am now pretty well," he said in the same letter,[86] "but my home is uneasy to me still, and I am therefore wandring about all this summer." His headquarters seem to have been sometimes at Dawley, sometimes at Oxford's London home. In September he visited the Carylls at Ladyholt; he spent early October with Lord Peterborough. Where and when he finished the fourth epistle of *An Essay on Man* we do not know[87]—perhaps again during one of his stays with Bolingbroke at Dawley. There is no reason to doubt Pope's statement to Swift in a letter of September 1, 1733: "I have written nothing this year." But a letter to Caryll, October 23, 1733[88] suggests that by this time Pope was beginning to think of his poetry, since he indicated that he had made some changes suggested by Caryll in the *Epistle to Cobham*, then added: "And I believe the author of the *Essay on Man* will end his poem in such manner as will satisfy your scruple." On New Year's Day, 1734, Pope wrote Caryll: "The *Essay upon Man* is a more serious thing; therefore it will be sent you." The *Essay* and the *Epistle to Cobham* both appeared in January 1734.[89]

Pope was gradually returning to work, but he was still too restless to settle down indefinitely at Twickenham, even though he occasionally entertained friends there and was

[86] 9 August 1733, III. 381.

[87] Professor Mack, in the Introduction to his Twickenham edition, p. xiv, says: "Whether having once embarked upon the fourth Epistle Pope carried it to a speedy conclusion in the autumn of 1731, it is impossible to say . . . nothing further of consequence is said about the composition of the *Essay on Man* until the summer and autumn of 1733, when it is evident that Epistle IV is still undergoing revision."

[88] III. 390.

[89] During 1734, in July and December, appeared also *Imitations of Horace* (Satire II, ii) and *Sober Advice from Horace*. The major work of 1734 was *An Epistle to Dr. Arbuthnot*, published January 1735, shortly before the doctor's death.

beginning to show some of his later interest in improving the place.[90] Reporting to Mallet "a smaller share of Health than ever," he hoped to amend it by a series of rambles around the Kingdom, which occupied him for four months during the summer and autumn of 1734. Bolingbroke's account of his itinerary makes one wonder how so frail a body as Pope's stood the rigors of those visits: "He is actually rambling from one friends house to another," Bolingbroke wrote Swift on June 27 and July 6, 1734.[91] "He is now att Cirencester, he came thither from my Lord Cobhams; he came to my Lord Cobhams from Mr Dormers; to Mr Dormers from London, to London from Chiswick; to Chiswick from my Farm, to my Farm from his own Garden, and he goes soon from Lord Bathursts to Lord Peterborows, after which he returns to my farm again. The Daemon of verse sticks close to him."

Casual readers of Pope's correspondence at this period are likely to attribute to him much more physical strength than he had actually had for some years, and to forget the progress of the kyphoscoliosis which was gradually taking from him power of locomotion. Indeed, such casual readers may have visualized him at Dawley striding to and from his "Dam," a matter of sixteen miles a day. It is doubtful that ever in his life Pope had been able to walk any such distance. There is no way of dating the period reported by the anonymous biographer and popularized by Johnson when Pope became completely dependent on maid-servants to get him into and out of bed and fasten around him the rigid "stays" which alone permitted him to stand. Sir John Hawkins in his *Life of Johnson*[92] said: "This weakness was

[90] He wrote Caryll and others that he had been stuccoing his "palace" which was now more truly *"Little Whitehall."* III. 406. The following spring (22 March 1735, III. 453) he reported his garden in good condition and added that he was building a stone obelisk, installing new ovens and stoves and "a hot-house for anana's." Later letters report his pride in sending pineapples to his friends. For the eighteenth-century interest in growing pineapples, see G.S. Rousseau, "Pineapples, Pregnancy, and *Peregrine Pickle*," forthcoming.

[91] III. 413.

[92] Quoted in *Lives of the English Poets*, ed. G.B. Hill (Oxford,

so great that he wore stays, as I have been assured by a waterman at Twickenham, who, in lifting him into his boat, had often felt them. He had a sedan-chair in the boat, in which he sat with the glasses down." In such a chair, carried by Bolingbroke's servants—or in another of the many conveyances undoubtedly available on Bolingbroke's farm —Pope probably made his trips to the pasture. Two comments by Swift during Pope's long stay at Dawley suggest Pope's increasing physical limitations: "I can walk 8 or ten Miles a day," Swift wrote on January 15, 1731,[93] "& ride 30 Irish ones. You cannot ride a mile nor walk two." Swift was sixty-four at this time, Pope forty-three. In his letter in response to the joint one from Bolingbroke and Pope, Swift wrote: "The misfortune I most lament is your not being able by exercise to battle with your disorders, as I do by riding and walking." On various occasions Pope said in effect to his friends: "If I could but ride on Horseback, it would make me some amends." Swift wished that Pope were "rich enough to keep a Coach and use it every day you are able." It seems curious that Pope never invested in one of the many kinds of coaches numerous in his time, the cost of which would seem to have been well within his means in middle life.[94] Not until 1740 did he mention owning any kind of conveyance. His references

---

1905), III. 83n. No further detail is given in *The Life of Samuel Johnson, LL.D. . . . Extended into Two Volumes . . . by Sir John Hawkins* (London, 1787). We have found nothing further on the matter in the modern abridged edition by Bertram H. Davis (New York, 1961), nor in the same author's *Johnson Before Boswell* (New Haven: Yale University Press, 1960).

[93] III. 161, 190. Two years later, on March 31, 1733, Swift wrote Pope: "I am almost every second day on horseback for about a dozen Miles" (III. 363).

[94] It seems that Sarah, Duchess of Marlborough, had tried to present Pope with a coach, among various gifts she offered him. Pope wrote her in June 1743 (IV. 457), indicating certain embarrassments of riches she had apparently offered, among them, "Secondly, I owe you a Coach & Horses, notwithstanding I fought you down to an Arm-Chair." According to Ruffhead (*Life*, p. 305), Pope was offered a coach by the government, but refused the offer.

to that are almost as perplexing as his sentence on the "Dam's pasture." Writing to Allen on October 14, 1740, he said: "I need not give you All the Trouble you propose of sending your Chariot, for I would chuse to come in my own little Chair, which would be highly useful to me when with you, in securing my very crazy person from Cold in the works in your Garden, Rock, &c."[95] This passing reference raises a question of what kind of "chair" or "chaise" —the words were often used interchangeably—Pope may have owned toward the end of his life. Even if we dismiss this reference to Allen as if spoken in jest, there is an indubitable reference to some sort of "chaise" in one of Pope's last letters, written on March 26, 1744 to Lords Marchmont and Bolingbroke,[96] telling them that Mr. Warburton wishes to wait upon them both, and adding: "If he comes to Battersea in a morning, pray furnish him with my chaise to come on hither, and let the chaise be left here, of whose earthly part I shall make use in my garden, tho not of its aquatic." Pope probably possessed some form of "Bath chair," or what we think of as "wheel chair," which he used to assist him in gardening in Twickenham and on the estates of friends. At no time did he ever mention owning a horse or renting or building a stable. His "earthly" and "aquatic" chaise remains a mystery, but it would hardly have been capable of a journey to Bath.

95 IV. 280. It is possible that Pope intended a mere laughing allusion to "the little green chair" the Allens kept for him at Prior Park. Sherburn mentions (IV. 229) an untraced letter from Dr. William Oliver of Bath to Pope, in which he says that he is to dine the next day with the Allens, "where I shall see the little green Chair, shall try by all the Strength of Imagination to replace you in it." Sherburn concludes that Pope had his own undersized chair at Prior Park. Indeed such chairs may have been provided for him at Bolingbroke's or Oxford's or in other houses to which he made long visits.

96 IV. 513. Ralph Straus, in *Carriages and Coaches: Their History and Their Evolution* (London: M. Secker, 1912), Chap. VI, discusses the "one-horse chaise" or "one-horse chair," some of which were very small, intended for children, which would have suited Pope well. He mentions also the *desobligeant*, "a chaise so called in France from its holding but one person," as Laurence Sterne said when he purchased an old one for his *Sentimental Journey*.

Such journeys were becoming more and more of a night-mare to Pope. They were over post roads, the best in England, but still far inferior to those in France, as English journal-keepers from Evelyn in 1620 to Thomas Gray in 1739 frequently noted. Cross-country journeys were often over little more than cart tracks.[97] Pope wrote Martha Blount about a proposed visit:[98] "I dread that [Ramble] to Worcester & back, for every one tells me tis perpetual Rock, & the worst of rugged roads; which really not only hurt me at present, but leave Consequences very uneasy to me." His letters make clear that extensive "rambles" of the sort Bolingbroke reported to Swift and which Pope made the following year also, were possible only because his hosts sent him by coach from one aristocratic home to another. Pope frequently stipulated that a visit must be long rather than short, since it took him some days to recover from a journey. As he wrote Bathurst in August 1735: "Riding is Physick & Strength at once to your Lordship, whereas to me it is Sickness & Pain."[99] Frequently he indicated his dread of travelling in a coach alone. We must remember that, in addition to fairly constant pain, Pope's weight was far less than that of a normal man, and he was consequently even more violently tossed about on rough roads. Too, he had the chronic affliction of piles, which he mentioned several times, one that made coach travelling particularly irritating. Writing to Allen on November 17, 1740, about his apparent procrastination in coming to visit him at Prior Park, Pope said that George Arbuthnot had promised to accompany him if he would delay his visit, adding: "His Company will not only comfort me, but render every Jolt on the road less sensible to me. Indeed Mr.

[97] Cf. his letter to Mrs. Ann Knight, August 5, 1734 (III. 425-26), cancelling a visit he had planned to make, which would have been cross-country. A clergyman from Mrs. Knight's district "told me the way was farther and worse than ever my fears had imagined." There are various references to his dread of "abominable stoney roads," where he had been "Half-jumbled to death."

[98] IV. 185.

[99] III. 483-84. Cf. letter to Allen, August 2, 1739, IV. 190.

Ches. [Cheselden] told me plainly, a Coach would be a Herse to me, if I went in one alone."

The year 1734-35 was saddened by the serious condition of Dr. Arbuthnot in what he himself recognized as his final illness. "A Recovery in my Case, and at my Age, is impossible," he wrote Pope on July 17, 1734.[100] "The kindest Wish of my Friends is *Euthanasia*." As his "Last Request" to Pope, he urged him to "continue that noble *Disdain* and *Abhorrence* of Vice, which you seem naturally endu'd with, but still with a due regard to your own Safety; and study more to reform than to chastise." In one reply Pope wrote: "I determine to address to you one of my Epistles, written by piece-meal many years, & which I have now made haste to put together."[101] From Southampton, where he was visiting Lord Peterborough, he wrote Arbuthnot on September 3 that the piece was finished. *An Epistle to Dr. Arbuthnot* was published in January 1735, shortly before Arbuthnot's death on February 27.

Pope's letters during the years 1734-38 are singularly free from the reiterated details of poor health which mark those that preceded and those that are to follow. To be sure he refers occasionally to poor eyesight, frequent bouts of headache, and occasional attacks of rheumatism. One severe illness, referred to in several letters, but in none described, introduced the surgeon William Cheselden (of whom we shall hear more), who of all his many medical practitioners most aroused Pope's enthusiasm. During this period he published little after the *Epistle to Arbuthnot*—one short *Moral Essay* in 1735, nothing in 1736; in 1737 and 1738 only a few of the *Imitations of Horace*. His comment to Swift early in 1736[102] sets the tone of this period, so far as literature was concerned. Pope had been talking of the possibility of another volume of "Epistles in Verse," presumably of about the same length as *An Essay on Man*:

But alas! the task is great, and *non sum qualis eram*!
My understanding indeed, such as it is, is extended

100 III. 417.   101 III. 428.   102 25 March, IV. 5-6.

rather than diminish'd: I see things more in the whole, more consistent, and more clearly deduced from, and related to, each other. But what I gain on the side of philosophy, I lose on the side of poetry: the flowers are gone, when the fruits begin to ripen, and the fruits perhaps will never ripen perfectly. The climate . . . is but cold and uncertain; the winds rise, and the winter comes on. I find myself but little disposed to build a new house; I have nothing left but to gather up the reliques of a wreck, and look about me to see what friends I have!

There were two main reasons for the change in tone that marks the correspondence of these years, when Pope was approaching fifty; one psychological, the other physiological. So far as the first was concerned, Pope had now settled into a routine of comparatively normal living, impossible for him during the last years of his mother's life when his attendance upon her had reduced him to a humdrum of melancholy, as a result of which he inevitably watched his own symptoms and exaggerated them frequently in the many letters that took the place of visits to and from friends. Now he was entertaining and being entertained. At least during the summers he "rambled," sometimes making rounds of visits. On some of these occasions he took an active part in assisting friends who were building or restoring houses, and—on his visits to Lady Peterborough—helping perfect the gardens at Bevis Mount. In addition, his attention was diverted from his own aches and pains by other matters which at the time assumed greater importance in his mind: in the second half of 1735 his attention was largely on his controversy with Edmund Curll over the publication of Pope's letters; in 1737 he was concerned with preparations for his own edition of his letters, and his apparently futile attempts to recover his letters from Swift. He was remodeling his house and intent upon his garden. He wrote to Allen, November 6, 1736: "I am now as busy in Planting for myself as I was lately in planting for another. And I thank God for every Wet day & for every Fog, that gives me the headake, but prospers my works."[103]

A physiological basis for the improvement in his health was the fact that, for almost the first time in his life, Pope was living on a fairly strict diet, undoubtedly recommended by his physicians but in part self-imposed as a result of experience. Pope had always been inclined toward gluttony. Professor Sherburn quotes a letter from Lord Bathurst to Lady Suffolk, written during a visit of Pope's in July 1734: "You do well to reprove him about his intemperance; for he makes himself sick every meal at your most moderate and plain table in England. Yesterday I had a little piece of salmon just caught out of the Severn, and a fresh pike that was brought me from the other side of your house out of the Thames. He ate as much as he could of both, and insisted upon his moderation, because he made his dinner upon one dish."[104]

Restored to society as he now was, he found that rich living at the homes of his aristocratic and wealthy friends was having a drastic effect on his constitution. As he wrote to Fortescue, August 23, 1735: "I shall dye of Hospitality, which is a Fate becoming none but a Patriot or a Parliament Man in the Country."[105] "I find," he wrote Mrs. Ann Knight in October 1736, "I must never attempt to dine so late as a fashionable hour. I really dread the consequence of doing it at Marble-Hill; when you set out thence after twelve, it will be three before you can be there, and four before they'll dine."[106] Pope began to decline such invitations, if they were not command performances, and, even if it meant that he ate alone, ate dinner no later than two. Supper he omitted entirely, and wine-drinking, which he had frequently carried to excess, became the exception rather than the rule in his life. He described this new regimen to Dr. Cheyne at Bath. "The Dr," he wrote Bethel,

[103] III. 40-41.
[104] III. 414-15; the quotation is from the *Suffolk Correspondence*, II. 81.
[105] III. 486.   [106] IV. 38.

"magnifyed the Scarborow waters, & indeed all Waters, but above all, Common Water. He was greatly edifyed with me for having left off Suppers, & upon my telling him that most of my Acquaintance had not only done so, but had not drunk out 3 dozen of wine in my house in a Twelvemonth, he blessed God, & said, my Conversation was with Angels!"[107]

In 1739, however, we begin to find a marked change in Pope's references to his health. The first half of that year was placid enough. He wrote to Martha Blount in July:[108] "I am extremely well, as well as ever I expect to be in every thing, or desire to be, except my Constitution could be mended." To Swift he described his way of life in detail: "I come to what is now my chief care, my Health & Amusement: The first is better, as to Headakes, worse as to Weakness & Nerves, the changes of Weather affect me much, otherwise I want not Spirits, except when Indigestions prevail. The Mornings are my Life; in the Evenings I am not dead indeed but sleep. . . . I love Reading still, better than Conversation; but my Eyes fail; and at the hours when most people indulge in Company, I am tired, & find the Labour of the past day sufficient to weigh me down: So I hide my self in bed, as a Bird in his Nest, much about the same Time, & rise & chirp the earlyer the next morning."[109] Pope's first mention of a new and serious condition occurred in a letter to Fortescue on August 17, 1739:[110] "I dined yesterday with Jervas upon a venison pasty, where we drank your health warmly, but as temperately, as to liquor, as you could yourself: for neither he nor I are well enough to drink wine; he for his asthmatic, and I for another complaint, that persecutes me much of late." This marks the beginning of a urinary condition that was to add to the difficulties of his last years, and lead to the experience of an operation.

The first of various treatments suggested by his medical men was a prolonged stay at the spas in Bath and Bristol.

107 25 September 1737, IV. 85.　　108 IV. 187.
109 17-19 May 1739, IV. 179.　　110 IV. 193-94.

This journey to the north was no pleasure trip. "Among my Complaints," he wrote Allen on September 14,[111] "I have one, & the most dangerous of any, that may as the Doctors tell me, be mended by drinking the Waters warm at Bristol." In part because Pope was seriously concerned about his health, in part because the treatment forced him to spend a long cold winter in uncomfortable surroundings, the tone of many letters of this period is a combination of tedium and exasperation. Bristol accommodations were far inferior to those to which he had been accustomed at Bath. Threatened constantly with colds, which he was warned would be dangerous to his condition, he went to Bath, where he was advised to "mix Bristol water with a small Quantity of Bath at the Pump." His health improved somewhat, in part, as he realized, because he was living very quietly on a restricted diet, and drank little or no wine. He noticed a difference shortly after he left the spas and went to London in February. "Since I came to London," he wrote Bethel, February 18, 1740: "I am not so much in Spirits, nor in the same Quiet, as at Bath. The Irregular hours of Dining (for as to Nights, I keep the same) already have disordered my Stomach, & bring back that Heaviness & Languor upon me after dinner, which I was almost entirely free from. Tho I still continue to make Water my ordinary drink, with as little Mixture of Wine as before."[112] The contrast between his casual attitude in 1736 to the colds and headaches that unsuccessfully attempted to interrupt his gardening, and his realization that the present condition was serious, is well indicated by sentences in a letter to Allen, March 25, 1740:[113] "The weather gives me Cold upon Cold, & I cannot attend my works in planting. . . . the severe Northwinds would kill me, with a Damp in my Grotto as fatal as those in Mines, if I presumed to work there now." Headaches and colds of the sort about which he had formerly complained had not been sufficient to keep him from his garden.

[111] IV. 195. The reference is to the Hot Wells Spa, in Clifton, on the Avon near Bristol.
[112] IV. 225.   [113] IV. 230.

Spa waters and diet having proved ineffectual, Pope was "at last *resolvd* (tho perhaps *compelld* were the truer word) to submit to the Operation of Mr Cheselden; he comes to me to morrow for that End." So he wrote on August 2, 1740 to Hugh Bethel. When Pope first mentioned Cheselden's name to Swift,[114] he was surprised that Swift had no idea to whom he was referring, and said in reply: "I wondered a little at your quaere, who Cheselden was? it shews that the truest merit does not travel so far any way as on the wings of poetry; he is the most noted, and most deserving man, in the whole profession of Chirurgery; and has sav'd the lives of thousands by his manner of cutting for the stone." A grateful patient did not exaggerate the skill and fame of his doctor, since William Cheselden was at this time the most famous surgeon in England. Possibly one of the reasons for Pope's surprise that Swift did not recognize his name was the fact that both Pope and Arbuthnot had known Cheselden for many years. Indeed Pope had thought of Cheselden at first not as a surgeon but as a member of a group interested in art and letters. His first mention had been in a letter to Jonathan Richardson, February 6, 1722,[115] when Pope was preparing republication of his edition of Shakespeare. He asked Richardson to "tell your friend Mr. Chiseldon, I shall be obliged to him if he will put upon a paper those conjectures of some passages of Shakespeare which he mentioned to Dr. Arbuthnot, or any others that may have occurred to him." The next month, when Richardson was arranging a "Shakespeare evening," at his home, Pope wrote him: "Let Friend Cheselden be of the party."[116]

[114] This letter is no longer extant. Swift's reply may be found IV. 3-4, and Pope's answer IV. 5-6.

[115] II. 100-101.

[116] II. 106. Cheselden had been one of the original subscribers to Pope's translation of the *Iliad* in 1725. Richardson suggested that Cheselden was well known among his friends as host, as well as guest, in lines he wrote, presumably in a letter to Pope, which are quoted, without reference, by Sir Zachary Cope, *William Cheselden, 1688-1752* (Edinburgh and London: Livingstone, 1953), p. 87:

Well before Pope mentioned him to Swift, Cheselden had become known as the most expert practicing surgeon in England, famous particularly for the technique he had developed during his period as lithotomist at St. Thomas' Hospital for "cutting for the stone,"[117] a technique that remained standard in surgery until 1885. In that age of non-specialization, Cheselden specialized more than most surgeons, simply because his fame brought so many stone patients to his doors. But during the 1730's he also achieved great importance in the history of ophthalmology by

---

Cheselden, with candid wile,
Detains his guest; the ready Lares smile;
Good Chiron so, within his welcome bower
Received of verse the mild and sacred power.
With anxious skill supplied the best relief
And healed with balm and sweet discourse his grief.

Professor Maynard Mack, in his edition of *An Essay on Man*, pp. 38n., 39n., suggests analogies between Cheselden's *Anatomy of the Humane Body* (London, 1713) and some of Pope's most familiar lines: those on the "microscopic eye," and on the sense of smell in the lioness, I. 213. He says, p. 42n., "I find nowhere the curious misinformation of Pope's note that lions hunt by ear. He may have owed it to his friend, the anatomist Cheselden, whose name he has placed beside this verse in the Harvard MS." Cheselden's *Anatomy* was very popular throughout the century; by 1778 it had gone into eleven editions, and later was translated into eight languages.

[117] The most complete account of Cheselden as surgeon is that of Sir Zachary Cope, mentioned in the note above. Sir Zachary kindly replied to an inquiry of ours, saying that he knew of no extant diary or case-book of Cheselden's, in which we might seek further reference to Pope's case. A most interesting account of Cheselden's operations—in part in the surgeon's own words—is given by Sir D'Arcy Power, "Cheselden's Operation," *British Journal of Surgery*, XVIII (January 1931), 353-57. He says, p. 356, that a French surgeon, sent to England by the Royal Academy of France in 1729, stated that he had often seen a stone removed in twenty-four seconds, and that it rarely took more than a minute. He watched Cheselden cut twenty-seven patients without losing one, and spoke so favorably of the method that it soon became known and practiced throughout Europe. Cheselden himself said, p. 354: "Publicly in St. Thomas' Hospital, I have cut two hundred and thirteen; of the first fifty, only three died; of the second fifty, three; of the third fifty, eight; and of the last sixty-three, six." Several of the patients who died had developed smallpox or another infectious disease during the period of their cure; they did not all die as a result of the operation.

techniques he developed in several eye operations,[118] a fact that explains an already quoted allusion by Pope in the *Imitations of Horace*:[119]

> I'll do what MEAD and CHESELDEN advise,
> To keep these limbs, and to preserve these eyes.

Cheselden's fame in ophthalmology lay not only in his having been the first ever to make an artificial pupil, but even more upon his theory about the nature of cataract and the technique he had developed for its removal, which, although opposed by some, was widely accepted and practiced by many eye surgeons. Pope was commenting on his reputation in that field when he wrote Cheselden from Bath, November 21, 1741:[120] "How does Mrs Cheselden? Had it not been for her, you had been here. Here are three Cataracts ripened for you—Mr Pierce assures me. Don't tell your Wife that." Pope was here referring not to his own eyes, as John Butt thought, but informing Cheselden that Jeremiah Pierce, surgeon at Bath Hospital, had three patients whose cataracts he was permitting to "ripen" in the hope that the distinguished surgeon Cheselden would remove them.

So successful a surgeon inevitably had his foes, as well as his admirers.[121] It is amusing to find that one rival, Dr. James

118 See Chap. XII, "Cheselden as an Ophthalmic Surgeon," in Cope, *Cheselden*.

119 Epistle I. 1. 51-52. In his edition of the *Imitations of Horace*, IV. 353, John Butt states that "Pope seems to have become acquainted with Cheselden about the year 1735," apparently not having noticed Pope's allusions in much earlier letters.

120 IV. 372. In the "Biographical Appendix" to *Imitations of Horace*, pp. 283, 353, Butt says that Cheselden "was treating Pope for cataract." The statement seems to have been based merely on his interpretation of this letter. There is one passing remark in Pope's letters which might lead to such a theory. He wrote to Warburton, January 18, 1743 (IV. 438): "my Eyesight grows every day shorter and *dimmer*." (Italics ours.) At no other time does he use the word "dimmer" about his sight. But if Cheselden had been treating him for cataract, surely Pope would have mentioned treatment of his eyes as well as of other symptoms.

121 An interesting example of the opposition aroused by Cheselden's

60

Monro, physician to the Bethlehem Hospital, suggested that Cheselden attempted to shine in light reflected from Pope. Horace Walpole included in a letter to Horace Mann, October 8, 1741,[122] "a new epigram that you will not dislike: it is made by Dr. Monro on two of his brethren, a physician and a surgeon." His barb was first turned against Edward Hulse, physician to George II, who had apparently attempted to offset a charge of heresy by appearing on various occasions with a parson in his coach. Cheselden, he implied, sought to gain credit with "the Wits" in a similar way:

When Cheselden saw that the scheme had success,
He conceiv'd in some sort it might suit his own case;
So to take an unlucky damn'd censure away,
He contriv'd to be seen with a wit every day:
And with Pope by his side in the pride of his soul,
'Now damn ye,' says he; 'now d'ye think I'm a fool?'

Cheselden was associated in his treatment of Pope by Richard Mead, one of the most distinguished physicians in

---

eye-technique is a pamphlet by Benedict Duddell, a surgeon, in the British Museum, *An Answer to Mr. Cheselden's Appendix, relating to the New Operation upon Iris of the Eye* (London, 1733). The antagonist opposed the "new" method proposed by Cheselden *circa* 1730, "an opening in the Iris for the Disease which is call'd a Syneresis of the Pupil." He reminded Cheselden that his own first method of cutting for the stone had been far from successful and that he had not hesitated to try another.

[122] The epigram was quoted by John Butt, *Imitations of Horace*, p. 353, from *The Letters of Horace Walpole*, ed. Mrs. Paget Toynbee (Oxford: Clarendon Press, 1903-05), I. 106. The characters are identified in *Horace Walpole's Correspondence with Sir Horace Mann*, ed. W.S. Lewis, W.H. Smith, and G.L. Lam, Yale Edition (New Haven, 1954), I. 168.

Monro may well have been piqued by Pope's passing—but slighting—reference to him in *Imitations of Horace* (Epistle II. ll. 70-71):

Sure I should want the care of ten *Monroes*,
If I would scribble, rather than repose.

This epistle was published in 1737. Pope's flattering reference to Mead and Cheselden in Epistle I. ll. 50-51, was published the next year.

London with whom also Pope had been acquainted for many years. "Dr. Mead," said Samuel Johnson,[123] "lived more in the broad sunshine of life than almost any man." He had inherited the lucrative practice of Dr. John Radcliffe (whose name we associate with the Radcliffe Library, Observatory and Infirmary), once physician to Princess Anne of Denmark. Through Radcliffe's influence Mead was summoned to the deathbed of Queen Anne, and thereafter became Physician in Ordinary to George II and Queen Caroline, the most popular—and most affluent—medical man of his time. In 1719 he had attracted much attention through his involvement in a truly medical quarrel, a sword duel with Dr. John Woodward in the quadrangle of Gresham College (both men were members of the Royal Society, Woodward since 1693, Mead since 1703). The subject of their quarrel was a disagreement about the treatment of smallpox, and particularly about Woodward's theory of bile. The engagement was halted by bystanders when Woodward tripped and lost his footing. This extraordinary duel must have excited the Scriblerians, who had so recently been engaged on their *Memoirs*. Woodward, one of many writers of "new theories" in the Burnet controversy and a collector who prided himself particularly on his fossils, had been bitterly opposed by Dr. Arbuthnot, himself a passionate collector. He became the "Fossile" of *Three Hours after Marriage*, a collaboration of Gay, Arbuthnot and Pope, and appeared in the *Memoirs of Martinus Scriblerus*, when Martinus "attended Dr. Woodward thro' a Twelvemonth's course of Vomition."[124] Woodward's theories of "Vomition" were echoed also by Pope in his satire on Walpole:

123 *Boswell's Life of Johnson*, ed. G.B. Hill, rev., L.F. Powell (Oxford: Clarendon Press, 1934-50), III. 355. The entry is for May 16, 1778, when Boswell dined with Johnson at Mr. Beauclerk's, with Mr. Langton, Mr. Steevens, Dr. Higgins and some others. The sentence is given, without connotation, as the first of Johnson's remarks that evening.

124 *Memoirs of the Extraordinary Life, Works, and Discoveries of Martinus Scriblerus*, ed. Charles Kerby-Miller (New Haven: Yale University Press, 1950), pp. 130, 274-75. There are passing references to Mead in this volume.

As one of *Woodward's* Patients, sick and sore,
I puke, I nauseate,—yet he thrusts in more.[125]

As with Cheselden the younger Pope had thought of
Mead as an associate among men of letters and arts rather
than as a physician. Mead had lived at first in the house
of John Radcliffe in Bloomsbury Square, but when Pope
visited him, he had moved to his home in Great Ormond
Street, where Cheselden also resided, close to Queen Square,
the home of Jonathan Richardson. At all these houses Pope
was a welcome visitor. Mead was justly proud of his library
of books and manuscripts, said to be the finest collection
in the British Isles. In his *Epistle to Burlington*[126] Pope
praised him for "collecting" as assiduously for his friends
as for himself, for his finding "Books for Mead, and Butterflies for Sloane," explicating the line in later editions
of his Works: "Two Eminent Physicians; the one had an
excellent Library, the other the finest collection in Europe
of natural curiosities; both men of great learning and
humanity." Samuel Johnson was responsible for localizing
at the Mead home the passage-of-arms between Pope and
Richard Bentley over Pope's translation of Homer, when
Bentley supposedly said: "a pretty poem, Mr. Pope; but
you must not call it *Homer*."[127] Johnson also, following
Ruffhead,[128] reported Mead's criticism of Pope's latinity,
the phrase "Amor publicus," in his inscription for Shakespeare, quoting the authority of Patrick, a dictionary-maker,
to which Pope replied, "that he would allow a dictionary-
maker to understand a single word, but not two words put
together," at which, according to Warton, Mead gave up
the struggle, quoting to Pope, "Omnia vincit amor, et nos
cedamus amori." On January 4, 1738 Pope made an ap-

[125] "The Fourth Satire of Dr. John Donne," ll. 152-153, in *Imitations of Horace*, ed. John Butt, p. 37. In the same satire Woodward is
mentioned also, ll. 28-31.

[126] *Epistles to Several Persons*, ed. F.W. Bateson, p. 136 and note.

[127] *Lives of the English Poets*, ed. cit., III. 213n. Bishop J.H. Monk,
Life of Richard Bentley, D.D., 2nd edn. (London, 1833), II. 372,
lays the scene at Atterbury's table.

[128] The passages from Ruffhead and Warton are given in *Lives*,
III. 201n.

pointment with Jonathan Richardson to sit to him for a portrait commissioned by Mead, whose biographer, Matthew Maty, second librarian of the British Museum, said:[129] "He was the friend of *Pope*, of *Halley*, of *Newton*, and placed their portraits in his house near the Busts of their great Masters, the antient Greeks and Romans."

Those earlier happy days were over. Cheselden and Mead were now attending Pope for a condition of great seriousness. Cheselden's operation marks the beginning of the last chapter of Pope's life.

VII

Apart from normal human dread of any operation in those pre-anesthesia days, Pope remembered vividly the sufferings of his close friend, Lord Peterborough, five years earlier as the result of an operation performed by a surgeon evidently much less skillful than Cheselden. Pope's letters in 1734 abound in references to Peterborough's sufferings, both before and after he underwent "the severest operation of being cut into the bladder for a suppression of urine." The operation had been performed at Bristol, and—indomitable as he was—Peterborough had insisted on going home to Bevis Mount, near Southampton, long before he was fit to make such a journey. Pope had gone to Southampton to see him. He wrote to Martha Blount, August 25, 1735:[130] "I found my Lord Peterborow on his Couch, where he gave me an account of the excessive Sufferings he had past thro', with a weak voice, but spirited. . . . I lay in the next room to him, where I found he was awake, & calld for help most hours of the night, sometimes crying out for pain: In the morning he got up at nine, & was carryd into his Garden in a Chair; he fainted away twice

129 *Correspondence*, IV. 91. Matthew Maty, *Authentic Memoirs of the Life of Richard Mead, M.D.* (London: Whiston, 1755), pp. 62-63; quoted in *Epistles to Several Persons*, 132n.

130 III. 487-88.

there. He fell about 12 into a violent pang which made his limbs all shake & his teeth chatter, & for some time he lay cold as death. His Wound was drest (which is done constantly 4 times a day) & he grew gay, & Sate at dinner with ten people. After this, he was again in torment for a quarter of an hour; and as soon as the Pang was over, was carried again into the Garden. . . . Nothing can be more affecting & melancholy to me than what I see here: yet he takes my Visit so kindly, that I should have lost One great pleasure had I not come." Pope added a fitting epitaph for the man who fulfilled his intention of going by yacht to Lisbon, where he arrived only to die: "This Man was never born to dye like other men, any more than to live like them."

At the time of his own operation, Pope was concerned, too, about the sufferings of his friend, William Fortescue, who was experiencing the "severe Distemper" of "the Gravel," a generic term for gallstones or kidney stones. In the letter to Bethel, informing him of the approaching operation, Pope added specific details, which he divulged to no other friend. Hugh Bethel seems to have taken the place of confidant long occupied by John Caryll, who had died April 6, 1736. Pope wrote: "The constant fear of being in Extremity, on every little Cold I catch, or upon any Heat by Motion, makes Life uncomfortable & precarious; and it is arrived of late to that point that I am waked five or six times in a night with a Pressure to make water, whatever Diet or Liquids I can use. You shall hear how it goes with me."[131] Bethel was to learn from the same letter, which Pope kept until the operation was over: "I kept this till another post that I might just tell you how I under go this

[131] IV. 254-56. Pope's letter gives no clue as to where the operation was performed. Before Cheselden joined the Royal Hospital, his home had often been Pope's London headquarters, particularly when Pope was ill. But Pope mentioned in a letter that Cheselden had moved his family away from London. Pope's London residence during the recent past had been at the home of Erasmus Lewis. Cf. IV. 177, 237. It is possible that Pope was writing from the Royal Hospital, where he went on two or three later occasions for treatment by Cheselden. Sir Zachary Cope, *Cheselden*, pp. 35, 43, says that Cheselden was permitted to continue his private practice upon persons who might come to him in his new surroundings.

operation. It is with a good deal of pain. the Stoppage is found by the Probe, and lies within an inch of the Os Pubis; it must be often repeated in hopes to wear the passage wider. The worst is the Pain upon every making water after it, for six or seven hours, the Salts of the Urine stimulating the Sore places; which must continue till by Use it grow more open & callous. The Remedy is (at present) worse than the Disease, for that gives me no pain, but Uneasiness."

Painful though it was, the operation was no such ordeal as Lord Peterborough had suffered. Pope's was a urethral dilatation, the therapy for which was the passing of a metal sound (dilator) into the penis. Such urethral stricture as Pope experienced, medical authorities tell us, was probably the result of gonorrhea, contracted in youth. The date of the operation was August 2, 1740, two years before Colley Cibber published his *Letter to Mr. Pope*,[132] with its statement that in Pope's youth Cibber had rescued him from a diseased bawd in "a house of carnal recreation," a charge that Pope vehemently denied, though there is little question that in that halcyon period of his youth, 1714-18, as Professor Sherburn says, "Pope, conscious of his physical infirmity, put up a brave front at being a rake." So far as Cibber's specific charge is concerned, we may let Cheselden, who performed the operation, speak:[133] "I could give a more particular account of his [Pope's] health than perhaps any man. Cibber's slander of a carnosity [is] false. [He] had been gay, but left it on his acquaintance with Mrs. Blount."

Pope said that the probing "must be often repeated," but his letters give no account of further operations by Cheselden though he mentioned such a possibility close

---

[132] *A Letter from Mr. Cibber to Mr. Pope* (London: 1742), pp. 47-49. Ault gives an account of Pope's early escapades, *New Light on Pope*, pp. 301-303. See also Sherburn, *Early Career*, particularly pp. 156-57. Ault dates the episode 1714-15, Sherburn, 1716-17. Cibber's *Letter* was probably a basic reason for Pope's changing Cibber for Theobald in *The Dunciad*.

[133] Spence, *Anecdotes*, I. p. 111.

to the end of his life. In the next extant letter to Bethel, on September 26, he said of his "progress in the Operation for the Strangury," that "the Severity of it, & the present Consequences from the Soreness of the Parts, made it too much for me to repeat often enough to obtain any effectual remedy. . . . So I must compound with the Piles, and Indigestion, and suffer them to get ground, in hopes to defeat the pains of the Strangury."[134] Since Cheselden had apparently warned Pope that his comfort would depend on diet and drink—"Vegetable diet & cool liquors," he noted—Pope began what was to be a series of journeys to Bath and Bristol. He spoke of the possibility of his going to Bath as early as October 14, but delayed decision for some time. Problems of conveyance were, as always, uppermost. On two occasions a private coach seems to have been available but, because of his dread of being "tumbled" alone in a coach, he delayed until he could write Allen on December 2 that George Arbuthnot had arranged to travel with him—presumably in a public coach—to Reading and to Newbury where Allen's carriage would meet them, "& he will poise your Chariot well with me, the rest of the way, if you can spare it so far."

Unfortunately Pope's letters written at Bath do not afford any clue to his health. A sentence in a letter to Mallet (January 25, 1741) may well be literal truth: "I have written to few or none of my Friends since I have been here." Not until well after his return in February do we find any reference to health. On April 14, 1741[135] he wrote Bethel, whose asthmatic condition was becoming steadily worse, expressing his concern, then adding: "Your Eyes I know are weak (and so truly are mine, weaker & weaker) tho otherwise my health, Colds excepted, tolerable of late." Like his mother, Pope had reached a plateau, where he was to linger for some months. Indeed he wrote Fortescue August 12, 1741: "As for my own health, it is not worse, but rather better than twenty years ago, when we first knew one another." The diet and the water

[134] IV. 268-69.   [135] IV. 340.

had had an effect, and other interests were distracting his attention from his symptoms, as he succinctly implied in a letter to Allen: "My Grotto is finished, & my Letters are printed." Still another reason for the diversion of his attention was hinted in a letter to Allen, June 5, 1741, postponing a trip to Bath: "Mr Warburton is with me, & intends to go to Oxford . . . He & I must necessarily return together to Oxford (I'll acquaint you with the reason) ." Pope had been offered the degree of LL.D. by Oxford, and Warburton said that he had been approached "by a person of eminence in that place, with an usual compliment, to know if a Doctor's degree in Divinity would be acceptable to him." The degree for Pope seems to have been offered, but that for Warburton failed. Thanks to his loyalty to his "learned" friend, Pope was never to wear academic regalia, never to join the procession of those "Dunces" in cap and gown at whom he shot barbs in *The Dunciad*, on the enlarged version of which he and Warburton were engaged at this time. Warburton joined him early in December at Bath, to which Pope had accompanied the Allens in November 1741.

From this time, more frequent references to ill health enter Pope's letters. An unusually cold winter and spring did not add to the comfort of a man so susceptible to colds. Travelling in Allen's coach, he and Warburton made their way from Bath to Twickenham over "Alps of Snow." The bad winter was followed by a "very unwholesome Spring, with continual North-east Winds, and in France there has been as great or a greater Mortality," he commented to Bethel, May 21-23. We pause over these details, since this was the period during which Pope was developing asthma, a secondary cause of his death two years later. As Peterborough's sufferings had made Pope dread still more the Cheselden operation, he was now even more conscious of his increasing affliction because he had recently seen his friend and confidant, Hugh Bethel, close to death through asthma.[136] Bethel had been able to do what Pope could

136 Pope wrote Martha Blount, August 11, 1741 (IV. 355): "I am

not: he had spent more than a year in Italy, but finding himself no better, decided to return home, presumably to die.

Although at the very end of 1742 Pope reported to Allen that "my health (Colds excepted) is much the better,"[137] this is the last time he was to speak about his health optimistically. His eyesight was increasingly bad,[138] his asthma definitely progressing. It is natural that his first statement about this should have been to Bethel:[139] "I have delayd writing any account of my own health which I knew would occasion as much uneasiness to you, as yours had given comfort to me. For I have these 3 months or more, been advancing to an Asthmatic Complaint, (from one Cold to another, as I believe, for I saw no further Cause for it). It is now at such a height, that I can scarce walk, or go up a pair of Stairs, or move much in my bed, without quite losing breath; And it is attended with a difficulty of urine, which makes me fear a Dropsy (the quantity I make is daily so much diminished), & a pain in the Breast is joynd to it, which I would willingly impute to Wind." This reference to "a pain in the Breast," which is repeated in the next letter to Allen, is the first indication that Pope had developed a cardiac condition, "commonplace," Dr. McKusick writes, "with severe kyphoscoliosis—so-called kyphoscoliotic heart disease, or cor pulmonale, embarrassment of pulmonary and cardiac function from the thoracic deformity."

Letters during this period are few and brief, perhaps because of Bolingbroke's return to London, and the fact that he and Pope had been together for five weeks at Twickenham and elsewhere. On May 21, 1743[140] he wrote War-

very glad I did not defer seeing Mr Bethel. I found him last night so bad, & panting for breath, that I can scarce imagin he ever will recover. . . . perhaps we shall never see him more."

[137] December 27, (1742); IV. 433.

[138] To Warburton, January 18, 1743, IV. 438: "My Eyesight grows every day shorter & dimmer." To Allen, March 12, IV. 443: "I don't care to be always complaining, but so it is, that my Eyes grow so weak it is almost a pain to write a common letter."

[139] IV. 445-46. Pope wrote Allen on March 24, 1743, IV. 449: "The worst is an excessive shortness of breath & pain in my breast, but I'm tired of tiring my friends with Complaining."

[140] IV. 455-56.

69

burton that his lawsuit with Lintot was at last at an end, the quarto edition of *The Dunciad* half printed, and Pope himself planning to visit the Allens in Bath. He wrote George Arbuthnot from Bath, July 23[141] that he was somewhat improved, but still "unable to move much about, especially to go upstairs or up-hill. I have let blood, & I take Medicines from Prescriptions of Dr Mead."

A long letter of Pope's to Bethel, February 20, 1744,[142] is prophetic of the declining health of both men, though Bethel was to outlive Pope for four years: "As often as I think of you I sigh, and look upon myself: Methinks our Fates grow more alike, & we go down the Hill arm in arm. For every month this winter I have been lower & lower; & yet I fear when you are at best, you are worse than I; yet if I live on, I shall certainly overtake you. . . . I am grown so tender as not to be able to feel the air, or get out of a multitude of Wastcotes. I live like an Insect, in hope of reviving with the Spring, and above all, my favorite Project would be to keep my self alive till you could come this way, & try if we can get up the hill together, instead of going down. But I am sincerely of the mind (and I believe you are) that it is hardly worth while to do so, unless we can enjoy this world better, or unless this world were better. . . . I have lived long enough, when I have lived to despise & lament the Worthlessness, Perfidiousness, & Meanness of half my Acquaintance, & to see the Dirtyness & Dishonesty of those we thought best of."

Embedded among these lines of despondency and the diatribe against humanity by the poet who not long before had published the *Fourth Dunciad*, are various details of medicines both Pope and Bethel were taking for asthma, and Pope's account to his friend of a recent alarming experience: "a week ago, I was seizd with a violent fit, & totally stopt from Expectorating & almost from breathing. The Case was pressing & Mr Cheselden came to me to Battersea, where it happend, & let me blood. The Relief was

141 IV. 461.   142 IV. 498-500.

instant; & (which is more than I expected) I have now for
2 days been infinitely better, not only than before but than
I have been in three months, if it will hold. I breath, sleep,
& expectorate, without the Pills, yet they will have me take
them on 6 in a day . . . I am inclind to repeat bleeding,
which Cheselden is confident I may, often & securely. What
do you think or know of that practise?"[143]

Relief by blood-letting proved only temporary. A letter of
mid-March to Fortescue reports that Pope has been very ill
and "confined to my Chamber at Twitnam for these last
3 weeks, with Doctors, Surgeons & Apothecarys for an inveterate Asthma."[144] Dr. Burton[145] wished Pope to come to
his house in Savile Row, London, but Pope dared not

---

[143] In other letters of this period, Pope adds a few more medical
details. He wrote Warburton, February 21 (IV. 501) that it was
Bolingbroke and Lord Marchmont who sent for Cheselden. He mentioned the blood-letting to Allen, February 25 (IV. 503). An undated
letter of Pope to the Duchess of Marlborough, which Sherburn places
earlier than the letters to Bethel, Warburton, and Allen is, we think,
later. Pope says (the italics are ours): "I was taken so ill of my
Asthma, that *I went to Chelsea*, to be let blood by my Friend Cheselden, by which *I had found* more good than by any other practice in
four months. But at my return to Town, I was worse & worse. . . .
I can scarce breathe, or sleep, *tho I've again let blood*." The letters
to Bethel, Warburton, Allen, from February 20-25, say that the good
effects of Cheselden's first blood-letting lasted for a week or longer.
Pope is telling the Duchess about later experiments with the treatment.
[144] March 15, 1744, IV. 507.
[145] On receipt of a letter from Bethel, Pope had gone to Dr. Simon
Burton, one of his physicians—who was to die just twelve days after
Pope—who advised continuation of pills both Pope and Bethel had
been taking. Simon Burton (1690-1744) was a distinguished physician
who practiced for several years at Warwick, and then in London at
Savile Row. One of the six chief physicians on the staff of St. George's
Hospital, he was also the Royal Physician in Ordinary at the time
he was attending Pope. With him on the staff of St. George's were
Drs. Noel Broxolme and G.L. Tessier (Teissier), both of whom treated
Pope briefly during the last years of his life (see *Correspondence*,
IV. 395, 450). Together with Dr. Edward Hulse, Broxolme and
Tessier attacked Thompson for his excessive purges in 1746. See
G.C. Peachey, *The History of St. George's Hospital* (London, 1910-
14), with marginalia by the author, in the British Museum. For some
of the information in this note we are greatly indebted to Sir Zachary
Cope, F.R.C.S.

"remove while this cold Weather lasts." As usual his fullest account of his condition was in a letter to Bethel on March 19:[146] "These inveterate North Easterly Winds give me much apprehension for yours [health], as they very greatly affect mine. Within these 3 weeks I have been excessive ill. The Asthma in every Symptom increasd, with a Swelling in my legs & a low fever. I have been so long & yet am confind to my chamber at Twitnam & the whole business of my two Servants night & day to attend me. Dr Burton is very watchful over me, he changd the warm Pills into a cooler regimen. I drink no wine, & take scarce any meat. Asses milk twice a day. My only Medcines are Millepedes & Garlick, & Horehound Tea. He is against crude Quicksilver till he is sure there is no fever, but prescribes Alkalizd Mercury in 5 Pills a day: & proposes an Issue, which I fear may drain & waste me too much, it can't be imagind how weak I am, & how unable to move, or walk."

Bethel replied in detail to Pope's letter, comparing the prescriptions for their pills, reporting that Dr. Cheyne of Bath had recommended blood-letting for his own case.[147] He had heard of cases of asthma in which phlebotomy had given immediate relief. "It did so to me once or twice formerly; but of late it has failed me." He believed that Pope was "too thin and weak for an issue, and it would be very painfull to you." He himself had found no good from such treatment. He commented on alkalized mercury and asses' milk, then added a postscript, which, for all its goodwill, probably hastened his friend's death: "I have heard of a great cure one Dr. Thompson has made upon Sir John Eyles,[148] who had a violent asthma." This post-

146 IV. 508.

147 IV. 511-12.

148 Cheselden would have had reason to be interested in Bethel's reference to Thompson's treatment of Sir John Eyles, whom Thompson was said to have saved from an attack of asthma. In the manuscript archives of the Royal Society, London, is a holograph letter from William Cheselden to Dr. James Jurin, written in 1725, describing "The Cases of Master & Miss Eyles," whom Cheselden had inoculated against smallpox when "Miss" was thirteen years old, "Master," eleven. The boy made a good recovery, but the girl died. Whatever

script brings into the story Pope's last physician, Dr. Thomas Thompson (Thomson).

VIII

When Pope first mentioned Bethel's postscript to his physicians—Cheselden, Mead, and Burton—he met a lack of enthusiasm. He wrote Bethel in an undated letter that his "own doctors [had] disagreed with your Yorkshire Dr. Thomson, on the use of waters in a dropsical asthma." Temporarily Pope accepted their decision and followed their treatment, which reduced still more his medication—"gum ammoniac, sal volatile, and sena, in small quantities, and to take comfortable things, rather than much physic"—and forbade mineral waters, either internally or externally. Thompson, on the other hand, in addition to purging his patients, excessively prescribed the use of "waters" to his asthmatic patients. "At the head of this class [of asthmatic cures]," he wrote, "I rank chalybeate waters . . . as one of the best prophylactic remedies."[149] Which of Pope's physicians in particular disagreed with Thompson we do not know, but it was apparent that some cure must be found

Thompson's treatment of Eyles, the case must have attracted attention, since Eyles was a man of importance in England, having been a governor of the South Sea Company and of the Bank of England, Lord Mayor of London in 1726-27, and a member of Parliament from 1713 to 1734. He was also the patron of the Abbé Prevost, who had been the tutor of Eyles' son. Curiously enough, Eyles is not listed in *DNB*. Our information here comes from Claire-Eliane Engel, *Le véritable Abbé Prevost* (Monaco: Editions du Rocher, 1957) .

[149] *Medical Consultations on Various Diseases: Published from the Letters of Thomas Thompson, M.D.* (London, 1773) , p. 217. From the Preface we learn that the anonymous editor compiled this casebook from Thompson's "Friends correspondence." Two cases of asthma are fully described, with Thompson's various remedies given. The editor hopes that the casebook, "being written in the epistolary form, will prove more useful, especially to young physicians, than more labourd systems." It is impossible to date cases of patients treated, since all names and dates have been deleted by the editor. The casebook is in the British Museum.

for their distinguished patient. Apart from the personal affection of Cheselden and Mead for Pope, they had reason to remember the public interest aroused a few years earlier by an erroneous newspaper report that the poet was ill at Bath. Now he was seriously ill, surrounded as he said by "Doctors, Surgeons, and Apothecarys," yet daily becoming worse before their eyes.

In justice to Cheselden, Mead, Burton—and even Thompson—we must realize that no doctor in this era had knowledge of either the cause or cure of asthma.[150] The physicians of Hugh Bethel, Alexander Pope, and Henry Fielding a few years later faced a serious quandary. So far as treatment was concerned, phlebotomy, clysters, emetics, massage, warm embrocations, cold baths, and dozens of expectorants all had their adherents. "I am now so weak," Pope said in his letter to Bethel, "that I can hardly read or write at present." It is significant that this letter, like a majority of the remaining few, was dictated to an amanuensis. Pope mentions here the last book he had read—probably the last he was to read—ironically enough, the tract of his old friend, Bishop Berkeley, *Philosophical Reflections and Enquiries concerning the Virtues of Tar-Water*. No one of Pope's physicians suggested for his case this "uni-

---

[150] An excellent discussion of medical knowledge and treatments of asthma is Ralph H. Major, "A Note on the History of Asthma," in *Science, History, and Medicine: Essays Presented to George Sarton*, ed. E.A. Underwood (Oxford: Clarendon Press, 1957), pp. 518 ff. The disease had been known among the Greeks, since Hippocrates mentioned it nine times but left no account. Aretaeus, Major says, in the second century A.D. left "easily the best account in ancient times, for that matter [it] has never been excelled." Unfortunately any influence he might have had was counteracted by that of Galen, persisting well through the Renaissance. He taught that "respiration of the brain was necessary to life itself," and declared that excess mucus in the throat or trachea was caused by excess secretion of the brain. Paracelsus and Van Helmont in turn had posited other theories that were passed on to the iatrochemists but their theories were as unclear and as useless as that of Galen. In spite of a few recorded spectacular "cures" (John Floyer, *Treatise of the Asthma*, 1717) and a few tracts that were later to prove of historical importance, no important theory or therapy had emerged by Pope's time.

versal panacaea," the secret of which Berkeley had learned from Indians in Rhode Island.

Pope's despondency at this time had been deepened by news that his Great Dane, "Bounce," whom he had given to the Orrerys, had been bitten by a mad dog and presumably destroyed. Pope wrote to Orrery on April 10:[151] "I dread to enquire into the particulars of the Fate of Bounce, Perhaps you conceald them, as Heav'n often does Unhappy Events, in pity to the Survivors, or not to hasten on my End by Sorrow. I doubt not how much Bounce was lamented." The last couplet of Alexander Pope was written to his dead pet:

Ah Bounce! ah gentle Beast! why wouldst thou dye,
When thou hadst Meat enough, and Orrery?

Pope added to Orrery that his days were "more supportable" than when he had last seen Orrery, because his nights were better, "tho the grand Cause of all, & the Shortness, & sometimes almost Stoppage of breath, continue without any alteration from the first, notwithstanding the heap of Medicines so constantly taken. And the Effect of my Confinement & utter Inability to use Exercise, make me so excessive weak of Limb & Nerve, that my Legs swell, & I have convulsive Catchings all over my body."

[151] IV. 517-18. Sherburn has included in the *Correspondence*, IV. 507-508, a letter of March 19, 1744, from the Countess to the Earl of Orrery, which begins abruptly: "An ugly accident has happened, poor Bounce is bit by a Mad Dog." Evidently the news was kept from Pope for some time. We agree with Sherburn that the letter addressed to Warburton, IV. 520, while "authentic" is "improbable" on the grounds he discusses, and particularly because of the mention of rheumatism. At this point of his critical illness, Pope would certainly not have emphasized the discomforts of rheumatism, nor, indeed, has he mentioned rheumatism for several years—not since the spring of 1739 when he reported a severe bout on April 17, and noted on May 18, that the warm weather had almost cured his rheumatism. If this letter is an adventitious conflation by Ruffhead, we suggest that this section at least may be as early as 1739. Since Sherburn has tentatively placed the previous letter to Warburton with relation to the "improbable" one, this letter may well have been later, after Thompson took over the case. For Pope says here, "I have been kept in constant purging these 3 days," and Thompson's emphasis in the case of Pope was on purging.

Since practically all letters of this period are undated, it is impossible to determine exactly the order of events, particularly so far as the entrance of Dr. Thompson into the medical picture is concerned. Pope wrote to both Warburton and Fortescue that he was expecting to go to Mr. Cheselden for what he calls "an Operation" in one letter, in the other, "an Experiment he is to try upon me." Whether this was for Pope's urinary condition or whether Cheselden planned some "experiment" to relieve the asthma we cannot determine. In any case it must have been about this time that Pope wrote Bethel of the disagreement of his attending physicians with the "Yorkshire Dr. Thomson," and that he made a remark reported by Spence about a change in physicians:[152] "On somebody's coming to see him in his illness and saying that they heard he was going to put his faith in a new physician, he said, 'No, I have not laid aside my old physician and given myself a new one, any more than I have renounced the errors of our Church, and taken up with those of yours.'" But as his paroxysms increased, Pope—like many other human beings —inevitably reached for any possible means of relief. He wrote Orrery early in May:[153] "I have indeed a new Physician," and continued, "who tells me I shall be grateful to all my friends [particularly, no doubt, to Hugh Bethel] & mend apace. He has chang'd the nature of my disease, from an Asthma into a Dropsy; & certain it is, he has drawn from me a great quantity of pure water by stool; & after these evacuations, I am more spirited than I used to be . . . I go abroad almost every day in a chariot; but am very lethargick."

Thompson had begun to treat Pope before the letter to Allen that we usually consider Pope's last, dated from "Chelsea College, May 7, 1744":[154] "I am now not able to

---

[152] *Anecdotes*, ed. cit., p. 261.

[153] IV. 521. Sherburn notes that the letter was listed by Orrery as "Mr. Pope's last Letter, signed but not written, by himself; received at Marston: May 5, 1744. his account of his new Physician Dr Tomson:—(who is said to have hastened his death)."

[154] IV. 522.

express a great part of my good sentiments for you, much less to write, my weakness has encreas'd every day, yet in order to get rid of my disease, I am forc'd to purge"—a reference to the drastic treatment on which Thompson insisted. Then follows an allusion to the postscript in Bethel's letter: "I am following Sir Jno Isles with as much Vigour as my constitution will admit of, and I have the Comfort to find Dr Burton, and Mr Cheselden, do not disapprove, allowing my Asthma to be Hydropical."

To what extent Burton and Cheselden "approved," we do not know, particularly in view of the fact that a contemporary satire indicates that Burton and Thompson quarreled about Pope's case.[155] These anonymous verses, *Discord, or One Thousand Seven Hundred Forty Four*, which purport to have been written "By a Great Poet lately deceased," are in form a dialogue between Pope and Warburton. Four Doctors—Thompson, Burton, Broxholm, and Mead—are mentioned briefly. In this passage Pope is presumably speaking on his deathbed:

> B—— and T—— always disagree,
> Wild are their Quarrels, but they're Death to me:
> And I, whose Writings rul'd the restless Age,

[155] The poem was mentioned, under the subtitle only, by Robert Carruthers, *Life of Alexander Pope* (London: Henry Bohn, 1857), p. 383. According to notes in *Correspondence of Horace Walpole*, ed. W.S. Lewis and Robert A. Smith (London and Oxford: Yale University Press, 1961), Vol. 30, p. 49, it was advertised as 'this day is published' in *Old England*, 23 June, less than a month after Pope's death. Walpole described it and quoted lines from it in a letter to Conway, 29 June, 1744. He also mentioned it in a letter to C. H. Williams, 26 June, 1744, to which the notes we mention are attached. The editors say: "The author of the poem is unknown, though Henry Fox thought it might be by Whitehead." This seems highly improbable in view of Whitehead's admiration for Dr. Thompson. Since the unknown author knew enough about the situation in Pope's bedroom to be aware that Bolingbroke had wept, he may be correct in his suggestion that all four doctors attended Pope at the end. The passage quoted in our text is ll. 57-64. In ll. 74-75 is another reference to two of Pope's physicians:

> To Br——x——m I had trusted still, or M——,
> From them less Incense, but more Health enjoy'd.

Die by a Brace of Quacks' conceited Rage.
This prates of Colleges, and Books, and Schools,
That damns all Reading, Method, Arts and Rules,
Till his hot Brain inflames his red'ning Eye,
While St. J——n weeps, and while just fainting I.

Pope himself in his last letter mentioned only the agreement of the physicians, and concluded with a tribute to the physicians of Chelsea and St. George's Hospital: "there is no end of my kind treatment from the Faculties they are in general the most Amiable Companions, and the best friends as well as the most learned men I know I hope both you and I shall preserve the friendship of all we know."

The career of Dr. Thomas Thompson[156] is much better known after his treatment of Pope than before. Evidently a Yorkshireman, he seems to have achieved some fame there and possibly at Bath before this Assyrian came down like a wolf on the fold of London. Pope's is the earliest of the London cases of which we have found any detailed record. Of his later career, we offer an Appendix in which it is discussed.

IX

Pope's letter of May 7, 1744 from Chelsea Hospital was his last. For accounts of the end of his life we are dependent on two letters of David Mallet, jottings of Spence for his *Anecdotes*,[157] and Ruffhead's *Life*. Thompson had begun to attend Pope regularly shortly before that last letter. Mallet, coming to see him some five days later,[158] sent Lord

[156] His name is spelled both "Thomson" and "Thompson" by his contemporaries and by later writers who mention him. We use "Thomson" only when it is the spelling in the original. For further information on Thompson, see the Appendix.

[157] *Correspondence*, IV. 524-25, includes as postscript an earlier and previously unpublished draft of the anecdotes concerning Pope's last days, from Huntington Library MS. 1271, ff. 518-26.

[158] The letter (IV. 522-23) is dated 19 May 1744. Since May 31,

Orrery an account of the alarming condition he had found: "I shall only afflict your lordship by what I have to say to him. He still breathes, but cannot be said to live, for he has not the smallest enjoyment of his life, hardly of his reason. I have watched the progress of his distemper with much and anxious attention. After having been treated several months for an asthma by some eminent physicians without the least abatement of that supposed distemper, there comes at last Dr. Thompson, who asserts that his illness is a dropsy of the breast,[159] and that the asthmatic complaint is only a consequence of it. He says too that he can cure him, weak and attenuated as he is. For this end he ordered Mr. Pope several doses of physic, with what judgment I will not say, but they have evacuated him into absolute inanition. His strength, as well as his senses, is, I think, irrecoverably impaired. I staid with him all Friday evening and Saturday without being able to understand a word of what he would have said to me, till towards noon that I had him carried into the garden. There he recovered into some coherence of thought, talked intelligibly and rationally for above an hour, but grew weary, would return into the house, where I left him, without the satisfaction of taking a last farewell of him. I beg pardon, my lord, for this melancholy detail, but it is the overflowing of a heart that long loved and esteemed him as a good man, no less than an excellent writer."

Owen Ruffhead[160]—with no mention of the authority for

---

the day of Pope's death, was Wednesday, May 19 would have been Friday; Mallet mentions the preceding Friday and Saturday, which would have been May 12 and 13. Mallet's letter to Orrery crossed one from him of the same date, in which Orrery wrote: "What is become of our dear and matchless friend Mr. Pope? My accounts of him have been so various and have alarmed me so much, that I have not a moment's ease when I think of him; and to banish him from my mind is beyond my power or inclination."

159 In his casebook, *Medical Consultations*, Thompson distinguished two kinds of asthma, "tubercular" and "nervous" (p. 212). His "course of purges" was apparently less severe for the second variety, as we learn from the cases of asthma described in his book. Presumably he considered that Pope's asthma was tubercular.

160 *Life of Pope*, ed. cit., p. 368.

his statements—said that Pope "seems to have risen superior even to his last infirmities. But two days before he died, he sat in the garden for three hours in a sedan; and took an airing in Bushy-park the very day before he died." This is not the impression one gains from Spence, whose account indicates marked degeneration throughout the last two weeks, with periods of lucidity and others of apparent delirium. Spence's own phrase, introducing one of the lucid moments, is significant: "on every catching & recovery of his mind." A small procession of Pope's friends crosses Spence's pages: George Lyttleton, Nathaniel Hooke, a Catholic friend responsible for Pope's receiving the last sacrament, Anne Arbuthnot, shocked at Pope's appearance— "such that we all thought him dying," when Pope insisted on his being carried to the dinner table five days before his death; Spence himself, and Bolingbroke, "crying over him," all apparently spending their time with him during the last days. Ruffhead dates on the day of the death, Spence[161] much more probably two weeks earlier, the last flash of characteristic humor we are to hear: "The fifteenth, on Mr. Lyttleton's coming in to see him, he said, 'Here am I, dying of a hundred good symptoms!'—[This was just after Dr. Thompson had been telling him, that he was glad to find that he breathed so much easier, that his pulse was very good, and several other encouraging things.]"

Among the last visitors—not mentioned by Spence— was David Mallet, who left an account of the end, again in a letter to Lord Orrery, written on June 1, 1744:[162]

At last, my Lord, we have lost that excellent Man! His Person I loved, his Worth I knew, & shall ever cherish his Memory with all the Regard of Esteem, with all the Tenderness of Friendship. . . .

On Monday last I took my everlasting Farewell of him. He was enough himself to know me, to enquire after Mrs Mallet's Health, and anxiously to hasten

161 *Anecdotes*, I. pp. 263-64.
162 IV. 523-24.

his Servant in getting ready my Dinner, because I came late. The same social Kindness, the same friendly Concern for those he loved, even in the minutest Instances, that had distinguished his Heart through Life, were uppermost in his Thoughts to the last.

He dyed on Wednesday, about the Middle of the Night, without a Pang, or a Convulsion, unperceived of those that watched him, who imagined he was only in a sounder Sleep than ordinary. —But I cannot go on. . . .

Like his mother's, Pope's passing was imperceptible. The long disease was over.

David Mallet and Pope had come to be close friends during the fifteen years since they had begun to correspond, but the last word from Alexander Pope's deathbed belongs to a much earlier acquaintance, "Friend Cheselden," whose glossing of Shakespeare Pope had admired, who had attended a "Shakespeare evening," with Pope and Jonathan Richardson. He had saved Pope's life in one of his worst attacks, and had done everything he could to prolong it and ease his suffering. When Spence reported Pope's quip about dying of a hundred good symptoms, after Thompson had told him that his pulse was very good, he added, "Ditto. (Like a fine ring of Bells, jangled out of tune. Quoted by Chiselden, from Shakespear.) "[163] Spence implied that the surgeon, like Thompson, was speaking of Pope's pulse, but William Cheselden, good Shakespearean that he was, may have been using Ophelia's lament for Hamlet as his epitaph for the friend whose life he could not save:

> Now see that noble and most sovereign reason,
> Like sweet bells jangled out of tune and harsh.

As one of Joshua Reynolds' descriptions of Pope served as Prologue to this "medical history," another may serve

[163] In the published version, ed. cit., p. 264, Spence transferred the equivalent quotation to Bolingbroke, and gave it a different connotation. We follow here the version in the Huntington Library manuscript, as quoted by Sherburn, IV. 525.

as Epilogue.[164] During the week of March 8-13, 1742, two years before Pope's death, Cock, the auctioneer, was selling the pictures of Pope's friend, Lord Oxford, in Covent Garden. James Boswell's account of that occasion will close our story: "The room was much crowded, Pope came in. Immediately it was mentioned he was there, a lane was made for him to walk through. Everyone in the front rows by a kind of enthusiastic impulse shook hands with him. Reynolds did like the rest and was very happy in having that opportunity. Pope was seldom seen in public, so it was a great sight to see him. He got within the rails at the head of the room. Sir Joshua said he had an extraordinary face, not an everyday countenance—a pallid, studious look; not merely a sharp, keen countenance, but something grand, like Cicero's. It was like what Petronius Arbiter says, [*grandiaque indomiti Ciceronis verba*]. He said there was an appearance about his mouth which is found only in [the] deformed, and from which he could have known him to be deformed."

[164] *Portraits of Sir Joshua Reynolds . . . recently discovered among the Private Papers of James Boswell and now first published*, ed. Frederick W. Hilles (London: William Heinemann, Ltd., 1952), pp. 22-23.

Part Two
Pope and Medicine

Pope and Medicine

MY FATHER," Pope wrote to Henry Cromwell on July 11, 1709,[1] when he was twenty-one, "has sometimes recommended the Study of Physick to me." The sentence occurs in an amusing account of his experience in a stagecoach that stopped for a passenger temporarily ill. When she removed her hood, Pope realized that she was one of the handsomest young gentlewomen he had ever seen, who recognized him as he did not her, causing him to blame Nature all the more for making him nearsighted. *"The Dev'l take me,"* he continued to Cromwell, "if ever I had any Ambition to be a Doctor till this Instant. I ventur'd to prescribe her some Fruit (which I happen'd to have in the Coach) which being forbidden her by Her damn'd Doctors, she had the more Inclination to. In short, I tempted, and she Eat. . . . I put on the Gallantry of the old Serpent, & in spite of my Evil Forme, accosted her with all the Gayety I was master of. . . . I had the pleasantest Journey imaginable, so that now, as once of yore, by means of the *forbidden Fruit,* the *Devil* got into *Paradise."*

This reminiscence serves well as an introduction to "Pope and Medicine," with its youthful light-hearted scorn of "damn'd Doctors," its self-conscious reference to the young man's "Evil Forme," and Pope's fleeting wish that he had followed a vocation his father had considered for him, the "Study of Physick." As we look back over "that long Disease," we can well understand why medicine looms large both in Pope's allusions to doctors and remedies, and in passing figures and references in his poetry. Any attempt to mention every doctor to whom he referred—apart from the major physicians who have played their parts in his

---

[1] *Correspondence,* I. 66-67.

"case history"—or to pick up every casual allusion to medicine, physiology, anatomy, would result in the dullest kind of catalogue. We shall attempt rather to give some ideas of his interests, serious or satirical, in matters pertaining to medicine in a broad sense. The last words Pope ever wrote, as we have seen, were a tribute to the medical "Facultie" of Chelsea College, "the most Amiable Companions, and the best friends as well as the most learned men I know." On his return from his last visit to Bath the preceding autumn, he had written to Dr. William Oliver: "The Medicine you gave me cannot relieve my breast & stomach more, than the Medicina Animae, administered in your Conversation, did my Spirits."[2] After sending his compliments to Dr. David Hartley, for whom Coleridge named his son, he concluded: "I have had such obligations to the best of your faculty, during my whole life, that I wish all others, both my Friends and my Enemies, were their Patients; in which I show that I wish well to my Friends, and not ill to my Enemies."

Yet when occasion warranted he could turn his barbs upon members of the medical profession, who might better have put themselves to school to some laymen, as he suggested in a tribute to Allen Baron Bathurst,[3] among whose many interests was "the Art of Medicine." "Witness those Instructions, which Physicians, instead of giving, Receive from You, even while you are their Patient: They come, to feel your pulse, and prescribe you physick! presumptuous Men! they return with their own pulses examind, & their own Bodies purgd, vomited, or blooded." Pope too could purge, vomit or bleed dishonest or pretentious doctors.

2 *Ibid.*, IV. 470.
3 *Ibid.*, III. 130; September 11, 1730.

I
Circulation and Transfusion

Pope's earliest essay into physiology would seem to have been a couplet on the circulation of the blood, preserved in *The Dunciad*:

> As man's Maeanders to the vital spring
> Roll all their tides, then back their circles bring.

Pope's account of the origin of the lines was included by Spence in the *Anecdotes*: "I wrote things, I'm ashamed to say how soon. Part of an epic poem . . . when about twelve. The scene of it lies at Rhodes and some of the neighbouring islands, and the poem opened under water, with a description of the court of Neptune. That couplet on the circulation of the blood in the *Dunciad*, was originally in this poem word for word, as it is now."[4] Nothing more is known of the epic, which Pope implies was written about 1700. It had probably been lost or destroyed long before Pope made this remark to Spence between 1728 and 1730.[5]

Pope first used the circulation couplet as III. 47-48 of *Dunciad A*, published in May 1728, and later as III. 55-56 in the expanded version of *Dunciad B*, published in 1742. It is possible that these were the only lines from the boyish epic he ever used, or—since Spence's memory was frequently inaccurate—that these were the only lines Spence remembered his mentioning. It is not difficult to see why

---

[4] *Anecdotes*, I. 16.

[5] This boyhood epic is not to be confused with Pope's later plans for an epic entitled "Brutus." The invocation is extant, as well as some of Pope's plans for its structure. Cf. *Minor Poems*, pp. 404-405. A fragment containing the invocation is preserved in Egerton MSS., 1950, in the British Museum. See Friederich Brie, "Pope's Brutus," *Anglia*, LXIII (1939), 44ff. Possibly the "Two CHORUSES to the Tragedy of BRUTUS," which Pope wrote for John Sheffield, Duke of Buckingham (*Minor Poems*, pp. 151-55), might also have found a place in the epic.

Pope introduced the lines where he did. In Book III the King of Dunces (Theobald at that time) experiences visions of *virtuosi* of various kinds. Pope wrote in the Argument: "After the other persons are disposed in their proper places of rest, the Goddess transports the King to her Temple, and there lays him to slumber with his head on her lap; a position of marvellous virtue, which causes all the Visions of wild enthusiasts, projectors, politicians, inamoratos, castle-builders, chemists, and poets." As Pope developed the satire on various branches of science, his youthful couplet on a physiological theme came back to his memory.

Not in boyhood but still early in his poetic career were much more perplexing couplets on a physiological subject, a group of lines on blood transfusion that Pope first included in, then excised from, the manuscript of *An Essay on Criticism*. This second earliest of Pope's references to what we today call "science" is a series of four couplets included in the 1709 manuscript of *An Essay on Criticism*, between the present lines 25 and 26.[6] Pope deleted the lines from the *Essay* before it was published in 1711:

> (*Good Sense*, which only is the Gift of *Heav'n*,
> And tho no *Science*, yet is worth the *Sev'n*.)
> Many are spoil'd by that *Pedantic Throng*.
> Who, with great Pains, teach Youth to reason wrong.
> *Tutors* like *Virtuoso's*, oft, inclin'd
> By strange *Transfusion* to improve the Mind,
> Draw off the Sense we have, to pour in *new*;
> Which yet, with all their Skill, they ne'r cou'd do.

Professor Robert Schmitz, in his edition of the *Essay*, thinks the reason for the excision was that "Pope was caught by an equivoque."[7] The word "Science" in the second line "carried its normal meaning—of the seven liberal arts—but

6 *Pope's Essay on Criticism, 1709,* ed. Robert M. Schmitz (St. Louis: Washington University Press, 1962), pp. 32-33. Neither Professor Schmitz nor F.W. Bateson, editor of *Epistles to Several Persons*, noted that Pope picked up the first couplet, with only one slight verbal change, in the *Epistle to Burlington*, ll. 43-44.

7 *Ibid.*, p. 10.

within three lines it became entangled with natural science, with *Virtuosos*, and with *Transfusions*, such as were reported to the Royal Society." We question whether Pope's mind made the association of the word "Science" as he used it in his manuscript, with "natural science," in the sense the term brings to Professor Schmitz and to us. The word carries only the old conventional meaning in the three other instances of its use in *An Essay on Criticism*:

One *Science* only will one *Genius* fit;
So *vast* is Art, so *narrow* Human Wit. (ll. 60-61)

O may some Spark of *your* Coelestial Fire
The last, the meanest of your Sons inspire . . .
To teach vain Wits a Science *little known,*
T'*admire* Superior Sense, and *doubt* their own!
(ll. 195-200)

While from the bounded *Level* of our Mind,
Short Views we take, nor see the *Lengths behind,*
But *more advanc'd,* behold with strange Surprize,
New, distant Scenes of *endless* Science rise! (ll. 221-24)

Not earlier than *An Essay on Man*, published in 1733, did Pope use the word "science" in the limited sense of "natural science":

Go, wond'rous creature! mount where Science guides,
Go, measure earth, weigh air, and state the tides;
Instruct the planets in what orbs to run,
Correct old Time, and regulate the Sun. (ll. 19-22)

Indeed, "scientists" of the period of *An Essay on Criticism* ordinarily used the terms "philosophy" or "natural philosophy" for their particular craft. It is, of course, Pope's use of the word "Virtuoso's" which brings to modern minds natural science, and led Professor Schmitz to the idea that Pope was caught by an equivoque, and that deletion was chiefly for semantic reasons, an example of Pope's deliberate choice of words or phrases.

The real problem about these lines is not why Pope took them out, but why he ever put them in. Young as he was when he was working on this *Essay*, perhaps still resentful of the little he himself had learned from the few "Tutors" under whom he had studied, why did he coin a phrase for them from forgotten attempts at blood transfusion on human beings? Such therapy had been unknown in England for forty years. Blood transfusion had first been performed privately at Oxford in February 1665 by Dr. Richard Lower, following directly upon a series of experiments by Christopher Wren of infusing opiates and poisons into the veins of animals.[8] Repeated at meetings of the Royal Society, these experiments and others, with their possibility of curing some animals and changing the nature of others, had attracted widespread attention in England and on the Continent. One of the most important pioneers and discussants had been Robert Boyle. Record remains of four human transfusions in France during 1667-68, the last one resulting in the spectacular trial of Dr. Jean Denis, who had earlier transfused Anthony Saint Amant, and was about to attempt another transfusion when the patient suddenly died. It was proved that death had been the result of arsenic introduced into Saint Amant's food and drink by his wife, and that the second transfusion had not taken place. The physician was acquitted, but the Court added a ruling that no further human transfusions were to be attempted without "the Approbation of the Physitians of the Parisian Faculty," which—since the medical faculty of the University of Paris was notably conservative—was tantamount to ending the practice. Under conservative influence an *Arrêt* in 1670 entirely forbade transfusion. Although we have found no corresponding Act of Parliament, French publicity had its effect in England so that references to both animal and human transfusion disappear from the minutes of the Royal Society and the *Philosophical Transactions*. We

[8] For an account of the first infusions and transfusions, see Marjorie Nicolson, *Pepys' Diary and the New Science* (Charlottesville: The University Press of Virginia, 1965), pp. 55-99. The first transfusion performed for the Royal Society was at a meeting on November 14, 1666; the first English transfusion into a human being in November 1667. A human transfusion had been performed in France about four months earlier.

have noticed no indication of any eighteenth-century interest in the subject earlier than that of Erasmus Darwin in *Zoonomia*[9] in 1794, shortly before transfusion began to be revived as a therapeutic measure—chiefly in childbirth—in the nineteenth century.

How did it happen that Alexander Pope coined a figure from the forgotten practice around 1709—possibly earlier, if we accept his statement in editions of 1717 and later, that the poem had been "Written in the Year 1709," or date the writing of some sections even earlier on the basis of Joseph Spence's memory that Pope had showed William Walsh his *Essay* in 1706?[10] We suggest that Pope's attention had been called to transfusion by the most extensive and hilarious satire on Restoration science, Thomas Shadwell's *The Virtuoso*, which had first been played at the Duke's Theatre in May 1676.[11] Sir Nicholas Gimcrack, the "virtuoso," had performed most of the experiments attributed to the Royal Society, among others both animal and human transfusion. When one of the characters remarked, on a "rare experiment performed by the scientists, of transfusing the blood of a sheep into a man," Sir Nicholas boasted that it had been short of many of his: "I assure you I have transfus'd into a human vein sixty-four ounces, avoirdupois weight, from one sheep. The emittent sheep died under the operation, but the recipient madman is still alive. . . . The patient from being maniacal or raging mad became wholly ovine or sheepish: he bleated perpetually and

[9] Geoffrey Keynes calls attention to this in "The History of Blood Transfusion, 1628-1914," *British Journal of Surgery*, XXXI (1943), 38-50. This is the best treatment of the subject in the history of medicine. Keynes adds that a few authors of medical textbooks included short accounts of the procedure in their writings; he mentions some of the works. Apart from these scattered references, the subject of blood transfusion became a dead issue.

[10] *Anecdotes*, I. 41-42.

[11] See "Theatrical History" in *The Virtuoso*, ed. M.H. Nicolson and D.S. Rodes (Lincoln: University of Nebraska Press, 1966), pp. xi-xiii. See also discussions of the satire on transfusion in the comedy, pp. 173-75. There is a brief satire on transfusion in Tom Brown, *Amusements Serious and Comical*, ed. Arthur L. Hayward (London: Routledge & Kegan Paul, 1927), p. 77.

chew'd the cud; he had wool growing upon him in great quantities; and a Northamptonshire sheep's tail did soon emerge or arise from his anus or human fundament."[12]

Well received in its own time, the comedy was revived and presented at Lincoln Inn's Fields on March 31, 1705. Pope was at this time a boy of sixteen. Possibly he attended the performance. We know that he had either seen or read Shadwell's farce and that he had discussed the play with his early friend, William Wycherley. Spence quotes Pope as having said: "The *Virtuoso* of Shadwell does not maintain his character with equal strength to the end, and this was that writer's general fault. Wycherley used to say of him that 'he knew how to start a fool very well, but that he was never able to run him down.' "[13]

Why did Pope delete the lines before publishing the *Essay* in 1711? Possibly because one or another friend to whom he showed the manuscript was not even familiar with the word "transfusion" in its medical sense. This seems entirely likely since the *OED* quotes no example of such use between 1678 and 1802, so completely had knowledge of blood transfusion disappeared from human knowledge. It is significant that the *Memoirs of Martinus Scriblerus*, upon which Pope was to be engaged with Swift, Arbuthnot, and others in 1714, contains no reference to this spectacular medical practice, which had seemed uproarious to an audience in 1676, with the Royal Society experiments freshly in mind. At that time, as Professor Kerby-Miller says,[14] Shadwell's scientific scenes had been "fresh and amusing," and the play continued to provoke mirth "for more than a quarter of a century—until, in fact, the scientific allusions had lost their topical effectiveness." The only one of the Shadwellian scientific parodies that found its way into the

---

12 II.ii. 184-94, in *ibid.*, p. 51.

13 *Anecdotes*, I. 205-206. Steele published "The Will of a Virtuoso," purportedly that of Sir Nicholas Gimcrack in the *Tatler* for August 26, 1710. That, however, had to do only with the "collections" left by Sir Nicholas and did not include reference to blood transfusion.

14 *Memoirs of the Extraordinary Life, Works, and Discoveries of Martinus Scriblerus*, ed. Charles Kerby-Miller (New Haven: Yale University Press, 1950) , p. 76.

Memoirs was "the device to relieve Consumptive or Asthmatick persons, . . . by pipes of the nature of Recipients of Air-Pumps; and to introduce the native Air of a man's country into any other in which he should travel."[15] Probably Martinus' adoption of this was a result of Dr. Arbuthnot's personal interest in the problem of the relation between the human body and the air surrounding it, on which he was later to write a treatise.[16] That was a lively medical issue in Arbuthnot's time; "the Choice of Air," as he said, was "a Subject about which a Physician's Advice is often demanded." Most of Shadwell's scientific satire was passé by the period of the *Memoirs*, and even to Dr. Arbuthnot, who had been only an infant when the French *Arrêt* forbade the practice, blood transfusion was an unknown technique, not taught in medical schools.

The lines on transfusion in the manuscript of *An Essay on Criticism* may have been among the earliest, possibly written in 1706 with Shadwell's *Virtuoso* fresh in Pope's memory. He himself may well have realized before 1711 that they no longer carried the barb he had intended when he dismissed his "Tutors" in lines reminiscent of Shadwell's scathing indictment of virtuosi: "If the blood of an ass were transfus'd into a virtuoso, you would not know the emittent ass from the recipient philosopher."

II

Animalitarianism

Norman Ault, in "Pope and his Dogs,"[17] stressed Pope's

---

[15] *Ibid.*, p. 345.

[16] *Essay concerning the Effect of Air on Human Bodies*, 1733. The quotation is from Lester M. Beattie, *John Arbuthnot: Mathematician and Satirist* (Cambridge: Harvard University Press, 1935) , p. 366.

[17] *New Light on Pope* (London: Methuen, 1949) , pp. 337-50. The substance of this essay had appeared on the bicentenary of Pope's death in *The Nineteenth Century and After* (May 1944) , pp. 212-21. The sentences we quote are in the text and note, *New Light*, p. 339.

"ceaseless advocacy of a more humane treatment of animals (in which he may be said to have led the modern
world)" and added in a note: "It is not widely realized
even now, that in his humanitarianism Pope was born so
long before his time." Ault exaggerated Pope's priority in
humanitarianism—certainly Montaigne had glorified animals more than Pope—though he was quite correct in em-
phasizing Pope's feeling for his dogs and his sympathy for
the brute creation, a recurrent theme in his poetry, which
may have been due, in part at least, as Ault suggests, to
"the miseries of his puny frame and physical infirmities."[18]

A thoughtful consideration of the problem of the nature
of animals had been provoked throughout Europe by Descartes' theory of a "beast-machine" in *Le Discours de la
Méthode*. Animals, he declared, are automata, acting purely
by mechanical processes, utterly devoid of reason. The possibility of a "beast machine" gained widespread acceptance
in France,[19] but, in spite of a few defendants, it was largely
opposed in England, beginning particularly with the Cambridge Platonists, Henry More, Ralph Cudworth, Isaac Barrow,[20] and continuing with John Locke in his *Essay concerning Humane Understanding* (1690). Locke's comments

---

On p. 337 Ault attributes the "slowly dawning recognition of the
poet's innate humanitarianism" to Edith Sitwell's *Alexander Pope*
(London: Faber and Faber, 1930). Actually Miss Sitwell devoted only
a brief section, pp. 101-102, to the subject, quoting the Spence
anecdote we discuss. She did, however, include as an Appendix Pope's
Guardian paper on animalitarianism, which Ault also included in
The Prose Works of Alexander Pope (Oxford, The Clarendon Press,
1936), I. 107-14, under the title "Against Barbarity to Animals."

[18] Ault says, p. 339n., that Pope's "zealous interest" in the well-
being of animals "anticipated by nearly a hundred years the first of the
various humane crusades, on which the early Victorians prided themselves."

[19] The Cartesian theory and French reaction to it has been studied
by Leonora Cohen Rosenfeld, *From Beast-Machine to Man-Machine*
(New York: Oxford University Press, 1941), and in a series of papers,
which are mentioned in the volume.

[20] Wallace Shugg has studied English attitudes toward the "beast-
machine" theory in *The Beast-Machine in England*, unpub. Ph.D.
diss. (Columbia University, 1966). We are indebted to him for some
of our references in the next section.

on animals are scattered throughout the *Essay*.[21] Brutes have ideas received from sensation, but they are simple ideas; they have memory, so that they retain simple ideas in their minds; "brutes abstract not," said Locke, but went on to insist, "yet are not bare machines." They have some degree of reason, consisting in "particular ideas" as they are received from the senses. On one occasion he developed in more detail the distinction between an animal and a machine, such as a watch: "in an animal the fitness of the organization, and the motion wherein life consists, begin together, the motion coming from within; but in machines the force coming sensibly from without, is often away when the organ is in order, and well fitted to receive it."

Dix Harwood, in *Love for Animals, and How it Developed in Great Britain*,[22] considers that the experiments of the Royal Society on animals, in the early Restoration period, indicated that the virtuosi shared the Cartesian belief that animals were mere automata. A closer examination of their experiments on respiration, infusion, and transfusion[23] proves that the scientists were aware that they were inflicting severe pain on sentient creatures, but considered that their experiments must be continued because—in phrases of their spiritual father, Francis Bacon—they would prove for "the benefit and use of mankind" and "the relief of man's estate." As Isaac Barrow is reported to have said, "The sanguinary curiosity which has recently ended the life of many a dog or fish or bird [is] a perfectly innocent cruelty and an easily excusable ferocity."[24] Robert Boyle, who performed a number of animal experiments that sounded particularly cruel to laymen, said it would be a "savage cruelty

21 John Locke, *An Essay concerning Humane Understanding*, ed. Alexander Campbell Fraser (Oxford: Clarendon Press, 1894), Vol. I, Book II, Chaps. 1, 2; Vol. I, Book II, Chaps. 10, 11, 27; Vol. IV, Chap. 3.

22 (New York: Columbia University Press, 1928), pp. 102-14.

23 Details about these operations will be found in Nicolson, *Pepys' Diary and the New Science*, pp. 63-83. Wallace Shugg has also studied these experiments and reached the same conclusion.

24 Percy H. Osmond, *Isaac Barrow: His Life and Times* (London: Society for Promoting Christian Knowledge, Limited Edition, 1944). p. 40.

to dissect . . . human bodies alive," as some of the ancients were said to have done. But if science was to reach important conclusions that would prolong or save human life, "it must, therefore, be of use to physicians, to see living irrational animals dissected."[25] It is significant that Boyle, writing of the first experiment in blood transfusion made on animals, when the emittent dog was killed by the emptying of its blood stream, said at this point, "when this tragedy is over." One of the cruelest animal experiments performed for the Royal Society—a landmark in the history of respiration—was that of Robert Hooke on the "bellows dog," described briefly in the minutes of the Royal Society:[26] "to open the thorax of a dog, and to keep him alive with blowing into the lungs with bellows." John Evelyn described the operation which he witnessed on October 10, 1667, and added: "This was an experiment of more cruelty than pleased me."[27] Although he was one of the founding fathers of the Royal Society, Evelyn was a layman, not a scientist or physician. Much more significant was the reaction of the scientist who had originally devised the experiment, Robert Hooke, as important as Robert Boyle in the history of English science. When the Royal Society requested him to perform the operation publicly, Hooke procrastinated from one meeting to another, and, when the demonstration was finally made, it was not by Hooke but by Dr. Richard Lower. Hooke indicated his reason for refusing to perform the operation a second time in a letter to Robert Boyle, November 10, 1664:[28] "The other experiment (which I shall hardly, I confess, make again, because it was cruel) was with a dog . . . I shall hardly be induced to make any

[25] *The Works of the Honourable Robert Boyle* (London, 1772), II. 65.

[26] Thomas Birch, ed., *The History of the Royal Society of London* (London, 1756), II. 25.

[27] *The Diary of John Evelyn*, ed. E.S. De Beer (Oxford: Clarendon Press, 1955), III. 497-98. The entry is for October 8, 1667.

[28] R.T. Gunther, *The Life and Work of Robert Hooke* in *Early Science in Oxford* (Oxford: Clarendon Press, 1930), VI. 217.

further trials of this kind, because of the torture of the creature: but certainly the enquiry would be very noble, if we could any way find a way so to stupify the creature, as that it might not be sensible, which I fear there is hardly any opiate will perform."

There had probably always been animal lovers in England, as in Greece and Rome. The little dogs Chaucer's Prioress fed on choice morsels were pets over which she could laugh or cry:

> But soore wepte she if oon of hem were deed,
> Or if men smoot it with a yerde smerte;
> And al was conscience and tendre herte.[29]

Robert Herrick's "Grange, or Private Wealth" consisted not in broad acres, but in his orphaned lamb, his cat and "Treasy" (spaniel), his goose, his cock and the hen

> which creeking day by day
> Tells when
> She goes her long white egg to lay.

Marvell's "Nymph Complaining for the Death of her Faun" may have as many levels of meaning as critics have read into it, but basically it is the lament of a girl for the pet she had fed "with sweetest milk and sugar," which it had "nurst" from her fingers and with whom she had frolicked in play. Shot by "the wanton Troopers riding by," it dies slowly, weeping "Amber Tears" that mingle with her own.

At the Restoration of Charles II, attitudes of the royal family towards their pets undoubtedly set the stamp of the highest authority upon the fashion of pet-keeping. Probably in no other period has there been a greater contrast between the callousness and cruelty to many animals and the sentimentality shown to lady's lap-dogs like Shock in *The Rape of the Lock*. By Pope's time, disparate attitudes were obvious. In Pope's immediate circle, his friend

---

[29] "General Prologue to the Canterbury Tales" in *The Works of Geoffrey Chaucer*, ed. F.N. Robinson (Boston: Houghton Mifflin, 1961), ll. 148-50.

John Gay wrote indignantly against the mistreatment of horses in London:

> Here laden carts with thundering waggons meet,
> Wheels clash with wheels, and bar the narrow street;
> The lashing whip resounds, the horses strain,
> And blood in anguish bursts the swelling vein.
> O barb'rous men, your cruel breasts assuage,
> Why vent thee on the gen'rous steed your rage?[30]

Henry St. John, Viscount Bolingbroke, entered into the controversy over the Cartesian beast-machine on various occasions.[31] He considered the Cartesian hypothesis a paradox, that had not "maintained much credit in the world," and declared that human beings persist in believing "that there is some difference between the parish clock and the town bull." Like Locke, Bolingbroke said that beasts "perceive ideas both simple and complex that come in by the senses, and they retain them too, as we do. That they compare these ideas, in some degree, is certain. How far they compound them, by any intellectual operation, I much doubt." His most vigorous passage on the subject is in *Essay the First: Of Human Knowledge,* where he protested against the absurd notion that animals are devoid of all reason: "Absurd and impertinent vanity! We pronounce our fellow animals to be automates, or we allow them instinct, or we bestow graciously upon them, at the utmost stretch of liberality, an irrational soul, something we know not what, but something that can claim no kindred to the human mind. We scorn to admit them into the same class of intelligence with ourselves, though it be obvious, among other observations easy to be made, and tending to the same purpose, that the first inlets, and the first elements of their knowledge, and of ours, are the same."[32]

[30] *Trivia* (London, 1716) , p. 28. In later editions, the reference is Book II, ll. 229-34.
[31] See *The Works of Henry St. John Lord Viscount Bolingbroke* (London, 1809) , V. 339-42; VI. 276-80; VII. 370-71; VIII. 351-53.
[32] *Ibid.,* V. 121.

98

Pope's sympathy with animals appears in his poetry at least as early as the first version of *Windsor Forest*, certainly in the manuscript of 1712, if parts of it had not been written as early as 1704, as Pope declared after the publication of the poem in 1713.[33] It is, of course, particularly clear in the frequently quoted lines on the pheasant (ll. 111-14):

> See! from the Brake the whirring Pheasant springs,
> And mounts exulting on triumphant Wings;
> Short is his Joy! he feels the fiery Wound,
> Flutters in Blood, and panting beats the Ground.

Throughout the central sections of the poem runs Pope's critique on English huntsmen who sacrifice hares and birds, all at the mercy of the sportsman's "Tube":

> Oft as the mounting Larks their Notes prepare,
> They fall, and leave their little Lives in Air.

The "wild-breath'd Beagles" that "trace the Mazes of the circling Hare" are following the teachings of men:

> (Beasts, urg'd by us, their Fellow Beasts pursue,
> And learn of Man each other to undo.)   (ll. 123-24)

In view of the pathetic—or other—fallacy in which Pope indulges in the earlier version of the poem, it is amusing to notice lines in the conclusion, which herald the Treaty of Utrecht. In that vision of a glorious future of peace:

> The shady Empire shall retain no Trace
> Of War or Blood, but in the Sylvan Chace,
> The Trumpets sleep, while chearful Horns are blown,
> And Arms employ'd on Birds and Beasts alone.
>
> (ll. 371-74)

Pope's most extensive youthful expression of humanitarianism was in the *Guardian* No. 61, May 21, 1713.[34] His "authorities" in this essay are largely classical and Biblical.

[33] See *Pastoral Poetry and an Essay on Criticism*, I. 125.
[34] *Prose Works*, ed. Ault, I. 107-14.

He quotes most extensively from Plutarch's *Life of Cato the Censor*, approving the idea that it is the part of "a well-natured Man" to take care of animals, not only during the years when they profit their masters, "but even when old Age has made them incapable of Service." Since he mentions Locke among the *moderns*, perhaps some thought of the Cartesian controversy was in his mind in one quotation from Plutarch: "Let us consider, that 'tis in its own Nature Cruelty to put a living Creature to Death; we at least destroy a Soul that has Sense and Perception." He inveighs against "our beloved Pastimes, *Bear-baiting, Cock-fighting*, and the like," in which men show themselves as cruel as children who have not reached the age of Reason, who torture dumb animals for their own pleasure. As in *Windsor Forest*, hunting comes in for the chief attack: "When we grow up to Men, we have another Succession of Sanguinary Sports; in particular Hunting." He pauses, too, over the irony of the "Savage Compliment our Huntsmen pass upon Ladies of Quality, who are present at the Death of a Stag, when they put the Knife in their Hands to cut the Throat of a helpless, trembling and weeping Creature." The last phrases anticipate those in *An Essay on Man* (I. 81-84) where the stag becomes a lamb:

> The lamb thy riot dooms to bleed to-day,
> Had he thy Reason, would he skip and play?
> Pleas'd to the last, he crops the flow'ry food,
> And licks the hand just rais'd to shed his blood.

Inevitably Pope has much to say of animals in the First Epistle of the *Essay on Man*, particularly in Sections VII and VIII, the theme of which he describes in the prose Argument:

VII. That throughout the whole visible world, an universal *order* and *gradation* in the sensual and mental faculties is observed, which causes a subordination of creature to creature, and of all creatures to Man. The gradations of *sense, instinct, thought,*

100

reflection, reason; that Reason alone countervails
all the other faculties. . . .

VIII. How much farther this order and subordination of
living creatures may extend, above and below us.

This he develops in the First Epistle:

> Far as Creation's ample range extends,
> The scale of sensual, mental pow'rs ascends;
> Mark how it mounts, to Man's imperial race,
> From the green myriads in the peopled grass.
>
> (I. 207-10)

Since in this Epistle Pope is deliberately stressing Reason
as the peculiar faculty of man, his emphasis is on the indefinite and subtle gradation of instinct in animals which
are far from being beast-machines in his mind. In one couplet he suggests the possibility of a degree of Reason in one
animal:

> How Instinct varies in the grov'ling swine,
> Compar'd, half-reas'ning elephant, with thine.

In the Third Epistle, Pope returns to the theme of the close
relationship between human and animal kingdoms:

> One all-extending, all-preserving Soul
> Connects each being, greatest with the least;
> Made Beast in aid of Man, and Man of Beast;
> All serv'd, all serving! . . .
> Man cares for all: to birds he gives his woods,
> To beasts his pastures, and to fish his floods.
>
> (III. 22-25, 57-58)

Far from counting himself lord and master of the lower orders, let Man consider the extent to which man in the past
put himself to school to animals and learned "from the
beasts the physic of the field," from the bee "the arts of
building," from "the mole to plow, the worm to weave."
Pope's is the perennial lesson of Proverbs: "Go to the ant,
thou sluggard; consider her ways and be wise." The "State

101

of Nature" of *An Essay on Man* was at the farthest possible remove from a warfare of all against all:

> Nor think, in NATURE'S STATE they blindly trod;
> The state of Nature was the reign of God. . . .
> Pride then was not; nor Arts, that Pride to aid;
> Man walk'd with beast, joint tenant of the shade;
> The same his table, and the same his bed;
> No murder cloath'd him, and no murder fed.
>
>   (III. 147-54)

The extended primitivism of the *Essay* seems at first in sharp contrast to the animal imagery of *An Epistle to Dr. Arbuthnot*, though the two poems appeared within a year or two of each other. Elias F. Mengel, Jr., in "Patterns of Imagery in Pope's *Arbuthnot*,"[35] stresses the unpleasantness of the animal images: "Five main images emerge, all connected in a kind of evolution: animal – filth – disease– persecution – virtuous man. The animal image yields the filth, the noxious element out of which disease arises, disease turns into persecution, and persecution reveals the virtuous man." We seem at first in a different world of discourse when we turn from *An Essay on Man*:

> The spider's touch, how exquisitely fine!
> Feels at each thread, and lives along the line.
>
>   (I. 217-18)

to the "Codrus" lines in *An Epistle to Dr. Arbuthnot*:

> Who shames a Scribler? break one cobweb thro',
> He spins the slight, self-pleasing thread anew;
> Destroy his Fib, or Sophistry; in vain,
> The Creature's at his dirty work again;
> Thron'd in the Centre of his thin designs;
> Proud of a vast Extent of flimzy lines.
>
>   (ll. 89-94)

[35] The paper was originally published in *PMLA*, Vol. 69 (1954), 184-97; we quote from the republication in *Essential Articles for the Study of Alexander Pope*, ed. Maynard Mack (Hamden, Conn.: The Shoe String Press, 1964), pp. 528-38.

The delicate insect-images of *An Essay on Man* seem far away, too, from lines on "Sporus";

> "Satire or Sense alas! can *Sporus* feel?
> Who breaks a Butterfly upon a Wheel?"
> Yet let me flap this Bug with gilded wings,
> This painted Child of Dirt that stinks and stings;
> Whose Buzz the Witty and the Fair annoys,
> Yet Wit ne'er tastes, and Beauty ne'er enjoys.
>
> (ll. 307-12)

The "lesson" of the animal imagery in the two poems is not basically different but similar. "The State of Nature," in the *Essay* "was the reign of God."

> Heav'n's attribute was Universal Care,
> And Man's prerogative to rule, but spare.
> Ah! how unlike the man of times to come!
> Or half that live the butcher and the tomb;
> Who, foe to Nature, hears the gen'ral groan,
> Murders their species, and betrays his own.
>
> (III. 159-64)

In the "State of Nature" man was not conscious of animal or human filth or of disease following in their wake. These are the result of "civilization," as in the *Essay*:

> But just disease to luxury succeeds,
> And ev'ry death its own avenger breeds.
>
> (III. 165-66)

What the animal world has become to man is the inevitable result of what man has made of man.

Pope's most extended comment on the problem provoked by the "beast-machine" controversy—the rationality and possible immortality of animals—was dated by Spence in his *Anecdotes* toward the close of Pope's life (10-14 January, 1744) in a dialogue between Pope and his would-be biographer.[36] Spence begins the conversation:

[36] *Anecdotes*, I. 118-19.

"I shall be very glad to see Dr. Hales; and always love to see him; he is so worthy and good a man"

Yes he is a very good man, only—I'm sorry—he has his hands imbrued with blood.

"What, he cuts up rats?"

"Aye, and dogs too! (and with what emphasis and concern he spoke it.) Indeed, he commits most of these barbarities with the thought of its being of use to man. But how do we know, that we have a right to kill creatures that we are so little above as dogs, for our curiosity, or even for some use to us?"

How long Pope had known Dr. Stephen Hales cannot be definitely determined but probably ever since Pope removed to his villa at Twickenham at the end of 1718. Hales had become Curate of Teddington in 1709, a position he held most of his life. Pope at Twickenham and Hales at Teddington were neighbors, their homes less than a mile apart. One of Hales' biographers says that "visits to each other's houses were frequent, Pope appealing for expert advice on horticultural problems, and Hales assisting in laying out Pope's grotto garden."[37] On one occasion, another neighbor coupled the names of Hales and Pope in verse. The Reverend Thomas Twining of Twickenham wrote in "The Boat: An Imitation of the *Dedicatio Phaseli* of Catullus"[38] lines showing his familiarity with some of Pope's physical idiosyncrasies:

[37] A.E. Clark-Kennedy, *Stephen Hales, D.D., F.R.S., An Eighteenth Century Biography* (Cambridge: Cambridge University Press, 1929), pp. 55-56. Hales' assistance in planning Pope's garden or grotto is mentioned by none of the various writers on those subjects. There is much information about Hales in the article by Francis Darwin in *DNB*, and also in a study by Henry Guerlac, "The Continental Reputation of Stephen Hales," *Archives Internationales d'Histoire des Sciences*, XIV (1951), pp. 393-403.

[38] *Recreations and Studies of a Country Gentleman of the Eighteenth Century: Being Selections from the Correspondence of the Reverend Thomas Twining, M.A.* (London: J. Murray, 1882). Although the poem is not dated, 1744—the year of the poet's death—seems likely, since it summarizes Pope's career.

Poetic Twit'nam, and its grot,
Where Pope caught cold when he was hot—
A thing (for let it have its due)
Exceeding pleasant to look through;
But Fate, alas! too near had placed
The Daemon dire of Anti'taste.

The versifier turns from Twickenham to Teddington to localize his "Daemon dire":

Green *Teddington's* serene retreat,
For philosophic studies meet,
Where the good Pastor, *Stephen Hales,*
Weigh'd moisture in a pair of scales:
To lingering death put mares and dogs,
And stripp'd the skin from living frogs
(Nature he loved, her works intent
To search, and, sometimes, to torment!) . . .
The antique Pars'nage undermined
By rats, and shaking to the wind;
Ducks, chickens, goslins, pigs, and cows,
The Parson, and the Parson's spouse!

Twickenham and Teddington, Pope and Hales were intermixed in the verses. As for "Ducks, chickens, goslins, pigs, and cows," the Parson of Teddington had dissected them all.

Stephen Hales was a remarkable man, a self-taught scientist of high distinction in his day, with a place in the history of anatomy and physiology. The title "Doctor" indicated "Doctor of Divinity," not "Doctor of Medicine." Even while he read for holy orders at Cambridge, he had recognized his own scientific bent, when as an undergraduate he and William Stukeley, later the distinguished antiquary, had followed William Whiston's course on "Hydrostaticks and Pneumaticks,"[39] of which we shall hear in "Pope and

[39] From a letter quoted by Clark-Kennedy, *Stephen Hales,* p. 19, it is clear that Hales spent much of his time at Cambridge repeating earlier experiments by Robert Boyle, particularly on hydrostatics.

Astronomy." When he left Cambridge in 1709 he settled down to become, as F. W. Bateson calls him, "the perpetual curate of Teddington." His arrival in the district preceded Pope's by nearly a decade. From the beginning of his Teddington career, he seems to have devoted the time not required by his curacy to scientific experimentation, particularly in connection with animal anatomy. He said in his *Haemastaticks* published in 1733: "Finding but little Satisfaction in what had been attempted on this subject by *Borellus* and others, I endeavoured about twenty-five years since by proper Experiments, to find what was the real Force of the Blood in the crural Arteries of Dogs, and about six Years afterwards I repeated the like Experiments on two Horses, and a fallow Doe; but did not then pursue the Matter any further, being discouraged by the disagreeableness of anatomical Dissections." Hales obviously recovered from his earlier distaste for dissection, since the *Haemastaticks* contains records of twenty-five experiments in dissection of animals: two mares, a gelding, an ox, a sheep, a doe, a frog and shellfish. The great majority of the experiments bears out Pope's statement to Spence, "Ay, and dogs too!" since ten experiments were on dogs, Hales himself reporting that he had used "twenty dogs of different weight" for these experiments. Some inevitably died, but Hales continued experimentation "for the beneficial progress of mankind."

Contemporary reaction to Hales' dissections varied from praise of his achievement to condemnation of "inhumanity." Satires and burlesques were written about him. J.R. Partington,[40] the late historian of chemistry, says that he performed his experiments "in the vicarage garden with the assistance of parishioners"; Clark-Kennedy insists that he performed the dissections "alone and unaided." Certainly

---

[40] J. R. Partington, *A History of Chemistry*, 4 vols. (London: Macmillan, 1961), III. 112-13; Clark-Kennedy, *Stephen Hales*, pp. 28-30. Partington calls *Haemastaticks* "a gruesome book," and is no more sympathetic to Hales's dissections than was Pope.

many residents of the district would have known about the dissections, whether or not they witnessed them. Some might have been reminded of the frontispiece of *The Anatomy of Melancholy* and lines "Democritus Junior" had written on his master:

> Old Democritus under a tree,
> Sits on a stone with book on knee;
> About him hang there many features,
> Of Cats, Dogs, and such like creatures,
> Of which he makes Anatomy.

Francis Darwin in his article on Hales in *DNB* says that "Frederick, Prince of Wales, the father of George III, is said to have been fond of surprising him in his laboratory." Such visits would not have passed unnoticed by parishioners. Some must have realized, too, that their curate enjoyed a high reputation among distinguished men of science and was the author of numerous scientific treatises. Elected a Fellow of the Royal Society in 1717, well before the publication of *Haemastaticks* and the more widely known *Vegetable Staticks* of 1727, Hales was an active member of the Society and contributed various papers to the *Philosophical Transactions*. In 1739 he received the Copley Medal of the Society, and was one of eight foreign members of the French Academy in 1753. His place in the scientific world was secure[41] no matter what the Teddington parishioners and the Twickenham poet might say. On one occasion Samuel Johnson commented in passing on Hales' "cruel and inhuman dissections," but on another, defended his animal-bleeding.[42] Johnson said: "Hales is of opinion, that every animal should be blooded, without having any

[41] In addition to his many contributions to pure science, Hales was widely known in England during the 1740's as the inventor of artificial ventilators for cooling rooms. (*A Description of Ventilators and a Treatise on Ventilators*, 2 vols. [London, 1743 and 1758]). The invention was registered in 1741.

[42] Boswell's *Life of Johnson*, ed. Hill, rev. Powell (Oxford: Clarendon Press, 1950), V. 246-47.

blow given to it, because it bleeds better." Boswell inter-
jected, "That would be cruel," to which Johnson replied:
"No, sir, there is not much pain, if the jugular vein be
properly cut."

Curiously enough, there is no reference to Stephen Hales
in Pope's extant *Correspondence,* although he must often
have seen him during the quarter-century they were
neighbors. He referred to Hales twice in poetry, the first
time by indirection in the *Epistle to Cobham,* written in
1733, the year of Hales' *Haemastaticks.* Pope's mind was
momentarily on matters scientific and philosophical, since
the preceding passage dealt obliquely with Newton's
Opticks, and this one carries echoes of Locke's *Essay*:

> Life's stream for Observation will not stay,
> It hurries all too fast to mark their way.
> In vain sedate reflections we would make,
> When half our knowledge we must snatch, not take.
> On human actions reason tho' you can,
> It may be reason, but it is not man:
> His Principle of action once explore,
> That instant 'tis his Principle no more.

His climactic couplet is an analogy between the moral
and scientific worlds, based on his neighbor's experiments:

> Like following life thro' creatures you dissect,
> You lose it in the moment you detect. (ll. 31-40)

Pope's other poetic reference to Hales in the *Epistle to a
Lady* was not to the scientist, but to the Curate of Teddington, the neighbor he knew so well that he was one of
the two witnesses to Pope's will. This has to do with Pope's
interest in sketching from life. He does not aspire, he implies, to draw such a "Helen" as the reigning beauty of
the Court, Catherine Hyde, Duchess of Queensberry, nor
does he turn for models to peers or bishops:

> From Peer or Bishop 'tis no easy thing
> To draw the man who loves his God, or King:

108

Alas! I copy (or my draught would fail)
From honest Mah'met, or plain Parson Hale.[43]

(ll. 195-98)

The section of Spence's anecdote to which we referred earlier has frequently been quoted by many others than Edith Sitwell, but she is one of the few who carries the dialogue to its end. Spence speaks first, reflecting the controversy aroused by the Cartesian theory of a beast-machine:

"I used to carry it too far; I thought they had reason as well as we."

"So they have, to be sure. All our disputes about that, are only a dispute about words.—Man has reason enough only to know what is necessary for him to know, and dogs have just that too."

"But then they must have souls too, as unperishable in their nature as ours. . . . Where would be the harm to us in allowing them immortality too?"

"None at all."

III
The Mary Toft Case

Some of Pope's earliest satire on members of the medical profession was written in connection with the extraordinary case of Mary Toft of Godalming who late in 1726 insisted that she had given birth to at least seventeen rabbits and

[43] F.W. Bateson, *Epistles to Several Persons*, p. 66, identifies "honest Mah'met" as "Servant to the late king, said to be the son of a Turkish Bassa, whom he took at the siege of Buda, and constantly kept about his person." It has usually been assumed that Pope had stopped sketching well before this period, 1733-35. A hitherto unpublished letter of Pope's shows that he was sketching in 1734. The letter, written to Martha Blount, dated 11 August [1734], describes, among other matters, Pope's sketching Netley Abbey, a romantic ruined monastery in Southampton. See G.S. Rousseau, "Pope to Martha Blount: A New Pope Letter," *PQ*, XLV (1966), 409-18.

other curious progeny. The case itself has recently been discussed in such detail[44] that we do not pretend to add new discoveries or theories, but will suggest that the Scriblerians found in the current gossip material for another chapter in the *Memoirs of Martinus Scriblerus* or for the *Miscellanies* to which he had given rise.

On December 5, 1726 Pope wrote to John Caryll who lived near Godalming and might be expected to have heard more details than Londoners: "I want to know what faith you have in the miracle at Guildford; not doubting but as you past thro' that town, you went as a philosopher to investigate, if not as a curious anatomist to inspect, that wonderful phenomenon. All London is now upon this occasion, as it generally is upon all others divided into factions about it."[45] If Caryll replied to Pope's inquiry, as he probably did, the letter is not extant. One of Pope's Scriblerian contributions was a series of verses, *"The Discovery: Or, The Squire turn'd Ferret. An Excellent New Ballad. To the Tune of High Boys! up go we; Chevy Chase; Or what you please,"* published on December 20, 1726, again on January 7, 1727, and several times thereafter.[46] Here Pope turned his light artillery particularly on two scientists, Nathaniel St André, a Swiss anatomist and medical attendant on the King, and Samuel Molyneux. Of the two, St André comes off the better, perhaps because he had treated Pope less than three months earlier at the time of the accident. Mary Toft had first been attended by John Howard, a

[44] The most complete account is by S.A. Seligman, "Mary Toft—the Rabbit Breeder," *Medical History*, V (1961), 349-60, which is based on extant contemporary accounts. There is another less extensive treatment by K. Bryn Thomas, *James Douglas of the Pouch and his pupil William Hunter* (London: Pitman Medical Publishing Company, Ltd., 1964), pp. 60-68.

[45] II. 418-19.

[46] We accept Norman Ault's attribution of this to Pope in *Minor Poems*, pp. 259-64. Spence, *Anecdotes*, I. p. 152, quotes Pope as having said toward the end of his life, that "the ballad on the rabbit-woman" was by him and Gay's friend, William Pulteney, later Earl of Bath. Ault says (p. 263): *"The Discovery* ran to at least three editions, was widely known, and has survived in several forms—in pamphlet, newspaper, and printed miscellany, besides MS copies."

Guildford surgeon and male midwife who had not known her until he was called in on her case. After having devoted most of his time to her for several days, delivering nine rabbits, he moved her to Guildford, to which he invited anyone who doubted the veracity of the reports he had been giving. St André, unfortunately for himself, accepted the invitation and made the trip to Guildford, taking with him Samuel Molyneux, Secretary to the Prince of Wales, a scientist of distinction, particularly important for his work in developing the reflecting telescope. He was a Fellow of the Royal Society and contributed papers to the *Philosophical Transactions*. In defense of Molyneux, let it be said that he was not a medical man and made no pretense to knowledge of midwifery; St André, on the other hand, although he had taken no degree, had been apprenticed to a surgeon, and had held the post of local Surgeon to the Westminster Hospital Dispensary. His appointment as Surgeon and Anatomist to the Court seems to have been made rather for his linguistic than his medical ability. Mary Toft's confession put an end to his Court position, and he was never again to attain medical recognition.[47] It was the unoffending Molyneux who bore the brunt of Pope's satire, perhaps because, as we shall see, Pope knew more about telescopes than about midwifery:

> But hold! says *Molly*, first let's try
> Now that her Legs are ope,
> If ought within we may descry
> By Help of Telescope.

[47] K. Bryn Thomas, *James Douglas*, p. 65, says: "St André was the chief target of satire and mirth, and his reputation never recovered. In the *Daily Journal* of 9 December, he published what amounted to his own recantation. He appeared once more at Court, only to be snubbed by the King, and he never again drew his Court salary. He shortly afterwards married the widow of his friend Molyneux, who died very suddenly; St André and the wife fled the same night, circumstances which certainly drew comment, but which were probably less suspicious than appearances would have suggested. St André lived to the age of ninety-six and died in great poverty in Southampton. It is said that he never allowed rabbits to appear on his table."

The Instrument himself did make,
  He rais'd and level'd right.
But all about was so opake,
  It could not aid his Sight. . . .

Why has the Proverb falsly said
  Better two Heads than one;
Could *Molly* hide this *Rabbit's* Head,
  He still might shew his own.

Pope may or may not have contributed another "ballad" on the Toft case to the *Flying Post*, published on December 19, 1726, four days after Pope's letter to Caryll. In the *Flying Post* it was "Said to be Written by Mr. Pope to Dr. Arbuthnot."[48] The published title is simply "Mr. P—— to Dr. A.——t." Here the satire is chiefly directed at Sir Richard Manningham, son of the Bishop of Chester and godson of Sir Hans Sloane, "society's most distinguished man-mid-wife," whose attention to Mary Toft had been ordered by the King himself. St André is introduced into the dialogue by the supposed Arbuthnot; "Pert Monsieur too deserves a Pat," to which "Pope" replies:[49]

Of him but little shall be said,
I wish a Man so finely bred,
Would use his Heels, and not his Head.

If Pope wrote the dialogue, the side-stepping for St André may again be the result of Pope's pleasant recollection of their association at the time of his accident. Into the concluding couplet of the brief satire, "Pope" introduced still another Scriblerian: "Thus will we then an Hour beguile/ We'll prate, & gentle *G–y* shall smile."

48 Ault includes the poem in his Appendix, pp. 444-46. He makes some comparisons between these verses and Pope's earlier rhymed epistles to Caryll. Two quotations from the poem are given in Hunter, *A Catalogue of Prints and Drawings in the British Museum* (London, 1877), pp. 637-38, in a section describing various satirical treatments of the Toft case by literary satirists and cartoons and prints by Hogarth and others.
49 We follow the text given by Ault in *Minor Poems*, VI. 444-46.

One set of verses has been attributed to Dr. Arbuthnot, and there is a strong possibility that a prose satire may have been his, all these possibly conceived as a Scriblerian scheme. In the library of the Royal Society of Medicine is an apparently unique scrapbook, "A Collection of 10 Tracts" on "Mary Toft, the celebrated pretended Breeder of Rabbits." Among these is a one-page set of verses, "The Rabbit-Man-Midwife," inscribed in an eighteenth-century pencilled hand, "by John Arbuthnot."[50] The ballad is a slight one of five stanzas without specific allusion to any of the medical men in the Toft case, containing a covert hint that the "father" of the Toft rabbits might be "a Lord/ Whose name does end in Burrough." This was probably intended as a sly dig at Charles Mordaunt, third Earl of Peterborough, who in 1722 had formed a liaison with Mrs. Anastasia Robinson, which before his death, both insisted had been a secret marriage. Shortly before the Toft affair, he was known to be making love—which may have had a political bias—to Mrs. Henrietta Howard.

The last stanza introduces a name that appears in no other of the contemporary satires we have seen:

> WHISTON, much plainer than his Creed,
>   Those Beasts in Scripture saw;
> But as the Story proves indeed
>   It was APOCHRYPHA.

The reference is to William Whiston, formerly Lucasian Professor of Astronomy at Cambridge, Isaac Newton's successor, under whom Stephen Hales had studied, who will become increasingly familiar to us in "Pope and Astronomy." Whiston had been dismissed from the University in 1710 for publishing anti-Trinitarian works. In the Royal Society of Medicine scrapbook is a tract of ten pages, *The Opinion of the Rev'd Mr. William Whiston concerning the*

---

[50] According to a footnote in the copy in the Royal Society of Medicine, these verses were included in *A Collection of Poems, entitled A New Miscellany*, printed in London for A. Moore, 1730. We quote from the scrapbook version.

Affair of Mary Toft, ascribing it to the Completion of a Prophecy of Esdras.[51] In the apocryphal book of Esdras, said Whiston, " 'Tis here foretold that there should be 'Signs in the Women' or more particularly that 'Menstrous Women should bring forth Monsters.' " Presumably writing years after the Mary Toft affair, when the story had been "long laughed out of Countenance," Whiston insisted that he believed it to be true "as the fulfilling of this Ancient Prophecy before us." How the hypothetical "John Arbuthnot" knew in 1727 a theory not published until 1753 must remain conjecture. Presumably Whiston, who preached on all possible occasions, delivered his opinion in a sermon at the time London was talking of the Toft case.

Early in 1727 when the small talk of London seems to have been divided between Mary Toft and Lemuel Gulliver —*Gulliver's Travels* had appeared the preceding autumn and provoked almost universal applause—it was inevitable that at least one pamphlet on the rabbit woman should be attributed to Jonathan Swift.[52] Those who have done him that honor have failed to notice that Swift had returned to Ireland a month before the Toft affair, and while he probably heard of it in letters, he had no such background for parody as Scriblerians in London. In the Royal Society of Medicine scrapbook is a pamphlet of 1727, purportedly written by "Lemuel Gulliver, Surgeon and Anatomist to the Kings of Lilliput and Blefuscu, and Fellow of the Academy of Sciences in Balnibarbi: *The Anatomist Dissected: or the Man-Midwife finely brought to Bed*, London, 1727." If one of the Scriblerians was responsible for this thirty-

[51] According to the title page of the tract, these pages were copied from the second edition of Whiston's *Memoirs*, published at London in 1753. The interpretation of the Toft case does not appear in the first edition of 1749, and, so far as we can determine, was not published separately.

[52] K. Bryn Thomas, *James Douglas*, p. 66, mentions a "false confession" by "Merry Tuft" called *Much Ado About Nothing*, and says: "It has been stated, though no evidence has been found to sustain the view, that this was written by Jonathan Swift." In his Bibliography, p. 68, Thomas inserts after *Gulliver, Lemuel* " (pseudonym for Swift, J. ?) ."

five-page pamphlet, it was Dr. Arbuthnot, who should not object to the attribution since *The Anatomist Dissected* is above the average tracts on the rabbit woman. It professes to be chiefly "an Examination of the Conduct of Mr. St André, Touching the late pretended Rabbit-bearer," based on St André's defense of himself, *A Short Narrative of An Extraordinary Delivery of Rabbits*. While *The Anatomist Dissected* is satirical, it also has its serious moments. It seems to be the work of a physician with a good knowledge of anatomy and experience in childbirth. He points out inconsistencies in St André's account, pausing over matters of the temperature and pulse of a woman in labor, and actions impossible for a person suffering as this patient should have been. In the central part of *The Anatomist Dissected* an experienced doctor is speaking, though speaking to laymen. Only at the beginning and end are we aware of Lemuel Gulliver who has returned to England after at least three of his four voyages. For the most part, a well-trained man of medicine seems to attend Mary Toft, and strip off the ignorance of an unqualified practitioner.

IV
Pope and "Vomition"

Cure or alleviation of many symptoms by "vomition" was standard therapy in Pope's time. Unlike a majority of his contemporaries, Pope established an aversion to such a "cure," which seems to have lain behind what became an *idée fixe* that he could not accept Swift's frequent invitations to Ireland because he could not cross the water. This was particularly ironic because Pope was a natural-born traveller, as his "rambles" attest, even though they were often accompanied by pain and discomfort. Joseph Spence said in his *Anecdotes*: "He should have travelled had it not been for his ill health, and on every occasion that of-

fered had a desire to travel, to the very end of his life."[53]
From the onset of curvature of the spine, his family seems
to have taken for granted that travel would be out of the
question, and the Grand Tour—in this period a normal
part of the education of a gentleman—impossible. Owen
Ruffhead said: "By the time he was fifteen . . . he expressed
a very strong desire of removing to London, in order to
learn French and Italian. His family, whose solicitude
chiefly regarded the improvement of his health, and who
knew that the miserable infirm state of body, would never
suffer him to travel abroad, where these languages might
be of most use to him, could not help considering the design as wild and extravagant. He nevertheless persisted in
it."[54]

For some years Pope seems to have cherished a hope of
going to the continent. George Berkeley said in a letter of
May 1, 1714,[55] when Pope was twenty-six: "I remember to
have heard you mention some half-form'd design of coming
to *Italy*." Pope himself wrote to Lady Mary Wortley
Montagu on November 10, 1716: "If you pass thro Italy
next Spring, & will give me timely notice & direction, It is
very possible I may meet you there. . . ."[56] One of Pope's
last references to such possibility's becoming a reality was
in a letter to John Gay, which can be dated only [1729], sent
during a serious illness of Gay's: "If I am so unfortunate
as to bury my poor Mother, and yet have the good fortune
to have my prayers heard for you, I hope we may live most
of our remaining days together. If, as I believe, the air of a
better clime as the Southern Part of *France* may be thought
useful for your recovery, thither I would go with you in-
fallibly; and it is very probable we might get the Dean
with us."[57]

It is well known that although Swift invited Pope to visit
him in Ireland many times, and even set aside part of his
house for Pope's occupancy should the poet decide to make

[53] *Anecdotes*, I. 22.
[54] *The Life of Alexander Pope* (London, 1769), p. 12.
[55] *Correspondence*, I. 221-22.   [56] I. 370.   [57] III. 1.

Ireland his permanent home, Pope constantly evaded favorable reply. He might indicate a desire to go to Swift on such an occasion as when he returned to Twickenham to find his mother apparently desperately ill in January 1728: "in that Day of trouble, I really thought of flying to You in my anguish, if it had pleased God to have taken her from me."[58] In less disturbed letters, both before and after this, a reader is conscious of the fact that Pope was making little effort. He did not mention the basic reason for his aversion to sea travel until 1733, when he was forty-five. After the death of his mother (whose condition had given Pope his alibi for several years), he wrote Swift: "In earnest, I would go a thousand miles by land to see you, but the sea I dread. My ailments are such, that I really believe a sea-sickness, (considering the oppression of cholical pains, and the great weakness of my breast) would kill me."[59] A year later, on November 1, 1734, Swift returned to the subject, saying: "I did never imagine you to be either inconstant or to want right notions of Friendship; but I apprehended your want of health."[60] On May 12, 1735, he wrote again: "God forbid that I should expect you to make a voyage that would in the least affect your health: but in the mean time how unhappy am I, that my best friend should have perhaps the only kind of disorder for which a sea voyage is not in some degree a remedy."[61] In a letter no longer extant Pope seems to have suggested a possible meeting in France. On March 23, 1737 he mentioned this again, "tho' I tremble at the sea, which only divides us . . . My sole motive in proposing France to meet in, was the narrowness of the passage by sea from hence, the Physicians having told me the weakness of my breast, &c. is such, as a sea-sickness might indanger my life."[62] Swift had already

[58] II. 468.   [59] III. 383.   [60] III. 438.
[61] III. 456. Among the "Additional Letters" in Vol. V. 13-16 Sherburn includes a longer version of this letter, from copies made for but not included in the Harleian transcripts. The sentence quoted here remains the same but one quoted later, in which Swift discusses his inability to go a day's journey, is added.
[62] IV. 62-64.

written Pope, May 12, 1735, of his own inability to go to either England or France, since he dared not venture even a day's journey from home "for fear of taking a fit of giddyness that sincks me for a month, & by which I lose ground that I never quite recover."[63]

One sentence on this subject in a letter of Pope's to Swift, May 17-19, 1739, must be taken with a grain of salt on the evidence of another letter recently published. In the first Pope had said: "I went some years agoe with Lord Peterborow about 10 Leagues at Sea, purely to try if I could sail without Seasickness, and with no other view than to make yourself & Lord Bolingbroke [at that time resident in France] a visit before I dy'd. *But the Experiment, tho almost all the way near the Coast, had almost ended all my Views at once.*"[64] Five years earlier, Pope and Lord Peterborough had started on a yachting trip to the Isle of Wight. In a letter to Martha Blount, dated August 11, 1734, Pope gave a detailed account of the expedition, beginning: "We had a mind to a Sea Voyage, & I some Curiosity to try if a Sea-Sickness would be supportable to me, in case I should ever run my Country."[65] They sailed "from the Port of Southampton . . . towds the back of the Isle of Wight." Because of the tide they were forced to change their plans and reached only a point on the mainland. The letter gives no indication that Pope suffered a qualm. One of the longest and most charming he ever wrote, it is a "romantic" description of the ruins of Netley Abbey, which Pope sketched after a picnic lunch which he apparently ate with gusto.

If Pope's frequent references to the "pain in my breast" had occurred later, we might surmise that he was referring to the cardiac condition that has been mentioned, but one of Pope's own statements indicates that the prohibition against taking a vomit went back for many years. In the letter to Swift of May 17-19, 1739 Pope wrote: "Why cannot I cross the Sea? The unhappiest Malady I have to complain

63 V. 15.   64 IV. 179-80. (The italics are ours.)
65 See G.S. Rousseau, *PQ*, XLV (April 1966) , 409-18.

of, the unhappiest Accident of my whole Life, is that Weakness of the Breast which makes the Physicians of opinion that a strong Vomit would kill me: I have never taken one, nor had a natural Motion that way, in fifteen years." On the basis of his extant letters, in which he constantly discussed his physical symptoms, the last phrase is an understatement. Pope's last extant reference to his having deliberately taken a vomit had been nineteen years before, when on January 22, 1720, he apologized for brevity to John Hughes,[66] "Being in the full operation of a vomit I have taken." From this occasion on, enforced vomits disappear from his correspondence. In Pope's early thirties, one of his physicians seems to have encouraged the patient to take a stand against "vomition," which at the very time Pope wrote Hughes was dividing London into two passionate camps. It may well have been Dr. Richard Mead, the leader of the anti-vomition party, who on June 10, 1719 challenged to a sword duel Dr. John Woodward, leader of the other and the chief butt of the scientific satire in *The Memoirs of Martinus Scriblerus.*

The battle was fought over Woodward's theories of "biliose salts" and his insistence on vomition rather than purgation in what came to be called "The Smallpox War."[67] In 1717 Dr. John Freind, a distinguished physician, published his edition of Hippocrates' *De Morbis Popularibus,* with an additional commentary in which Freind upheld Mead's position on purging rather than vomits. Woodward replied in 1718 with his *State of Physick and of Diseases,* insisting that purging was contra-indicated, since it drove the "biliose salts" essential to digestion into the bowels where they caused corrupt matter to pass into the blood, thereby increasing rather than diminishing fever. It is clear that some of his charges against purging were directed

[66] *Correspondence,* II. 28.

[67] Lester M. Beattie discusses this controversy in *John Arbuthnot: Mathematician and Satirist* (Cambridge: Harvard University Press, 1935), pp. 242-62. Some idea of the extensiveness of satire on Woodward may be seen from Beattie's Chap. III in which seventy-two pages are devoted to "Satires on Woodward."

against Dr. Mead, who on the occasion of the duel was quoted by Woodward as saying, "had he been to have given me any of the Physick, I would rather than take it, have ask'd for my Life of him; but for his Sword, it was very harmless."[68]

The duel had been preceded and was followed by a series of pamphlets on the moot question of vomition. Lester M. Beattie in his life of Arbuthnot[69] lists nearly a score of them, some written by physicians, some by journalists, others —particularly after the duel—by satirists, siding now with one, now with the other of the major contestants. Among the better known authors was Daniel Defoe who in *Mercurius Politicus* for June 1719 found for Woodward rather than Mead. Steele was probably the author of two papers on the subject in the *Free Thinker*, in which he also upheld Woodward. The controversy was not limited to pamphleteers. The anonymous *Life and Adventures of Don Bilioso de L'Estomac*,[70] a little sequel to *Don Quixote*, purported to be a French-Spanish manuscript found in Quixote's library, on which Woodward's *State of Physick* was declared to be based. Lester Beattie was of two minds about admitting this to the Arbuthnot canon, saying: "In 1750 its direct style and jocularity and its imaginative coloring apparently gave it the correct Arbuthnot ring — as they might do even now if there were any convincing reason for associating Arbuthnot with the quarrel."[71] This seems a curious statement, since, considering the fact that Woodward was more frequently attacked than any other scientist by the Scriblerians, it would seem strange if Arbuthnot did not enter the controversy.

[68] Woodward's account was published in the *St. James's Evening Post* and other papers. It is here quoted from Dr. V.A. Eyles, "John Woodward, F.R.S.," *Nature*, Vol. 206 (May 29, 1965), 870.

[69] It is impossible to give bibliographical references for some of the minor works listed in this section, since they are to be found only in *The Miscellaneous Works of the Late Dr. Arbuthnot*, 2 vols. (Glasgow, 1751), where they are attributed to Arbuthnot. On these volumes see Beattie, *John Arbuthnot*, pp. 308-17. The authenticity of a majority of the pamphlets was denied by George Arbuthnot, the son.

[70] This satire, which circulated shortly after the duel, is anonymous.

[71] Beattie, *op.cit.*, p. 255.

Another satire in the controversy was an allegory, *An Account of a strange and wonderful Dream, Dedicated to Doctor M——d*, published in the *Weekly Packet* for May 9-16. Purporting to be a petition from "the Confectioners, and Pastry Cooks of the City" to Mulso (Mead) and Amigo (Freind), the author begs the two physicians to publish other "learned Lucubrations" on the sickness, deaths, autopsies of their patients, promising to "disperse them along with Sugar Plumbs, Custards, and Mutton-Pyes." In one way this was the cruellest of the satires, since it asserted the infidelity of Mulso's wife. Mrs. Mead had died in February of the year of the controversy. One account of the duel was written in verse, an anonymous mock-epic, *Tauronomachia; Or a Description of a Bloody and Terrible Fight between two Champions, Taurus and Onos, at Gresham–College*. Onos, the ass, is Woodward, Taurus, the bull, Mead. Beattie describes part of the action:[72] "[Taurus] heaps scornful abuse on his opponent. Onos grasps a salamander and hurls it in his face, and next flings a scaly crocodile, and has a great store of crustaceous and testaceous ammunition; at last he is stunned and pierced by Taurus's horn, and his 'Anted'luvian Steel' is wrested from him—but his life is spared. . . . Woodward is the principal victim, but Mead endures all the liabilities of faint praise."

Another "Arbuthnot" paper, over which Mr. Beattie lingers, is one to which we wish to draw particular attention in connection with Pope and vomition. This is *An Account of the Sickness and Death of Dr. Woodward; as also of What Appeared upon Opening his Body*, by a pseudonymous "Dr. Technicum," who seems to have been John Harris, author of a compendious Latin dictionary called *Lexicon Technicum*. He had crossed swords with Woodward in the earlier controversy over theories of the Deluge. This paper Mr. Beattie considers superior to all its predecessors in the quarrel, although it seems to him to fall into two separate parts, possibly implying a composite authorship. In the first part the author sympathetically described the

[72] *Ibid.*, p. 259.

121

"last illness" of Dr. John Woodward (who was to live for a number of years). As a result of overdosing himself with "biliose salts," he became steadily worse. Not only did the salts have a malign effect on his body, but they brought on delirium and madness. Even in his ravings he would call aloud for an emetic. He "died" on April 1, some of his adversaries insisting that he died of fright at the appearance of "the late meteor," of which we shall hear more in "Pope and Astronomy." No natural phenomenon, "Dr. Technicum" insists, should have frightened to death a naturalist who had rebuilt our original world, who was "always prying into grottos and volcanoes, and the wonders of the creation."[73]

The second part of *The Sickness and Death of Dr. Woodward* differs in several ways from the first. This is an account of an autopsy, with a report on conditions found in every part of the body. Much more technical in language and style, carefully footnoted by reference to medical authorities, this was obviously written by a physician. Into most of it we shall not enter, but there is one section that might well have given Pope pause, even without the advice of a physician. This is an account of the effect of "biliose salts" on bones. In his *State of Physick and of Diseases* Woodward has discussed effects on various parts of the body caused by purging. Largely he limited himself to internal and softer parts of the anatomy, but on one occasion he suggested the serious effect purges might have on bony structure, mentioning a "Tendency to a Sphacelus in his Hip."[74] The autopsy on "Dr. Woodward" showed that as a result of "biliose salts," "the back, during the last days of his illness was very up, and appeared somewhat gibbose and humped."[75] "Dr. Woodward" has become a hunchback. If Pope read this paper, it alone might have led him to the stand on vomition which he reported to Swift.

[73] *An Account of the Sickness and Death of Dr. Woodward*, p. 467.
[74] *State of Physick and of Diseases* (London, 1718), p. 177. Medical Dictionaries define "Sphacelus" as gangrene, sometimes of the hip.
[75] *An Account of the Sickness and Death of Dr. Woodward*, p. 470.

The "smallpox war" subsided and pamphlets on the subjects of purgation and vomition ceased to flow from the press as they had in 1719-20. Dr. Mead seems never to have forgotten the situation that brought about the Gresham College duel. As late as 1747 he published a major work, *A Discourse on the Smallpox*. In the Preface, says Mr. Beattie,[76] are "lines on Woodward's 'bare-faced calumny' and his 'personal reflections and brawling' which are as bitter as anything penned in 1719. The tone suggests contemporary pamphleteering; yet this preface is dated September 29, 1747. And Freind and Woodward had then both been dead for nearly twenty years." Richard Mead never forgot Dr. John Woodward, nor, we shall suggest, did Alexander Pope the Scriblerian.

V

The "Mummius" Episode

One of Pope's passing allusions to a physician who attended Mary Toft we deliberately left for later consideration, since it leads to a familiar line in the *Fourth Dunciad*, written many years after the Toft case. In "The Discovery," Pope had written: "Some said that D——gl—s sent should be." Dr. James Douglas took an active part in the Toft affair, brought in by Sir Richard Manningham. Both Manningham and Douglas were temporarily deceived by the pretended rabbit breeder, though later they were largely responsible for forcing her confession, the first copy of which indeed Douglas wrote at the illiterate woman's dictation. But the harm had been done and in the public mind both physicians were tarred with the St André brush. Pope's satire on Dr. Douglas in the *Fourth Dunciad* consisted of only one line, "And Douglas lend his soft, obstetric hand," but that line was said to have hastened the physician's

---

[76] Beattie, *John Arbuthnot*, pp. 261-62.

death, which occurred not long after the publication of the *New Dunciad*.[77] It is the connotation that makes the single line devastating. The whole passage (ll. 371-94) is the "Mummius" episode. "Mummius," adapting a travel tale which we shall consider later, tells of a traveller who, to preserve antique medals, swallowed them. "Mummius" promptly bought them from him, subject to later delivery: "I bought them, shrouded in that living shrine, / And, at their second birth, they issue mine." "Soft Annius," the medal-bearer, replies that the medals are still in his paunch: "and that thus I eat, / Is to refund the Medals with the meat." But how are the medals to be recovered? Then come the climactic lines:

> "To prove me, Goddess! clear of all design,
> Bid me with Pollio sup, as well as dine:
> Then all the Learn'd shall at the labour stand,
> And Douglas lend his soft, obstetric hand."

The "soft obstetric hand" which had once delivered Mary Toft of rabbits in her "labour," surely can now perform another labour of Hercules by delivering the medals buried "deep in his Entrails." If Pope heard the story circulated by the Rector of Uppingham, that fact may explain the addition of a flattering and inconsistent "PW" note in the edition of 1743: "*Douglas*]. A Physician of great Learning and no less Taste; above all curious in what related to *Horace*, of whom he collected every Edition, Translation, and Comment, to the number of several hundred volumes." But Dr. James Douglas was already dead.

[77] See Sutherland, Biographical Appendix to *The Dunciad*, V. 438: "Mr. Jones, Rector of Uppingham thinks our friend Dr. Douglas's life was shortened by Pope putting him into his *Dunciad*." *Family Memoirs of the Rev. W. Stukeley*, 1882-87, II. 352. According to K. Bryn Thomas, *James Douglas*, p. 18, James Douglas died April 21, 1742. The *New Dunciad* had been published March 20, 1742. Dr. Thomas apparently did not realize that the line was satirical, nor did he mention the statement of the Rector of Uppingham. In his biography, p. 10, Thomas quotes the two couplets of which the line forms the climax as Pope's "appreciation" of Douglas.

The reference to Douglas is clear, since he is called by his own name, but what of "Mummius" in whose episode the physician's name appears? This has long been a matter of dispute.

Mummius o'erheard him; Mummius, Fool-renown'd,
Who like his Cheops stinks above the ground,
Fierce as a startled Adder, swell'd, and said,
Rattling an ancient Sistrum at his head. (ll. 371-74)

The "PW" note to the passage in the 1743 edition reads:[78]

This name is not merely an allusion to the Mummies he was so fond of, but probably referred to the Roman General of that name, who burn'd Corinth, and committed the curious Statues to the Captain of a Ship, assuring him "that if any were lost or broken, he should procure others to be made in their stead:" by which it should seem (whatever may be pretended) that Mummius was no Virtuoso.

James Sutherland adds at this point: "Walpole and Warton both identify Mummius as Dr Mead, the celebrated physician and collector: E[lwin] C[ourthope] suggests Woodward." In his Biographical Appendix,[79] Professor Sutherland refuses to accept the Mead identification, saying that Pope was on friendly terms with the physician when the passage was published and had been his patient. We emphatically agree. No one who has read the "case history" can believe that Pope would deliberately bring that distinguished gentleman, his close friend, into an intentionally vulgar and debasing episode. The mere fact that Mead was known to be the owner of two mummies is not sufficient evidence for identification, since, as Professor Sutherland shows, there were various other well-known mummy-collectors in England at that time. Professor Sutherland considers the Woodward identification "ill-founded: Woodward had been dead almost fifteen years when *The New Dunciad* was published.

[78] *Dunciad*, 379n.   [79] *Ibid.*, pp. 449-50.

Perhaps the likeliest candidate is John Montagu, fourth Earl of Sandwich," a Fellow of the Royal Society and virtuoso. "As President of the Egyptian Club he was the person who might most appropriately be described as 'rattling an ancient sistrum,' " a custom which in an earlier note Professor Sutherland had explained as a symbol of the President of the Egyptian Club.

We prefer to return to what seems to us a strong probability that "Mummius" *was* intended for Dr. John Woodward, "whose unenviable distinction it is," said Charles Kerby-Miller in the *Memoirs of Martinus Scriblerus*, "to have been the individual most frequently and severely satirized by our club of wits."[80] Woodward was a collector *par excellence* of almost anything that virtuosi of his age could collect, of fossils, of coins, of antiquities, and—the Scriblerians would have added—of rust in any form. Woodward was in Pope's mind when he wrote in the epistle "To Mr. Addison":

> With sharpen'd sight pale Antiquaries pore,
> Th' inscription value, but the rust adore;
> This the blue varnish, that, the green endears,
> The sacred rust of twice ten hundred years! (ll. 35-38)

Dr. Arbuthnot devoted much time over a period of twenty-five years to his study of Greek, Roman, and oriental coins. His *Tables of Ancient Coins*, first published in 1705, was greatly expanded in the 1727 edition. He opposed Woodward as numismatist as vehemently as he opposed him as collector of fossils. Indeed, various Woodward enthusiasms were presaged in the elaborate plans the father of Martinus Scriblerus made for his prospective son: "He had already determin'd to set apart several annual Sums, for the recovery of *Manuscripts*, the effossion of *Coins*, the procuring of

[80] *Memoirs*, p. 203. In addition to the various jibes in the *Memoirs*, the Scriblerians satirized Woodward in *Three Hours after Marriage, An Essay on the Origine of Sciences, An Epistle to the Most Learned Doctor W——dw—d*, and *An Account of the Sickness and Death of Doctor W——dw—rd*.

Mummies."[81] Woodward's interest in collecting had not been limited to classical antiquities. In his imitation of Donne's fourth satire, Pope's mind (as in the "Mummius" passage) associated him with the Nile:

A verier monster than on *Africk's* Shore
The Sun e're got, or slimy *Nilus* bore,
Or *Sloane,* or *Woodward's* wond'rous Shelves contain.

(ll. 28-30)

Although the name "Fossile" in *Three Hours after Marriage* recalls the controversy between Arbuthnot and Woodward over fossil-collecting, the satire in the comedy concerns itself also with collectors' enthusiasm for things Egyptian, as suggested when in Act III Fossile turns to "Underplot": "Sir, the Respect I have for Catacombs, and Pyramids will not protect you. . . ."[82] The central episode in *Three Hours after Marriage* involves the appearance in Fossile's museum of Underplot, masquerading as an alligator, and Plotwell concealed in a mummy. The scene is followed, as in the *Fourth Dunciad,* with a satire on virtuosi-collectors in general. To be sure, the comedy had been acted in 1717, many years before the *Fourth Dunciad,* but the probability that Woodward is "Mummius" is made much more striking when we remember that in the *New Dunciad,* the place of honor as villain of the piece, once occupied by Theobald,

[81] *Memoirs,* ed. cit., p. 97. In his notes on the passage (pp. 190-91), Kerby-Miller says: "One of the supreme marks of the comic virtuoso of the time was the possession of an Egyptian mummy." He lists numerous satirical references to mummy-collectors, points out that various of the well-known "visits" to London included seeing mummies at the Royal Society and elsewhere, and adds: "One of Lady Mary Wortley Montagu's first acts on arriving in Constantinople in 1717 was to 'bespeak' a mummy." In connection with the "Mummius" passage, it is interesting to note that the meaning of the word "effossion" is "digging out." On the lines to Addison, see also Howard Erskine-Hill, "The Medal Against Time: A Study of Pope's epistle *To Mr Addison,*" *Journal of the Warburg and Courtauld Institutes,* XXVIII (1965), 274-98.

[82] *Three Hours after Marriage,* ed. Richard Morton and William M. Peterson (Lake Erie College Studies, Painesville, Ohio, 1961), p. 50.

had been awarded to Colley Cibber—and Cibber, on the occasion of that dramatic presentation, had played the part of Plotwell, the mummy. Pope had not forgotten the altercation behind the scenes when Gay and Cibber had come to blows.

So much for various similarities and reminiscences between Woodward and "Mummius." There is still another which puts Woodward far ahead in the race, in comparison with John Montagu, Earl of Sandwich. We return momentarily to undertones in the speech of "Mummius," elucidated in the long note of "PW," pointing out similarities between the tale he tells and that of Vaillant, in "the *History of the Syrian Kings*, as it is to be found on medals." A collector of coins, Vaillant pursued by a "Corsaire of Sallee, swallowed down twenty gold medals. . . . He got to land with them in his belly. On his road to Avignon he met two Physicians, of whom he demanded assistance. One advis'd Purgations, the other Vomits." As we have seen, the chief authority on "Vomits" in Scriblerian days had been John Woodward, under whose tuition Martinus Scriblerus had studied for a year, as we learn in Chapter X of the *Memoirs*:[83] "Being weary of all practice on *foetid Bodies*, from a certain niceness of Constitution (especially when he attended Dr. Woodward thro' a Twelve-month's course of Vomition). . . ." The historic duel in the courtyard of Gresham College between Mead and Woodward had been fought over Woodward's theory of bile. Pope, with his aversion to vomits, remembered Woodward's enthusiasm when he wrote in the *Fourth Satire of Donne*: "As one of *Woodward's* Patients, sick and sore, / I puke, I nauseate,—yet he thrusts in more (152-53)."

To be sure, Dr. John Woodward was dead.[84] So was Dr.

---

[83] *Memoirs*, pp. 130, 274-75.

[84] Woodward's death had not marked the end either of his reputation or satiric attacks on his theories. Lester M. Beattie devotes a lengthy section of his *John Arbuthnot*, pp. 190-263, to "Satires on Woodward," carrying them down to 1747, the year in which Mead in his *Discourses on Small-pox* returned to their earlier controversy on this subject in his Preface dated September 29, 1747. G.S. Rousseau,

John Arbuthnot, so too John Gay. Swift still lingered in a living death. Pope had spent many days and weeks editing the *Memoirs of Martinus Scriblerus* and the miscellanies in which various Scriblerian papers appeared. He and Arbuthnot had collaborated with Gay in *Three Hours after Marriage*. From the early satire on "dunces" had come *The Dunciad*, in which Colley Cibber was finally enthroned as King of the Dunces. Pope had not forgotten the actions of Cibber on the occasion of the early farce; he had bitter reason to recall Cibber's scurrilous "Letter to Mr. Pope," published only a year before the *Fourth Dunciad*. "Mummius," we believe, Pope deliberately intended as a satire on Dr. John Woodward, with various Scriblerian undertones by the last of the Scriblerians.

Doctors and Medicine in the Novels of Tobias Smollett, pp. 87-90, points out that Woodward is specifically identified by name and his "salts" satirized in Smollett's *The History and Adventures of an Atom*, as late as 1769.

Part Three
Pope and Astronomy

"See Worlds on Worlds
Compose One Universe"

Alexander Pope and Astronomy

URIOUSLY enough, Pope's one extended reference to
an actual astronomer was not, as one might expect,
to Copernicus or Galileo, but to Tycho Brahe. Writing to
Pope on November 5, 1710,[1] Henry Cromwell had quoted
a line from Nicholas Rowe's translation of Lucan, "Then
looking down on the Sun's feeble Ray," and asked, "If
there be an *Error-Sphaericus* in this or no?" Pope replied
on November 11: "What you observe surely cannot be an
Error-Sphaericus, strictly speaking, either according to their
Ptolomaick, or our *Copernican* system; *Tycho Brahe* himself will be on the Translator's side. For Mr. *Row* here says
no more, than that he look'd down on the Rays of the Sun,
which *Pompey* might do, even tho' the Body of the Sun
were above him." Cromwell replied: "The System of *Tycho
Brahe* (were it true, as it is *Novel*) cou'd have no room
here. *Lucan*, with the rest of the *Latin* Poets, seems to follow *Plato*." Obviously nettled, Pope retorted on November
25, "I will tell you without any Preface, that I never took
Tycho Brahe for one of the Ancients, or in the least an
Acquaintance of Lucan's; nay tis a mercy that on this occasion I do not give you an account of his life and conversation, which perhaps I know a little more of than you
imagine; as how he livd some years like an Enchanted
Knight in a certain Iland, with a Tale into the bargain of
a King of Denmark's Mistress that shall be nameless."[2]

[1] The letters between Pope and Cromwell referred to in this section,
are in *Correspondence*, I. 102-106.

[2] Tycho Brahe spent many years on the Island of Venusia (Hveen,
Hvan) in the Danish Sound, a site given him for an observatory by
King Frederick II. The island is frequently called Uraniborg, although
Tycho's own description of the whole district shows that this was the
name of the castle-observatory that he built. His illustrated descrip-
tion, from his *Astronomiae Instauratae Mechanica*, is given in trans-

It would be interesting to learn what Pope had been reading that made a romanticized version of Tycho's life vivid in
his memory. We know from his own remarks and from the
Pastorals that he had spent much time reading Italian pastorals and also Italian romance. Of the important *romanzieri*
only Tasso and Tassoni were late enough to have mentioned
Tycho, who certainly does not appear in Tasso's *Liberata*.
Alessandro Tassoni's *Secchia Rapita*, we know, was one
source of Pope's *Rape of the Lock*, but, although there is
an enchanted island in Book IX, Tycho is not there, nor
does he seem to be mentioned elsewhere. Pope's association
of Tycho with an enchanted island (a commonplace of romance) and with the tale of the King's mistress,[3] would
seem to suggest a fictional rather than nonfictional source[4]
for his Tychonic reading, but as yet we have not been able
to discover it. Pope's discussion of Tycho Brahe in his letter
of November 25 is followed by a brief suggestion of a little
cosmic voyage, of a kind we shall meet again: "if once you
get so near the Moon, Sapho will want your presence in the
Clouds & inferior Regions; not to mention the great Loss
Drury Lane will sustain when Mr. Cromwell is in the
Milky-Way."[5]

lation in *Tycho Brahe's Description of his Instruments and Scientific
Work*, tr. Hans Raeder, Elis Strömgren, Bengt Strömgren (Copen-
hagen: I Komission E. Munksgaard, 1946), pp. 125-40. See also John
Alleyne Gade, *The Life and Times of Tycho Brahe* (Princeton: Princeton University Press, 1947), particularly Chap. IV.

[3] Such gossip would have been associated with Christian IV, rather
than with Tycho's original patron, Frederick II, who had worried his
family and councilors by his complete disregard for women, not
marrying until he was thirty-seven, and except for one minor escapade,
apparently living a blameless life. (See Gade, *Tycho Brahe*, p. 76).
Of his son Christian, on the other hand, C.V. Wedgwood writes
(*The Thirty Years War* [New Haven: Yale University Press, 1939], pp.
204-205): "Monogamy never suited his exuberant nature, and the number of his bastards grew in time to be a Danish problem and a Euro-
pean joke."

[4] The most important contribution to Tychonic studies in the
seventeenth century had been Gassendi's *Tychonis Brahei Vita* (Hagae
Comitum, 1655).

[5] Later we shall suggest that this passage, like one in a letter to

Pope's references to the telescope—with one important exception—were again largely conventional or generalized. In both versions of *The Rape of the Lock* (II. 179-80, V. 137-38), as Arabella's tress rose to become a new constellation, Pope wrote:[6] "This *Partridge* soon shall view in cloudless Skies,/ When next he looks thro' *Galilaeo*'s eyes." In *Peri Bathous*,[7] Pope spoke of the true artist: "His Eyes should be like unto the wrong end of a Perspective Glass, by which all the Objects of Nature are lessen'd," and in a letter to Caryll, December 5, 1712, he said that his failure to "render manifest the real affection and value" he felt for him, was like "glasses which are designed to make an object very clear, generally contract it into a smaller compass." As with the microscope, only on one occasion did Pope refer to a real instrument, but that reference is significant. Writing to Robert Digby on October 10, 1725, he said: "The Moon shines too, tho' not for Lovers these cold Nights, but for Astronomers. Have ye not Reflecting Telescopes whereby ye may innocently magnify her Spots and Blemishes?"[8] To the 1735 edition Pope added a note: "These instruments were just then brought to perfection." Pope's memory ten years after he wrote the letter was correct. During the period 1720-25 the *Philosophical Transactions of the Royal Society* had devoted an unusual amount of space to telescopic astronomy. Important papers were submitted by Edmund Halley, reporting observations of his own, and correspondence with Jacques Cassini who, after his father's death, had succeeded him as director of the Paris Observatory.[9] Pope's note referred specifically to a

---

Lady Mary Wortley Montagu, is based on Fontenelle's *Entretiens*, showing that Pope knew that work at least by 1710.

6 In 1736 Pope annotated: "John Partridge *was a ridiculous Stargazer, who in his Almanacks every year, never fail'd to predict the downfall of the Pope, and the King of* France, *then at war with the* English." There is a reminiscence, of course, of Swift's Bickerstaff papers.

7 *The Art of Sinking in Poetry*, ed. Edna Leake Steeves (New York: Columbia University Press, 1952), p. 19.

8 *Correspondence*, II. 330.

9 The first extended account of the new instrument appeared in

milestone in telescopic history, reached in the 1720's when John Hadley, F.R.S., began to report to the Society observations he had made with his "catadioptrick" or reflecting telescope. As the Reverend James Pound, F.R.S.—one of the best astronomical observers in England—pointed out in his discussion of "the curious Mechanism of that Catadioptrick Telescope," such an invention was worthy of its "original author, Sir Isaac Newton," which, he went on, "perhaps from the vain Attempts made by some for putting it into practice, hath lain neglected these 50 years."[10] Almost exactly half a century earlier Newton had developed the first reflecting telescope. He had realized that his instrument "hath its imperfections, both in the composition of the metals, and in its being badly cast." Hadley had attempted to correct both these faults in the instruments he had developed which he later presented to the Royal Society. The fact that Pope had been well aware of these matters in 1725 and still remembered them ten years later when he wrote the note gives evidence of an interest in astronomy more technical than we should expect of a layman, and may explain the reason that in "The Discovery," his verses on the Mary Toft case, he emphasized the use of the telescope by Samuel Molyneux, another pioneer in developing the reflecting telescope.

These later references will lead us back to the most momentous year of Pope's youth, his twenty-fifth in 1713, dur-

---

Phil. Trans., XXXII, No. 376 (March-April 1723), 303-12. "An Account of a Catadioptrick Telescope, made by John Hadley, Esq; F.R.S. With the Description of a Machine contriv'd by him for the applying it to use." This was followed in No. 378, pp. 382-84, by a letter from the Reverend James Pound, who had examined the instrument in collaboration with his nephew, James Bradley, Astronomer Royal. There was also a report made by Hadley on his observations of Jupiter and Saturn through the new instrument, pp. 385-86.

[10] "Accompt of a New Catadioptrical Telescope invented by Mr. Newton," *Phil. Trans.*, VII., No. 81 (1672), 4,004-10. An amusing passage in Newton's report is his description of various trials he made of his reflecting telescope, including pp. 4009-10: "And to day I found, that I could read in one of the *Philosophical Transactions*, placed in the Sun's light, at an hundred foot distance, and that at an hundred and twenty foot distance I could discern some of the words."

ing which his imagination was transformed by two major experiences: his study of painting with Charles Jervas and his introduction to Newtonian astronomy by William Whiston. This was a particularly happy period, spent in Jervas' studio and in coffee-houses where Pope sharpened his wits against those of the "Wits" of the day, from Addison and Steele down to lesser fry, like John Gay, who was to be very close to him. Norman Ault speaks of the Jervas experience as "an enthusiasm which has sometimes been regarded with an amused tolerance by his biographers, who have not always grasped the full significance of this study in his life and works."[11] He quotes from a letter of Pope's written to Gay in 1713, in which he wrote: "By Mr. Jervas's help, I begin to discover Beauties that were till now imperceptible to me," and speaks of Pope's "escape into a new world of colour, light, and form." In addition to these, Pope became conscious as never before of *space* on and beyond the palette. While his studio experience was still comparatively new to him Pope discovered a vaster conception—Cosmic Space, which at once enthralled and appalled.

I

In 1951 George Sherburn[12] called attention to Pope's attendance during the summer of 1713 at a popular lecture on science given at Button's coffee-house and the effect it had had on Pope's imagination. Pope so indicated in a letter he wrote to John Caryll on August 14, 1713, but which he printed in 1735, almost verbatim, as if it had been addressed to Addison:[13] "You can't wonder my thoughts are scarce consistent, when I tell you how they are distracted!

11 "Mr Alexander Pope: Painter," in *New Light on Pope*, pp. 68-71.
12 "Pope and 'The Great Shew of Nature,' " in *The Seventeenth Century: Studies in the History of English Thought and Literature from Bacon to Pope* (Stanford: Stanford University Press, 1951), pp. 306-15.
13 *Correspondence*, I. 185-86, 201-203.

Every hour of my life, my mind is strangely divided. This minute, perhaps, I am above the stars, with a thousand systems about me, looking forward into the vast abyss of eternity, and losing my whole comprehension in the boundless spaces of the extended Creation, in dialogues with Whiston and the astronomers; the next moment I am below all trifles, even grovelling with Tidcombe in the very center of nonsense. . . ." This had not been Pope's earlier attitude toward William Whiston. In a verse-letter to Cromwell, written—according to Curll's dating—on July 12 or 13, 1707, he wrote of a third-rate versifier:

> To *Brocas's* Lays no more you listen
> Than to the wicked Works of *Whiston*;
> In vain he strains to reach your Ear,
> With what it wisely, will not hear:
> You bless the Powers who made that Organ
> Deaf to the Voice of such a *Gorgon*,
> (For so one sure may call that Head,
> Which does not Look, but Read Men dead.)

Professor Sherburn questioned Curll's dating of this letter as of 1707. On the basis of Pope's phrase, "the wicked Works of Whiston," we are persuaded that the letter was not earlier than 1708 but probably written in that year.

In order to justify this contention, but chiefly to explain Pope's right-about-face, we must enter into a digression on William Whiston, who has briefly appeared on earlier pages. His early career had been a distinguished one. In 1701 he had been appointed deputy for Isaac Newton's Lucasian professorship of mathematics at Cambridge. In 1703 he succeeded to the professorship. Four years later he published "by the Author's permission," Newton's *Arithmetica Universalis*. In the same year—1707—he delivered the Boyle Lectures on the subject, *The Accomplishment of Scripture Prophecies*. His real troubles began in 1708, when the Vice Chancellor at Cambridge refused to license his essay *Upon Apostolical Constitution*, declaring that it upheld the Arian heresy, a charge that was promptly read back into the Boyle Lectures. During the same year Whiston addressed the archbishops on several subjects, one of which was his contention that the orthodox doctrine of the Trinity was erroneous. He was deprived of his professorship and banished from Cambridge in 1710, on the ground of heresy, particularly Arianism. Whiston himself denied Arianism, although later he declared himself Eusebian, which he defined as Unitarian. In London he published one of his chief works, *Primitive Christianity Revived*, and some pamphlets dealing with the charges against him. Although his case had been taken up by the Convocation, his trial before a court of delegates appointed by the Lord Chancellor did not occur until 1714. Interrupted by the death of Queen Anne, the case was not resumed and the proceedings against him were dropped. So much for his academic career and his increasing reputation as a heretic. In the mind of Pope, as of many, one of his "wicked Works" would have been the Boyle Lectures, published early in 1708. The other "wicked" work leads us into a very different subject.

Well before his appointment to the Lucasian chair, Whiston had attracted attention by the publication in 1696 of *A New Theory of the Earth*, one of many volumes in the "Burnet controversy," provoked by Thomas Burnet's *The Sacred Theory of the Earth*.[14] Burnet insisted that the earth as we know it was not the original earth, which had been smooth and regular, marked by no such gross irregularities as mountains and canyons and the channel of the sea. Our wild irregularities are the result of the Flood. Books and pamphlets poured from the press, some approving, some

[14] Whiston's religious heresies have recently been studied by E. Frank Manuel, *Newton as Historian* (Cambridge: Harvard University Press, 1963), pp. 56-69. The chapter is carefully annotated. On the "Burnet controversy," see Marjorie Nicolson, *Mountain Gloom and Mountain Glory* (Ithaca: Cornell University Press, 1959), particularly Chaps. V and VI; Ernest Tuveson, "Swift and the World-Makers," *Journal of the History of Ideas*, XI (1950), 54-74. An extensive summary of Whiston's theory, only one aspect of which can be discussed here, may be found in Katharine Brownell Collier, *Cosmogonies of Our Fathers* (New York: Columbia University Press, 1934), Part I, Chap. XXII.

inveighing against, others proposing still other theories. While Burnet's work was Whiston's point of departure, he was concerned less with the result of the Flood than with its cause. This he attributed to the "Choc" caused by the collision of the earth and a comet, which he identified with the comet of 1680, and which he traced as far back as 1770 B.C., one of several dates hypothesized for the Deluge. To some extent, Whiston's desire in his *A New Theory* was to make Genesis consistent with theories of Newton whom at this time he greatly admired and to whom he dedicated the work. Like Burnet and others of the controversialists, he was seeking to explain the origin of the world on natural rather than supernatural causes. Although—as in the cases of many writers in the "Burnet controversy"—this was heresy, it had nothing to do with Arianism or Eusebianism and certainly had not stood in the way of his appointment to the Newtonian chair. Yet the dangers implicit in such a new theory may be seen in the more cautious procedure of a greater "onlie begetter" of the comet theory, from whom Whiston seems deliberately to have borrowed[15] the hypothesis. In 1694 Edmund Halley had read before the Royal Society two papers in which he suggested as a natural cause for the Flood the "Choc of a Comet." Halley had not published the papers but had deposited them in the archives of the Royal Society, "he being sensible that he might have adventured *ultra crepidam*; and apprehensive least by some unguarded Expression he might incur the Censure of the Sacred Order." The papers remained in the archives for thirty years. In 1724 "at the Desire of a late

15 Whiston was not a member of the Royal Society, but Halley's papers provoked so much comment that he could hardly have been unaware of the theory. Nowhere in *A New Theory*, so far as we can see, does Whiston mention Halley. He may have been implying that the theory was not original with himself when he introduced his comet theory by saying: " 'Tis true, *when upon a meer Supposition of such a passing by of a Comet, I had in my own mind observ'd the Phaenomena relating for the Deluger to answer to admiration I was not a little surpriz'd and pleas'd at such a Discovery.*" (Italics ours.) In the first edition of 1696, the passage appears on pp. 126-27, in the second on pp. 181-82.

Committee of the Society," they were published in the *Philosophical Transactions.*[16]

Here, then, is the second of Pope's "wicked Works of Whiston." The appearance of an edition of *A New Theory* in 1708 gives added weight for the redating of the letter to Caryll as not earlier than that year. Pope, born in 1688, had been too young to experience the excitement caused by the "Burnet controversy," which was raging particularly during the 1690's. Publication of the second edition of *A New Theory* in 1708 coincided with the first charges of heresy read into the Boyle Lectures and proved that Halley's caution against incurring "the Censure of the Sacred Order" had been well founded, particularly in the case of a man like Whiston, now undoubtedly accused of scientific as well as theological heterodoxy. But what of Pope's spectacular change of attitude five years later?

In his article Professor Sherburn took for granted that Whiston's coffee-house lectures in London began soon after his expulsion from Cambridge in 1710; he says: "At this point that supposed model of orthodoxy, Joseph Addison, stepped in and arranged to have Whiston give popular lectures on astronomy and other subjects in the coffee-houses of London."[17] Evidence that has come to light since

[16] *Phil. Trans.,* XXXIII, No. 383 (May-June 1724), 118-25. The explanation for the long delay is given on p. 125. Either Halley or the editor of *Phil. Trans.* apparently had the suspicion of plagiarism we raise, since the note on this page concludes: "Here the Reader is desired to observe, that Mr. William Whiston's Book, entituled, A NEW THEORY OF THE EARTH, was not published till about a Year and a half after the Date hereof, and was not presented before June 24, 1696 to the Royal Society."

[17] "Pope and 'The Great Shew of Nature,'" p. 310. Whiston's *Memoirs* were published in 1749 and again in 1753. There also seems to have been a very early edition of the *Memoirs:* on the title page of the edition of 1753 in the British Museum, we read that these *Memoirs* were "first written in 1713 . . . and are now corrected." The British Museum also has a copy of another edition which we had not seen in the American libraries we consulted: *Memoirs of the Life and Writings of William Whiston, M.A. Part III. and Last.* (London, 1753). Professor Sherburn's reference here is to the 1753 edition, I. 257. Our references to the *Memoirs* will be to the first corrected edition of 1749, in which the passage appears, I. 302. We may point out that the *Memoirs* are frequently more confusing than

141

the time of Professor Sherburn's article indicates that Addison was not Whiston's original sponsor, and also that the lectures did not begin in 1710, immediately after Whiston's banishment. Pope may well have been one of Whiston's earliest auditors, may indeed have heard the first coffee-house lecture he gave in London.

Professor Rae Blanchard has shown that Steele and Henry Newman, Secretary of the Society for Promoting Christian Knowledge, were primarily responsible for plans enabling Whiston to earn at least a subsistence in London.[18] She quotes a draft letter written by Newman to Steele on August 10, 1713,[19] thanking Steele for the interest he had taken in Whiston and his evident intention of going further. Whiston had been a member of the SPCK[20] during his years at Cambridge, particularly active in their work for charity schools. One of several reasons for thinking that Steele even more than Addison was responsible for the inauguration of Whiston's popular lectures on science was

helpful, not only because they are diffused and rambling, but also because they were written at the end of Whiston's life, when he was in his eighties.

[18] "Richard Steele and the Secretary of the SPCK," in *Restoration and Eighteenth-Century Literature: Essays in Honor of Alan Dugald McKillop* (Chicago: University of Chicago Press, 1963) , pp. 287-95.

[19] Calhoun Winton, *Captain Steele: The Early Career of Richard Steele* (Baltimore: The Johns Hopkins Press, 1964) , pp. 157-58, also discusses this letter which he identifies as from *SPCK MSS. Letterbooks, CS* 2. He calls Henry Newman "the American Secretary of the Society"; Whiston calls him "Secretary."

[20] Whiston, *Memoirs*, ed. cit., I. 153: "About the Middle of the same Year, 1710, I wrote a small *Memorial* for setting up Charity-Schools universally in *England* and *Wales*: It was presented to that Society of which I was a Member, called *The Society for promoting Christian Knowledge*; which had Charity-Schools under their Care; and was I think one of the oldest of those excellent Societies greatly promoted, if not first founded by my dear Friend, Dr. *Thomas Bray*." Later in the *Memoirs*, I. 174-76, Whiston repeats some of this, then quotes a letter he had written to the Society after his banishment from Cambridge, "directed to Mr. Secretary Newman, who had long been my great Friend." The letter indicates that, although Whiston had frequently attended meetings when in London in the past, he did not intend to continue doing so, for fear of prejudicing public opinion against the organization, which was dependent for financial aid on public goodwill.

Steele's plan at exactly this time for his Censorium, a hall in York Buildings which he had leased apparently before January 1712. This he designed as a little theatre and lecture hall, in which he proposed to offer entertainments "to improve public taste," ranging from recitals of poetry with musical backgrounds to scientific lectures and demonstrations. "All Works of Invention,"[21] he wrote, "All the Sciences, as well as mechanick Arts will have their turn." Professor Blanchard writes: "Since March 1713 the arrangement and decorations of the Great Room had been in readiness for Steele's little theatre the Censorium." In spite of elaborate preparations no record has been found of any performance under Steele's aegis before May 1715. As Professor Blanchard says: "The delay from the spring of 1713, when the Great Room was made ready for such a project as the Censorium, to May 1715 in beginning the entertainments can be attributed to Steele's absorption in politics and possibly in part to lack of funds."[22] The first known use of the hall was on May 28, 1715, when a large company gathered, ostensibly to celebrate the King's birthday, probably also Steele's recent knighthood. It is possible that Pope was present, since, in honor of the occasion, Steele had had medals coined either as invitation or souvenir, one of which was discovered in Pope's house in Twickenham, when it was put up for auction in 1802.[23]

Since the Censorium was ready for use by August 1713 when Steele presumably arranged the first of the Whiston lectures at Button's, why did he not make use of Whiston to inaugurate the lectures on science he proposed for the

[21] The last two sentences are paraphrased and quoted from the best treatment of the Censorium, John Loftis, "Richard Steele's Censorium," *HLQ*, XIV (November 1950), 43-66. The quotation is from a manuscript draft, in Steele's hand, of *The Town Talk* No. 4, which Professor Loftis found among Steele's papers in Blenheim Palace.

[22] *Richard Steele's Periodical Journalism 1714 - 1716* (Oxford: Clarendon Press, 1959), p. 302.

[23] Loftis, p. 55. The medal bore on the obverse a picture of the sun surrounded by the inscription "Sensorium. Anno Primo. Georgii, 1715". On the reverse were two human figures and the Latin word "suadere."

Censorium? It is not difficult to answer the question. The "wicked Works of Whiston" were only too familiar to the public in 1713 and the trial for heresy was pending. When scientific or other lectures were to be given at the Censorium, they would be arranged either by subscription or by payment of an admission fee for individual lectures, as indeed was the case when Whiston lectured there on March 16, 1716 on one of the most spectacular celestial phenomena of the age (of which we shall hear more), "the surprizing Appearances in the Air, seen on Tuesday, the 6th Instant."[24] Steele had no way of anticipating whether Whiston would have the drawing power necessary for a paying audience. Indeed he may not have known whether the former Lucasian professor of mathematics was capable of the level of lecture necessary for the general public rather than for University undergraduates. Another problem that might have deterred Steele from Censorium lectures was the question whether Whiston could and would limit his lecture to science or whether he would take the opportunity to attempt to justify his heretical theological beliefs.[25] It seems to us probable that Steele initiated the coffee-house lecture or lectures deliberately as a trial run.

Pope's letter to Caryll offers all the evidence needed to prove that Whiston was a success in lecturing to laymen. On the basis of the response, Steele and Addison proceeded with plans for an extended series of coffee-house lectures for Whiston. Whether Addison knew Whiston personally or not, he had recently printed in *Guardian* No. 107, July 11,

24 From an advertisement in *The Daily Courant*, March 6, 1716, quoted, Loftis, p. 59. The advertisement shows that Whiston made his own arrangements to sell tickets either in advance or at the door.
25 Newman had warned Steele of this possibility in his draft letter from which we have quoted. He said, *Restoration and Eighteenth-Century Literature*, p. 292: "I only beg leave to suggest one thing to you when he does [lecture], because it will come with more authority from you than perhaps any man in the Kingdom beside, and that is that you will be pleas'd to conjure him Silence upon all Topicks foreign to the Mathematics in his Conversation or Lectures at the Coffeehouse. He has an Itch to be venting his Notions about Baptism & the Arrian Doctrine but your authority can restrain him at least while he is under your Guardianship."

1713, a letter from him on the project for determining the longitude. To this he prefixed some flattering remarks, saying that Whiston has "lately obliged the work with that noble plan, intituled, "A Scheme of the Solar System, with the orbits of the planets and comets belonging thereto, described from Dr. Halley's accurate Table of Comets, Philosoph. Trans. No. 297." This system, Addison added, was "founded on Sir Isaac Newton's wonderful discoveries," now described and explained by William Whiston.[26] Addison and Steele seem to have joined forces in arrangements for an extended series of lectures at Button's coffee-house, to begin in January 1714 and advertised well in advance. We wonder, indeed, whether "advance publicity" for these lectures may explain the fact that Pope printed in 1735 the letter addressed to Addison, as of December 14, 1713, which is almost identical with the letter to Caryll four months earlier, telling of the effect on Pope of hearing Whiston lecture. To be sure, Pope frequently repeated himself in letters and was not averse from later publishing a letter proved by its manuscript to have been addressed to one correspondent, as if it had been sent to another. It merely seems possible that Addison might have asked Pope for a "testimonial" which he might show to Button or to others whom he was trying to interest in backing the new series. Pope may well have felt that his sincere letter to his close friend was the best possible "testimonial" he could offer Addison.[27]

How many trial-run lectures Whiston delivered at Button's in 1713 and how many Pope heard are questions to which we have found no answer. The facts about the series beginning in January 1714 are abundant. The lectures were advertised in *The Englishman*, as beginning January 11,

[26] Whiston's Scheme of the Solar System will be mentioned again below. Halley's table to which Addison referred was his great *Astronomiae Cometicae Synopsis*, first published in *Phil. Trans.*, XXIV, No. 297 (March 1705), 1,882-98.

[27] We willingly grant that there is no particle of evidence for this supposition. Two letters of Addison to Pope in November 1713 are included in Addison's *Collected Letters* (Oxford: Clarendon Press, 1941), with no other until February 1714.

1713-14, "a course of Philosophical Lectures on Mechanicks, Hydrostatics, Pneumatics, Opticks. . . . This course of
experiments is to be performed by Mr. William Whiston
and Francis Hauksbee, the nephew of the late Mr. Hauksbee."[28] The outline of the experiments, which auditors
were undoubtedly urged to purchase, is extant.[29] There
is evidence that the lectures proved so popular that they
had to be moved from Button's to a larger hall.[30] All in all,
Addison and Steele had reason to be very much satisfied
with their plans for aiding the banished professor to support
himself in London, and he in turn every reason to be grateful to them—as he continued to be to Addison, though he
later expressed reservations about Steele. The longest discussion of the two men in Whiston's *Memoirs* begins: "Mr.
Addison who was excellent every Way, as a Traveller, as a
Prose-Writer, and as a Poet; who was my particular Friend;

[28] Rae Blanchard, *The Englishman: A Political Journal by Richard
Steele* (Oxford: Clarendon Press, 1955), p. 436. The statement about
Hauksbee here may well correct that in *DNB* that Francis Hauksbee
was the son of the elder Hauksbee.

[29] *A Course of Mechanical, Optical, Hydrostatical and Pneumatical
Experiments. To be perform'd by Francis Hauksbee; and the Explanatory Lectures read by William Whiston, M.A.* We have found three
copies of this in the United States, and have used the one at Columbia
University along with a Xerox copy of the one in the Clark Library of
the University of California in Los Angeles. No copy has a date. The
Clark Library goes no further than "17—?" The copy at Columbia
has an inserted "1713?", that at the Library of Congress an inserted
"1714?" The *Course* was not included in Lintot's monthly *Catalogues
of all Books.* . . . It contained twenty engravings and sold for five
shillings. In his *Memoirs*, I. 235-36, Whiston said that he and Hauksbee published this in 1714, and adds, "This has been several times
printed, and belongs to the Course itself." In his *Memoirs*, I. 136-37,
Whiston notes: "Mr. *Cotes* and I began our first Course of Philosophical Experiments at *Cambridge*, May 5, 1707. In the performance of
which, certain Hydrostatick and Pneumatick Lectures were composed:
they were in number twenty-four; the one half by Mr. *Cotes*, and
the other half by myself: Which Lectures were also afterward made
use of in the like (enlarged) Courses, which Mr. Hauksbee and I
performed many years in London."

[30] *The Englishman* reported two weeks after the commencement of
the lectures, on Tuesday, January 26, 1714: "Mr. Whiston's Mathema-
tick lectures will be this day removed from Mr. Button's Coffee-house
to a larger Room close by at Mr. Dale's, an upholsterer over the
Corner of the nearest Piazza in Covent Garden."

and who, with his friend Sir Richard Steel, brought me, upon my Banishment from Cambridge, to have many Astronomical Lectures at Mr. Button's Coffee-house, near Covent Garden, to the agreeable Entertainment of a good Number of Curious Persons, and the procuring me and my Family some comfortable Support under my Banishment."[31] He gives a brief biography of Addison, recalling his own futile attempt to see him in what proved Addison's last illness. Earlier he had mentioned collecting "the several ancient Testimonies" referred to by Addison in his *Discourse of the Christian Religion*. So far as Steele was concerned, Whiston commented briefly on one or two cases on which they apparently crossed swords. His critical attitude may be summed up in a single sentence: "He wrote very well but lived very ill."

From Pope's letter to Caryll of August 14, 1713 we may deduce that on the occasion Steele introduced Whiston to the coffee-drinkers he himself "presided" informally. "Now," wrote Pope, "am I recreating my mind with the brisk sallies and quick turns of wit, which Mr. Steele in his liveliest and freest humours darts about him." Steele was seeing to it that Whiston talked about science, not theology, and obviously felt free to interrupt whenever he feared that Whiston was about to ride his heretical hobby horses or possibly when momentarily he might seem above the comprehension of the layman. His subject was astronomy, not mechanics, optics, hydrostatics, and pneumatics later advertised for the series. His emphasis was clearly on the solar system. Possibly he was skimming the cream of the work he had evidently recently published, and praised by Addison in the *Guardian—A Scheme of the Solar System*—if that were indeed a pamphlet or a book.[32] If not based on his "Solar System,"

---

[31] *Memoirs*, I. 300-303. The earlier reference to Addison is I. 299. Whiston's own statement here that he gave "many Astronomical Lectures at Mr. Button's Coffee-house" adds weight to our belief that he gave a number of such informal lectures in 1713. We know from the advertisement that only the first two of the series of January 1714 were at Button's.

[32] An intensive search on our part has failed to discover this work which, the Library of Congress agrees, is listed in none of the usual

Whiston's lecture may well have been adapted to a coffee-house audience from a series of lectures he had given at Cambridge "for the use of young Students in the University," which he published in London in 1715 as *Astronomical Lectures.*[33]

We need no other evidence than Pope's letter to Caryll to know that Whiston's emphasis on that occasion was on the vastness of the universe, an infinity of worlds, the discovery of space, which had enthralled lay imagination (as it still does) from the time that Galileo's telescopic observations merged with Bruno's philosophy of the infinite. "This minute, perhaps," wrote Pope, "I am above the stars, with a thousand systems round about me, looking forward into the vast abyss of eternity, and losing my whole comprehension in the boundless system of the extended Creation." And then, as he turned from the lecture to the trivial talk of the coffee-house, he pondered: "Good God! what an Incongruous Animal is Man? how unsettled in his best part,

---

bibliographies or catalogues. Whiston listed it three times in his own bibliographies. In *Several Papers Relating to Mr. Whiston's Case before the Court of Delegates* (London, 1715), it is given a full title: *A Scheme of the Solar System, with the Planets and Comets: in a large sheet, Engrav'd on Copper, by Mr. Senex,* 2s, 6d. In the *Astronomical Principles of Religion,* London, 1717, it is entitled *A Scheme of the Solar System, with the Orbits of the 21 Comets. In a large Sheet.* In the Index to Mr. Whiston's Writings in the second volume of the *Memoirs,* it is entered as "Solar System." In the text, I. 222-23, Whiston says he published it "about 1712." From his description it would seem to have been not a book or pamphlet, but a sheet or sheets of diagrams describing the orbits of twenty-one comets. Addison's notation indicates that he was familiar with it. Since Whiston published many of his works at his own expense and marketed them himself, it is not strange that such an ephemeral "publication" should have disappeared. It seems to us possible that this work survives, at least in part, in the series of diagrams Whiston included in his *Astronomical Principles of Religion, Natural and Reveal'd,* pp. 34, 37, 50, 67-68, 72, 76. The first bears the heading, "The Copernican, or true Solar System," with a larger diagram of the Copernican system, smaller of the Ptolemaic and Tychonic systems. Each of the plates is signed "I. Senex, sculpt."

[33] *Astronomical Lectures, Read in the Publick Schools at Cambridge; By William Whiston, M.A. Mr. Lucas' Professor of the Mathematicks in that University. . . . For the Use of young Students in the University.* (London, 1715).

his soul; and how changing and variable in his frame of body? The constancy of the one, shook by every notion, the temperament of the other, affected by every blast of wind. What an April weather in the mind! In a word, what is Man altogether, but one mighty inconsistency." Like many before and after, Pope experienced a dual response to vastness —an expansion of his imagination, countered by a poignant awareness of the insignificance of man in a universe that had grown too vast for his comprehension.

A month after his letter to Caryll a letter now attributed to Pope appeared in *Guardian* No. 169[34] (Thursday, September 24, 1713) in which the themes of the Caryll letter continue. Here is Pope's awareness of a plurality or infinity of worlds, the vastness of the universe: "How many Foxhunters and Rural Squires are to be found in *Great Britain*, who are ignorant that they have all this while lived on a Planet, that the Sun is several thousand times bigger than the Earth; and that there are other Worlds without our View, greater and more glorious than our own." He had just said: "When I consider things in this Light, methinks it is a sort of Impiety to have no Attention to the Course of Nature, and the Revolution of the Heavenly Bodies. To be regardless of those *Phaenomena* that are placed within our View, on purpose to entertain our Faculties, and display the Wisdom and Power of their Creator, is an Affront to Providence of the same kind, (I hope it is not Impious to make such a Simile) as it wou'd be to a good Poet, to sit out his Play without minding the Plot or Beauties of it." And then he reflects on the contrast between the grandness of the universe and supposed "Human Grandeur": "Within this ample Circumference of the World, the glorious Lights that are hung on high, the

[34] *The Prose Works of Alexander Pope*, ed. Norman Ault (Oxford: Clarendon Press, 1936), I. lxviii-lxx, 137-40. In attributing the letter to Pope, Ault stresses "the presence of ideas which he is known to have entertained from time to time." He quotes "a few of the more separable doubles." Curiously enough he makes no reference to the more striking parallels with the Caryll letter, although the letter was available in the Elwin Courthope edition of the *Works*, VI. 190-91.

Meteors in the middle Region, the various Livery of the
Earth, and the Profusion of good things that distinguish
the Seasons, yield a Prospect which annihilates all Human
Grandeur."

Even though we have found no direct statement, other
than Pope's, about Whiston's earliest lecture at Button's,
we suggest that two other poets, also habitués of the
coffee-house, shared some part of Pope's imaginative response. John Gay was later to have his fun with Whiston,
as we shall see, but in the latter months of 1713 cosmological ideas were markedly present in his poetry.[35] Four
poems appeared in Steele's *Miscellany* in December 1713,
among them *A Contemplation on Night* and *A Thought
on Eternity*. The first includes a lengthy astro-theological
section:

> Wrapt in night's robe the whole creation lies.
> Yet still, ev'n now, while darkness clothes the land,
> We view the traces of th' almighty hand;
> Millions of stars in heav'n's wide vault appear,
> And with new glories hang the boundless sphere;
> The silver moon her western couch forsakes,
> And o'er the skies her nightly circle makes,
> Her solid globe beats back the sunny rays,
> And to the world her borrow'd light repays.
>
> Whether those stars that twinkling lustre send,
> Are suns, and rolling worlds those suns attend,

35 William Henry Irving, in *John Gay: Favorite of the Wits* (New York: Russell & Russell, 1962, reprint of edition of Duke University Press, 1940), p. 73, quotes some lines from *Rural Sports* about "Millions of worlds," with the comment, "Other passages in this poem make use of the *loose Newtonianism* of this time" (italics ours). There was, of course, much of such meditation on infinity and eternity in the astro-theological writers from whom various poets drew. However, it seems somewhat more than mere coincidence that both Gay and John Hughes were habitués of Button's, and that all the poems we quote here were written after Whiston's first lectures. The passage from *Rural Sports* quoted by Irving (beginning Canto I, 107) was earlier. That poem, dedicated to Pope, appeared in January, 1713. Our quotations from the other poems are from *Poems on Several Occasions* (London, 1737), II. 136-40.

Man may conjecture, and new schemes declare,
Yet all his systems but conjectures are;
But this we know, that heav'n's eternal King,
Who bid this universe from nothing spring,
Can at his *Word* bid num'rous world's appear,
And rising worlds th' all-pow'rful *Word* shall hear.

A Thought on Eternity combines themes of eternity and infinity with millenarianism, an enthusiasm of Whiston's:

Ere the foundations of the world were laid,
Ere kindling light th' Almighty word obey'd,
Thou wert; and when the subterranean flame
Shall burst its prison, and devour this frame,
From angry heav'n when the keen lightning flies,
When fervent heat dissolves the melting skies,
Thou still shalt be; still, as thou wert before,
And know no change, when time shall be no more.
O endless thought! divine eternity!
Th' immortal soul shares but a part of thee; . . .
She longs to wait, and wishes to get free,
To launch from earth into eternity.
For while the boundless theme extends our thought,
Ten thousand thousand rolling years are nought.

Another poet, then better known than Gay or Pope, seems to have experienced some of the same responses to Whiston's lectures. John Hughes was at this time a member of the Button group. Several of his canticles had been set to music and so well received that when in 1711 Steele first became interested in the Censorium, which Thomas Clayton was using for concerts, he sent to Hughes Clayton's adaptation of Dryden's "Alexander's Feast," requesting Hughes to "alter this Poem for Musick, preserving as many of Dryden's Words and Verses as you can."[36] Hughes' drama,

[36] The chief authority for the life of Hughes was William Duncombe, who published most of Hughes' poems after his death in 1720, in *Poems on Several Occasions. With some Select Essays in Prose* (London, 1735). This statement appears in I. xvii.

The Siege of Damascus, was acted at the Theatre Royal,
with the King and Queen present, on the very night Hughes
died, as Steele pointed out in his memorial essay in *Spectator* No. 15. Hughes had contributed to the *Tatler*, more
frequently to the *Spectator*, and probably also to the *Guardian*. He was recognized by his contemporaries as a translator of importance, both from the classics and from French.
For our purposes the most important of these was that of
the letters of Abelard and Eloisa, which appeared in July
1713, and became the basis for Pope's *Eloisa to Abelard*.[37]

In the "Ode to the Creator of the World," Hughes had
used astronomical materials. Published in 1713, presumably
before the Whiston lectures, the "Ode" contains little
specifically "modern" astronomy. In this way it differs from
Hughes' most extensive poetic treatment of astronomy in
his finest poem, "The Ecstasy." While this cannot be dated
exactly, Duncombe makes clear that it was published posthumously, and—his order throughout generally chronological—he placed it last among Hughes' poems. The earlier
verses are imitation, but the Advertisement indicates that
"the latter Part, which attempts a short View of the Heavens, according to the Modern Philosophy, is entirely Original, and not founded on any Thing in Latin Authors."
Hughes' is, indeed, the most extensive and most technically
correct poetic adaptation of the Newtonian cosmology be-

[37] Among his translations were some works of Fontenelle, to whom
we shall return later. In 1708 he published his translation of Fontenelle's *Dialogues of the Dead*. He also translated his "Discourse concerning the Ancients and the Moderns," which appeared with some
of the editions of the translation of Fontenelle's *Conversations* by
Mr. Glanvill. This we will mention again. Hughes was familiar with
the Latin text of the letters of Abelard and Eloisa, which had been
published in France in 1616, but he translated from a much more
romantic French version of 1693, which seems to have combined
French translations of three of the letters by Comte de Bussy (published in 1697 but circulated earlier in manuscript) with a later translation, published at The Hague in 1693. Among various versions of
Hughes' translation is one published at London in 1783. *Letters of
Abelard and Heloise. By the late John Hughes, Esq. . . . . Together
with the Poem of Eloisa to Abelard. By Mr. Pope. And (to which is
now added) the Poem of Abelard to Heloisa. By Mrs. Madan.*

fore Newton's death in 1727.[38] Turning from the conventional material in the opening stanzas, the poet beseeches the clouds and whirlwinds to raise a "raptur'd Bard" to the empyrean,

> Where Planets, in pure Streams of Æther driv'n,
>   Swim thro' the blue Expanse of Heav'n.
> And lo! th' obsequious Clouds and Winds obey!
> And lo! again the Nations downwards fly,
> And wide-stretch'd Kingdoms perish from my Eye.
>   Heav'n! what bright Visions now arise!
>   What opening Worlds my ravish'd Sense surprise!
> I pass *Cerulean* Gulphs, and now behold
> New solid Globes their Weight, self-balanc'd, bear,
>   Unprop'd amidst the fluid Air,
> And all, around the Central Sun, in circling Eddies roll'd.
>   Unequal in their Courses, see they advance,
>   And form the Planetary Dance!

The "Raptur'd Bard" looks up to the Galilean moon, then down to the earth which seems "a larger Moon." He sails among the planets, Mars with his "ruddy Rays," Jupiter presiding over his four moons, and finally comes to Saturn and his "bright Ring." Suddenly before the poet's eyes appears "a pointed Flame," which seems at first a "shining Meteor," but this meteor originates not in the celestial regions but on earth, and travels its path in reverse:

> And now it traverses each Sphere,
> And seems some living Guest, familiar to the Place.
>   'Tis He—as I approach more near
> The great Columbus of the Skies I know!
> 'Tis Newton's Soul, that daily travels here
> In search of Knowledge for Mankind below.

[38] In *Newton Demands the Muse* (Princeton: Princeton University Press, 1946), pp. 10-11, I suggested Halley's Latin poem, prefixed to the first edition of the *Principia*, as one of Hughes' possible sources, and said, "John Hughes alone suggested the kind of tribute we shall later find. . . . Hughes was a pioneer in combining in verse the theories of the *Opticks* with those of the *Principia*." MHN

Here, more than ten years before Newton's death, is the first extended poetic tribute to Newton (save Halley's dedicatory poem) of a sort that became increasingly familiar after 1727. In the finest lines of the Ode that immediately follow, Hughes deftly combines discoveries of the *Principia* with those of the *Opticks* as in ecstasy his imagination accompanies Newton on his cosmic voyages:

> Here let me, thy Companion, stray,
> From Orb to Orb, and now behold
> Unnumber'd Suns, all Seas of molten Gold;
> And trace each Comet's wand'ring Way,
> And now descry Light's Fountain-Head,
> And measure its descending Speed;
> Or learn how Sun-born Colours rise
> In Rays distinct, and in the Skies
> Blended in yellow Radiance flow,
> Or stain the fleecy Cloud, or streak the Wat'ry Bow;
> Or now diffus'd their beauteous Tinctures shed
> On ev'ry Planet's rising Hills, and ev'ry verdant Mead.

Hughes was in his thirties when Whiston began his coffee-house lectures, when Pope and Gay were in their twenties—Pope had recently passed his twenty-fifth birthday.[39] We have some evidence from an anonymous and highly prejudicial source that Whiston's coffee-house lectures were popular and influential, particularly on the young. *Will-with-a-Wisp; Or, the Grand Ignis Fatuus of London*[40] is an attack on Whiston's various heresies, includ-

---

[39] The relation between Hughes and Pope continued for several years, and was on the whole a pleasant one, although Hughes was said to have withdrawn most of his contributions from the *Miscellany* because he objected to Pope's translation of the *Wife of Bath*.

[40] The Yale University Library contains a series of nine volumes called "Whiston Controversies." These are pamphlets by and about Whiston, concerned with Whiston's supposed heresies, charges brought against him, and his defense of himself. For the most part they contribute nothing to our problem, but the one from which we quote includes some references to the coffee-house lectures, among many charges against Whiston: *Will-with-a-Wisp; Or, the Grand Ignis Fatuus of London. Being a Lay-Man's Letter to a Country Gentleman, concerning the Articles lately exhibited against Mr. Whiston.* (Lon-

ing "his beloved *Milennium*, a mere Whimsy, or a pleasant *Dream* of his wandering Mind." The attack continues: "I comes next to our *Will-with-a-Wisp's Mathematicks*, which *he* only sets-up in profess'd Praejudice and Contempt of both *Universities*." Here is a refrain reiterated since the first coffee-house had been established in Oxford shortly before the Restoration: the distrust of fellows and dons of Oxford and Cambridge for these "Penny Universities," in which youth sought some aspects of education which it did not always find in the academic lecture halls. The author continues: "A full Account of whose wonderful *Lectures* for *Mechanicks, Opticks, Hydrostaticks, Pneumatics,* &c.— so many *Bombast-Ticks* are as easily forgotten; I have read, with some Dissatisfaction at the designing *Project*, in a publick Paper at a certain *Coffee-house* in *London*." This was, of course, the series of lectures advertised to begin in January 1714, which were later moved from Button's to a larger hall. "He leads our *young People* astray thither, into the *City*, or back to *Button's* again; and takes them off from their more serious Duties, Studies, and Exercises of *Religion* or Business at *Home*. . . . In short they contract ill Habits and wrong Notions in Religion, as well as neglect their other worldly *Employments*, by following such admir'd designing, Arian Lectures in vogue."

Specific references to Whiston's lectures appear in the Pope correspondence on two occasions later than the Caryll letter. In April 1715 Gay and Pope sent a combined letter to Caryll.[41] Gay wrote: "There is a grand revolution at Will's Coffee-house. Morrice has quitted for a coffee-house in the City, and Titcombe is restored to the great joy of Cromwell, who was at a great loss for a person to converse with upon the Fathers and Church History. The knowledge

don, 1714). No author is given. A printed insertion on the first page reads, "By a Gentleman formerly of Queens' College, Oxon." The passage from which we quote is on pp. 56-57.

[41] *Correspondence*, I. 288-90. This letter is not dated; the second version to Congreve is dated April 7, 1715. (*Correspondence*, I. 290-91.) The "extraordinary copy of verses" on the longitude, mentioned in the first letter, will be discussed later.

I gain from him is entirely in painting and poetry; and Mr. Pope owes all his skill in astronomy and particularly in the revolution of eclipses to him and Mr Whiston, so celebrated of late for his discovery of the longitude in an extraordinary copy of verses which you heard when you were last in town." A letter from Gay and Pope to Congreve, dated April 7, 1715, is a shortened version of that to Caryll. The entry for these two letters in Professor Sherburn's index to the *Correspondence* reads: "He (Whiston) lectures at Will's coffee-house," a statement for which he offers no evidence. His surmise may well be correct, since Whiston's fame as a popular lecturer had increased during the eighteen months since Pope first heard him. How often he had heard Whiston later we have no way of proving, but Whiston himself said that he gave "many" lectures at Button's. One of Gay's phrases is significant as showing that in April 1715 Pope was particularly interested in Whiston's pronouncements on eclipses.

II

Pope was far from alone in his interest in "the revolution of eclipses" at this time. During the month of April 1715 was to occur the most widely heralded eclipse of the century, a total eclipse of the sun on April 22, 1715, in prediction of which Whiston was much involved. There is no reason to doubt his statement in the *Memoirs*: "this most eminent Eclipse, 1715, was exactly foretold by Mr. Flamsteed, Dr. Halley and myself: Its Beginning came to one Minute, and its End within four of the Calculations."[42] But let us turn from Whiston to the greatest English observer of that phenomenon, Edmund Halley,[43] to see why

42 *Memoirs*, I. 239.
43 *Observations of the late Total Eclipse of the Sun of the 22d of April last past, made before the Royal Society.* By Dr. Edmund Halley, *Phil. Trans.*, XXIX, No. 303 (March-April-May 1715), 245-62.

Pope and hundreds of others had their attention on eclipses in early April.

It surprises a modern reader to learn from Halley's account that there had been no total eclipse of the sun over England for five hundred and seventy-five years. The last, according to Halley's computations, had occurred in 1140.[44] Naturally great preparations for the occurrence were made by all astronomers and by the Royal Society. Halley had "caused a small map of England, describing the Tract and Bounds thereof, to be distributed all over the Kingdom, with a request to the Curious to observe what they could of it, but more specifically to note the Time of Continuation of total Darkness." Since this required no equipment on the part of the observer other than a pendulum clock, his request for cooperation met with a magnificent response. When the day came, "the Heavens proved generally favourable." At the headquarters of the Royal Society in Crane Court gathered members and invited guests, some among the aristocracy and dignitaries of the City, others "several foreign Gentlemen," including members of the Royal Academy of Sciences at Paris, most of whom had come particularly to view the eclipse, which was partial in various sections of the world, total only over England. It began at seven minutes past eight in the morning, and ended two hours and thirteen minutes later. During the eclipse, Jupiter, Mercury and Venus were clearly visible to the Royal Society observers, but of the fixed stars only Capella and Aldebaran were observed.

Even today a total eclipse of the sun arouses widespread interest. How much more engrossing it must have seemed to Englishmen, particularly Londoners, in 1715, realizing that no such phenomenon had been observed in more than five and a half centuries. Pope, like many others, had clearly been preparing for the experience by studying "the revolutions of eclipses" in some way with Whiston. We shall try to

---

[44] The last partial solar eclipse over England, which we have found mentioned in *Phil. Trans.* had occurred on September 13, 1699, when Pope would have been eleven years of age. It was readily observed in Germany, but not in England, because of the weather.

157

reconstruct what and how they had been studying. In exactly this period, William Whiston published a work, which he called *The Copernicus,* described briefly in his *Memoirs* as "an Astronomical Instrument by me first invented, and afterwards published, for the Examination of all those, and indeed of all the ancient Eclipses, that could possibly be seen in any Parts of the World, of which we have any ancient Histories preserv'd."[45] By this instrument Whiston had computed solar and lunar eclipses as far back as 400 B.C. Elsewhere in the *Memoirs* he mentioned the fact that the instrument sold for six guineas, while the explanatory text cost only one shilling.

No copy of *The Copernicus* is available in America, and until we obtained a microfilm of the British Museum copy of the text, *The Copernicus Explain'd,* we assumed that the instrument was some variety of telescope. It proved no such thing, but a very elaborate kind of perpetual calendar for the discovery or prognostication of celestial phenomena, past, present and future. It was made up of a series of circles, an outside "immovable Circle, and the small moveable central Circle within," as well as "ten intermediate concentrical *Annuli,* or broad circular Rings, fitted to revolve one within another; but so, as to be capable of being fix'd, by small Pins, in any situation whatsoever." Six of the *annuli* were removable; when inserted they were firmly connected with the frame and revolved as freely as the others. "The Copernicus" also provided a "Terrestrial Globe of Nine Inches Diameter, plac'd under the inner Circles, with its Hour Circle, turning along with it in the diurnal Motion." The globe could be elevated, fixed at any height "and so regulated by Screws, as to be ready for the Exhibition of those Eclipses, which the six outward Circles assist us to discover." Among other equipment of

---

[45] *Memoirs,* I. 181-82. The price is mentioned I. 241. The explanatory text was *The Copernicus Explain'd: Or a Brief Account of the Nature and Use of an Universal Astronomical Instrument, For the Calculation and Exhibition of the New and Full Moons, and of the Eclipses, both Solar and Lunar; with the Places Heliocentrical and Geocentrical of all the Planets, Primary and Secondary, &c.* (London, n.d.) .

this elaborate instrument was "a Pole, with a Groove, containing an Angle of $5°$ 37^1 for the Moon's Path in Eclipses"; "a round Plate of Glass, with 12 Concentrical Circles therein, for the 12 Digits in Solar Eclipses"; also "a dark Circle, representing that Season of the Earth's Conical Shadow, along which the Moon passes in its own Eclipses"; "also two Threads, with their Plummets, fix'd to the Center of the Instrument; of frequent Use in its Operations."[46]

"The Copernicus" had many uses. Indeed, it would have served as a basis for a course in descriptive astronomy. Whiston's reiterated emphasis on eclipses, and the dating of the instrument and text, indicates that both had been prepared for the eclipse of April 22, 1715.[47] The pamphlet bears no printed date, but was signed on page 55: "March 18, 1714/15. Will Whiston." Probably the elaborate instrument had been prepared earlier. Four weeks before the eclipse Whiston had the text prepared, and undoubtedly his printer—usually R. Senex of Salisbury Court —ready to print the pamphlet at once. So far as we can determine from the title pages of Whiston's more ephemeral pamphlets (though this is also true of the two-volume *Memoirs*) Whiston usually marketed his own wares and apparently always did so with material to accompany lectures. In a note to *Copernicus Explain'd* he urged readers who purchased "the Copernicus" and who desired to have it explained to "apply themselves to the Author, who will endeavour to make the several Parts and Uses of it easie and familiar to them." Thanks to the widespread popular in-

---

[46] This general summary is followed by a lengthy detailed description of the various parts of the instrument, and another passage indicating the various uses of "the Copernicus."

[47] In Section 12 there is a curious error which must have been typographical: "Thus the next great Solar Eclipse will begin here at London, April 21." The eclipse was on April 22, as Whiston well knew both from his own calculations and from Halley's map sent out over England, which Whiston mentions at this point. The hours mentioned agree with Halley's, Whiston says "about 8 h. 7 m. in the Morning." Halley had computed the beginning of the eclipse as 8 h. 7^1 (account cited, *Memoirs*, p. 247), but found it to begin one minute earlier. The end of the eclipse he timed as "exactly 10^h 20^1 correct time." The error had been not in the computation but in their clocks.

terest in the eclipse, Whiston reaped a rich reward from "the Copernicus" and his public lectures at this time, as he reported in the *Memoirs*:[48] "I myself by my Lectures before; by the Sale of my Schemes before and after; by the generous Presents of my numerous and noble Audience; who at the Recommendation of my great Friend, The Lord Stanhope, then Secretary of State, gave me a Guinea apiece; by the very uncommon Present of twenty Guineas from another of my Benefactors, the Duke of Newcastle; and of five Guineas at Night from the Lord Godolphin; gained in all about 120.£ by it. Which in the Circumstances I then was, and have since been, destitute of all Preferment, was a very seasonable and plentiful Supply: And, as I reckoned, maintained me and my Family for a whole Year together."

There seems to us little question that Pope, whose skill in "the revolution of eclipses" Gay reported to Caryll on or before April 7, 1715, had been following some of Whiston's lectures, during which he would certainly have seen "the Copernicus" demonstrated. Possibly he bought the instrument or text, and sought Whiston out for the personal instruction he offered. No letters are extant between April 7 and early June so that we have no comment by Pope about the eclipse. In view of the widespread interest in the phenomenon and Pope's study of the subject, it would seem incredible that he did not watch it from some vantage point, probably with a group of Whiston's auditors, who may well have followed the eclipse with "the Copernicus" and through telescopes. On that occasion amateur astronomers must have experienced even more profound emotions than those reported by England's greatest observer Halley,

[48] I. 239. Whiston dedicated *The Copernicus Explain'd* to General Stanhope, whom he particularly mentions here, as "A great Patron and Encourager of Learning, and of Understanding for the Public Good." James Osborn in his recent edition of Spence's *Anecdotes*, I. 394, is skeptical about the identification of Lord Stanhope. Whiston's comments here, as on the committee on the longitude, would seem to leave no reason to doubt that this was Charles, first Earl of Stanhope, who became Secretary of State.

who described "the Chill and Damp which attended the Darkness of this Eclipse, of which most Spectators were sensible, and equally Judges. Nor shall I trouble you with the Concern that appear'd in all Sorts of Animals, Birds, Beasts, and Fishes, upon the Extinction of the Sun, since ourselves could not behold it without some sense of Horror." A poetic parallel for Halley's account may be found in John Hughes, "To Urania, on her Arrival at Jamaica," written in the same year:

> So when of late our Sun was veil'd from Sight
> In dark Eclipse, and lost in sullen Night,
> A shivering Cold each Heart with Horror thrill'd
> The Birds forsook the Skies, the Herds the Field.
> But when the conqu'ring Orb, with One bright Ray
> Broke thro' the Gloom, and reinthron'd the Day,
> The Herds reviv'd, the Birds renew'd their Strains,
> Unusual Transports rais'd the chearful Swains,
> And Joy returning echo'd thro' the Plains.[49]

Pope may not have brought his dog to London, but there was always one at Binfield. The master may well have suffered vicariously at the terror of his current "Bounce."

The year 1715-16 proved an *annus mirabilis* in England, meteorologically speaking. In June 1715, two months after the eclipse, appeared in Collo Cygni a *nova*, which astronomers realized was a reappearance of one first described in 1686, the second *nova* which had been known to appear and disappear periodically. It was found to have a period of 404½ days. An account of it in the *Philosophical Transactions*, Number 346, for November, 1715 ("A Short History of the several New-Stars that have appear'd within these 150 years: with an Account of the Return of that in Collo Cygni"), begins: "Whether it be owing to the greater Diligence of the Moderns, or that in reality no such thing has happen'd for many Ages past, I will not undertake to determine; but this is certain that, within the

[49] In *Poems on Several Occasions*, I. lvii; the poem is dated at the end, MDCCXV.

Space of the last 150 Years, more Discoveries have been made of Changes among the Fixt Starrs, than in all Antiquity before." Among others, the author describes "the wonderful Star in Collo Ceti, seen by David Fabricius" in 1596, "which had been since found to appear and disappear periodically." The *nova* observed in 1715 had first been described "by Mr. G. Kirch in the Year 1686." Anticipating its return, astronomers observed it on June 15, when it "was first perceived like one of the very least Telescopical Stars; but in the rest of the Month of July it gradually encreased, so as to become in August visible to the naked Eye; and so it continued all the Month of September." By December 8 it had died away to such an extent as to be scarcely discernible even through the telescope, but its reappearance in the autumn of 1716 was anticipated. We have paused over this *nova* because it was naturally considered a comet by many laymen who had heard of its periodicity, and may be reflected in some of the popular literature of the time.

Astronomy apart, Englishmen had reason to feel that the strange portents in the heavens were presages of another kind of "meteorological" phenomenon that affected them much more directly. The winter following the total eclipse was to be long remembered because of its phenomenal coldness. The passage of "most memorable occurrences and events" in the *Historical Register* for that year reads: "The Frost, which began the latter End of November last, continu'd with small Intermissions, 'till the 8th or 9th of this Month (February), with greater Severity than had been known in the Memory of Man. The River Thames was quite frozen up, and abundance of Booths were built upon it. On the 19th of January, two whole Oxen were roasted on the Ice. It is remarkable also, that at different Times there fell vast Quantities of Snow, which, together with the great Lumps of Ice, render'd even the Streets of London very dangerous, and almost unpassable."

It is possible that there was some interrelation between the phenomenal cold, continuing into March, and another extraordinary celestial phenomenon, not anticipated by astronomers, and therefore even more terrifying to laymen than the total eclipse. Again, Edmund Halley has left the most authoritative "Account of the late Surprizing Appearance of the Lights seen in the Air, on the sixth of March last; with an Attempt to explain the Principal Phaenomena thereof."[50] Even expert astronomers were startled by a sight none of them had ever seen. "This Phaenomenon," said Halley, "found all those that are skill'd in the Observation of the Heavens unprepared, and unacquainted with what was to be expected; and so it left all of them surprized, and astonished at the Novelty thereof." His research had shown that no such appearance in England had been recorded since Camden and Stow had described the "meteor" of November 14-15, 1574. Halley, indeed, had despaired of ever seeing what he saw that night, which he correctly identified as "aurora borealis."

Visiting a friend that evening, Halley had not seen the most spectacular part of the aurora, the corona, since the display began about seven o'clock and Halley did not observe it until about nine o'clock.[51] Analogies he quoted from descriptions given him by others indicate the effect of this phenomenon, particularly on laymen: "Some likened it to that Representation of Glory wherewith our Painters in

[50] *Phil. Trans.*, XXIX, No. 347 (January-March 1716), 406-28. In the next number, pp. 430-32, are further accounts of the appearance of the aurora on March 31, April 1 and 2, less spectacular, some observed in London, others elsewhere. The corresponding passages in the *Historical Register* for 1716 are on p. 115.

[51] The "Account of Happenings in the Sky" in the *Historical Register* for the year 1716, p. 117, carries the account back one hour: "The same Evening, about Eight of the Clock, was seen a strange Phaenomenon in the Sky. It appear'd at first like a huge Body of Light compact within it self, but without Motion; but in a little Time it began to move and separate, extending it self towards the West, where it seem'd, as it were, to dispose it self into Columns, or Pillars of Flame: From thence it darted South-East with amazing swiftness; where, after many undulatory Motions and Vibrations, there appear'd to be a continual Fulguration, interspers'd with Green, Red, Blue, and Yellow. Then it mov'd towards the North; from whence, in a little Time, it renew'd its wavy Motions and Coruscations; as before, which continu'd to be seen 'till past Three in the Morning."

Churches surround the Holy Name of God. Others to those radiating Starrs wherewith the Breasts of the Knights of the most Noble Order of the Garter are adorned. Many compared it to the Concave of the great Cupola of St. Paul's Church, distinguished with Streaks alternating Light and obscure, and having in the middle a Space less bright than the rest, resembling the Lantern."

Naturally many amateur observers thought the aurora a comet with a spectacular tail; many, too, as often with comets, eclipses and other celestial phenomena, believed it a warning of the end of the world or other manifestation of divine discontent with humanity. Political significance was only too readily read into the aurora, which had appeared on the evening of the day on which the King "gave the Royal Assent to *An Act for the speedy and easy Tryal of the [Jacobite] Rebels.*"[52] Millenarian though he may have been, Whiston was also a competent astronomer, and although, like Halley, he had never seen one, he recognized the phenomenon from historical descriptions and correctly identified and explained it in the lecture, mentioned earlier, he gave in the Censorium ten days after the aurora borealis. He defined it by the other title familiar to us today, "northern lights."[53] We stop briefly over one of the "Notices" of the Censorium lecture, "A Letter to a Lady in the Country. By Humphrey Philroye," published in *Chat-Chat*: "It is of too Low a Consideration to Trouble you with the ridiculous Construction that the Disaffected put on the late Lightning, which appear'd in the upper Region of the Air by Night; their Accounts of it not being more Mon-

[52] Quoted from the *Historical Register* by Sherburn, *Early Career*, p. 160.

[53] Whiston did not give an outline of the lecture in his *Memoirs* but indicates, I. 280-81, that during the year he published what was either the lecture or a paper based on it, as "An Account of a surprising Meteor [or Northern Light] seen in the Air March 6th, 1715/6 at Night." This appeared in *Post Man* on April 26 and in the *Daily Courant* on April 25; it included a description of the northern lights as he had seen them; a historical account of such phenomena; letters he had received from elsewhere describing the appearance; the principal phenomena and conjecture about the causes.

164

strous, than their Observations drawn from it . . . but I hear Mr. *Whiston* has spoken on this Subject, and I will Communicate his Thoughts to you, with all the exactness I can, when I have learn'd them; and will only add, that many impute this great Degree of Light, and Refulgency to a Comet's passing by the Earth."[54]

Pope mentions neither the aurora nor Whiston's lecture in his letters, in which there is a hiatus from February 29 to March 20. Certainly his name seems to have been associated with the phenomenon on at least one occasion if we may judge from the unsigned epilogue written for Addison's unsuccessful play, *The Drummer*,[55] which was performed on March 10, 1716, four days after the aurora:

If any *Briton* in this Place appears,
A slave to Priests, or superstitious Fears,
Let these odd Scenes reform his Brainsick Notions,
Or *BYFIELD'S* ready—to apply his Potions.
Those Wits Excepted, who appear'd so wise,
To Conjure Spectres from the vap'ry Skies.
A very POPE (I'm told) may be afraid,
And tremble at the Monsters, which he made.
From dark mishapen *Clouds of many a Dye.
A different Object rose to every Eye:
And the same Vapour, as your Fancies ran,
Appear'd a *Monarch*, or a *Warming-Pan*.
Well has Friend WHISTON every Scene apply'd
And drawn th' unmeaning *Meteor* to our Side.[56]
*The late *Meteor*

[54] See Rae Blanchard, *Richard Steele's Periodical Journalism*, pp. 261-62.

[55] "An *Epilogue* written for the late celebrated New *Play* called the *Drummer*, but not spoke." The Epilogue did not appear in editions of the play until the fourth. We follow a copy in the Yale University Library.

[56] Professor Sherburn quoted the first eight lines from *State Poems*, London, 1716, in *Early Career*, pp. 160-61. We find his pages confusing. At the beginning of the section he speaks of "a series of nights made portentous by displays of the aurora borealis," and evidently thought that the first aurora had appeared earlier than March 6, since, when he mentioned the act passed that day, he said, "the same

But for a time we must leave the subject of astronomy and turn back chronologically to another work of Whiston's, frequently mentioned among the Scriblerians, and the subject of one of their satires in the *Memoirs*.

III

In 1714 Whiston, with Humphrey Ditton, had published *A new Method of Discovering the Longitude*. Of all the scientific problems of the Restoration and early eighteenth century, this was the most urgent to the government, far more important in the minds of monarchs and Parliaments than remote astronomical theories. England was preeminently a maritime power, shipping one of the great sources of her wealth. In spite of many improvements since the invention of the mariner's compass, no accurate way for mariners to determine their longitude had yet been discovered, although the most distinguished scientists of the Royal Society had devoted time and effort to the problem.[57] The names of Hooke, Newton, and Halley led the list. An amusing illustration of the great importance placed

evening followed more aurora borealis." As we have indicated there were "more" later, but Halley's account makes clear that this was the first aurora seen in England since the sixteenth century. Sherburn may have been correct in interpreting the couplet on Pope in the epilogue as referring to an article in the *Weekly Packet*, 18 February 1716, in which Pope's description of Minerva's descent like a comet (*Iliad*, IV. 95-106) was associated with Jacobite prophecies of further wars or uprisings. However, he apparently did not understand that "*the late Meteor" in the epilogue referred specifically to the aurora of March 6, since he said: "Such talk of meteors was likely to occur in the days of satire on astrologers and almanac-makers." He did not include the couplet on Whiston, and apparently it had slipped his mind when he wrote his "Great Shew of Nature" about Pope and Whiston many years later.

57 Some indication of the long search for such a scheme on the part of one distinguished scientist may be seen by following through the entries in R.T. Gunther, *The Life and Work of Robert Hooke*, in *Early Science in Oxford* (Oxford: Clarendon Press 1930), Vols. VI and VII, which cover a span of thirty years.

by the Crown on the problem of longitude was shown by Edmund Halley's presentation to King James of a copy of Newton's *Principia* in 1687. Quite aware that His Majesty was not likely to read or understand the abstractions and mathematical proof of the volume, Halley accompanied it by extracts he had made from a section the King might well consider of importance, "The True Theory of the Tides," adding a note: " 'Tis to be hoped, that . . . having perfected the Theory of the Moon, the long devised discovery of the Longitude (which at sea is only predictable this way) may at length be brought to light, to the great Honour of your Majesty and Advantage of your Subjects."[58]

There is no question of the public fame and rich reward that would be attained by anyone who could propose a scheme simple and practical enough to be used by mariners at sea. When William Whiston and Humphrey Ditton entered the competition, the field was as open as it had been when Hooke entered it in 1655. Their first appearance in print on the subject was a letter to the *Guardian* No. 107, dated July 11, 1713, just four weeks before Pope wrote Caryll about Whiston's lecture. Addison included this, with a little essay on "projects," some parts in light vein. Then he added: "I shall publish one of a more serious nature, which deserves the utmost attention of the public, and in particular of such who are lovers of mankind. It is on no less a subject than that of discovering the longitude, and deserves a much higher name than that of a project, if our language afforded any such term." Whiston was advertised by Addison as having "lately obliged the world with that noble plan, entitled, A Scheme of the Solar System." The letter itself is short. Whiston and Ditton were giving away no secrets. It dwelt rather on the social good

---

[58] *Isaac Newton's Papers & Letters on Natural Philosophy*, ed. I. Bernard Cohen (Cambridge: Harvard University Press, 1958), pp. 412-24. There are various references to the problem of longitude in *The Correspondence of Sir Isaac Newton*, ed. H.W. Turnbull (Cambridge: Cambridge University Press, 1959-61); and in *The Correspondence of Sir Isaac Newton and Professor [Roger] Cotes*, ed. J. Edleston (London: J. W. Parker, 1850).

such a discovery would have and predicted that "now that the longitude has been found it cannot be long before the latitudes of the earth are also discerned." Five months later a letter from Whiston and Ditton, dated December 7, 1713, appeared in the *Englishman*.[59] Again the contributors stressed their desire for the public good, but particularly requested "Patrons and Well-wishers of Learning and Ingenuity of all Nations" to send them word of "the several Rewards which are any where set apart for this Discovery, and on what Condition, and by what Methods the Discoverers may apply for, and obtain them."

Whiston and Ditton were laying their plans carefully.[60] Whiston communicated their method to Newton, and, apparently at his request, discussed it with Halley, Samuel Clarke, and Roger Cotes, Professor of Astronomy at Trinity College, Cambridge. Absurd as the Whiston-Ditton scheme seems today, it had at least qualified approval of some of these experts who encouraged them to apply to the House of Commons for a reward. The interest of the government in some means for discovering the longitude from ships at sea had become even more acute as the result of a petition brought before the House of Commons on May 25, 1714, by captains of the Queen's ships, merchants of London, and commanders of merchant ships, declaring that "The Discovery of Longitude is of such Consequence to Great Britain, for Safety of the Navy, and Merchant Ships, as well as Improvement of Trade, that, for want thereof, many ships have been retarded in their Voyages, and many lost." The Commons promptly established a committee to consider the petition, and so urgent the matter seemed, the committee was ordered to meet at once ("five o'clock this

---

[59] Ed. R. Blanchard, pp. 119-20.

[60] This section is based on two sources: *Journals of the House of Commons*, Vol. XVII (1711-1714) between 25 May and 13 July 1714, and a lengthy footnote by J. Edleston in his edition of *Correspondence of Sir Isaac Newton and Professor Cotes* (London: J. W. Parker, 1850), p. lxxvi. The main part of this note is a quotation from Whiston which Edleston identifies only as "Historical Preface, date probably 1742, inserted in some copies of his [Whiston's] *Longitude Discovered*, London, 1738."

afternoon"). The chairman of the committee was Lord Stanhope, Secretary of State, of whose later interest in Whiston we have heard. The report of this committee was considered in detail by the Commons on June 11. At some time between May 25 and that date, Whiston and Ditton had been called before the committee, together with Newton, Halley, Clarke and Cotes. Since the *Journal of the House of Commons* did not describe part of that meeting (although a long section of the report was concerned with the Whiston-Ditton proposal), we may turn to Whiston's account, written several years later. A chair was placed for Newton, the other witnesses standing, Whiston behind Newton's chair. The others spoke without notes; Newton alone read from a manuscript. "Upon the reading of this paper," said Whiston, "the Committee were at a loss, as not well understanding its contents: Sir I. Newton sitting still and saying nothing by way of explication.[61] This gave the chairman an opportunity which it was perceived he wanted of trying to drop the bill; which he did by declaring his own opinion to be that, 'Unless Sir I. Newton would say that the method now proposed was likely to be useful for the discovery of the Longitude, he was against making a bill in general for a reward for such a discovery, as Dr. Clarke had particularly proposed to the Committee.' " Upon his pronouncement and Newton's continued silence, Whiston feared his cause was lost. He himself spoke: "Mr. Chairman, the occasion of the puzzle you are now in is nothing but Sir I. Newton's caution. He knows the usefulness of the present method 'near the shores' (which are the places of greatest danger). Whereupon Sir Isaac Newton stood up and said, 'He thought this bill ought to pass, because of the present method's usefulness near the shores.' Which declaration of his was much the same with what he had said in his own paper, but which was not understood by the Committee, and determined them unanimously to agree to such a bill." A bill authorizing the establishment

[61] In his *Memoirs*, pp. 292-94. Whiston said that Newton "was of the most fearful, cautious, and suspicious Temper that I ever knew."

of a reward was passed by the House of Commons on July 13.[62]

To a modern reader the Whiston-Ditton proposal sounds as absurd as it seemed to the Scriblerus Club. It was basically a project for anchoring fire-ships at each degree of the meridian; from each of these daily at exactly noon would be discharged cannon and rockets which would burst at altitudes that would be known to mariners. Based to some extent on discoveries made in the nature of sound by men like Robert Hooke and Robert Boyle, the proposal would have seemed to many contemporaries "scientific," and an improvement on known ways of computing the longitude which Whiston and Ditton discussed at length in their book. Whatever Newton thought of it, it must have had at least modified support from the other scientists present, since all of them knew the principles proposed before they attended the meeting. The reward was offered, but Whiston and Ditton did not receive it.

The Scriblerus Club was born not long after Pope heard Whiston lecture at Button's. Pope's proposal for *An Account of the Works of the Unlearned,* in which the Club had its genesis, had appeared in *Spectator* No. 457, the previous year, on August 14, 1712. During the following year Pope maintained his association with Addison and Steele,

---

[62] Whiston and Ditton in their *New Method* mention the amount of the award both on the frontispiece and on p. 26 as £20,000, the same amount as quoted by Kerby-Miller, *Memoirs of Scriblerus,* p. 335 ("13 Anne c. 14"). The *Journals* include a long résumé of Newton's paper, under date of June 11, 1714. Newton briefly analyzed various methods then in use for determining longitude, and pointed out their limitations: (a) watches, but no watch had yet been invented to withstand the motion of a ship, variations in temperature, and the force of gravity at sea; (b) the eclipses of Jupiter's satellites, but most boats could not be equipped with the kinds of telescopes necessary, and few mariners had the necessary knowledge and skill; (c) the place of the moon, but lunar theory was still not exact enough to determine longitude within a degree. He raised various objections to the Whiston-Ditton scheme, and was not reported in the *Journals* as expressing any enthusiasm for it. From his reluctant addendum to his paper it would seem that Newton believed that Commons should offer a reward in order to stimulate further experimentation, but by no means recommending the award to Whiston and Ditton.

POPE AND ASTRONOMY

with Button's as headquarters for the Whig men of letters. For a time Pope continued to discuss with Addison and Steele his plan for a journal of sorts, a plan in which he had been enthusiastically joined by John Gay. Since there was nothing political in his project, Pope probably had hoped to bring together Whig and Tory contributors. Young as he and Gay both were, it was natural that they should seek among the Tories for a man of the maturity and stature of Addison. Inevitably they found one in Swift, with whom Pope seems to have become acquainted in the autumn of 1713.[63] Pope wrote happily to Gay that "Dr. Swift much approves what I proposed, even to the very title." Gradually Pope and Gay were weaned away from Button's to Will's, although the two young men continued to visit their friends at Button's for some time. Meetings of the Scriblerus Club—Swift, Arbuthnot, Parnell, Lord Oxford, Pope, and Gay—were held during the early months of 1714. Pope found his scheme radically changed by Swift and Arbuthnot, and his periodical of papers about the "unlearned" becoming the *Memoirs of Martinus Scriblerus.*

As the club developed and it became clear that one of the subjects to be satirized was inevitably science, Pope may well have found himself in a quandary, so far as Whiston was concerned. Whatever he thought now of the "wicked Works" he could not have failed to feel loyalty toward a teacher who had opened such worlds to the imagination as Whiston had for Pope. It is possible that a protest of Pope against satires on Whiston Arbuthnot designed for the *Memoirs* may be an additional explanation of Swift's rather curious analysis of the club members in a letter to Arbuthnot: "To talk of Martin in any hands but yours,

[63] All these matters have been discussed in careful detail by Charles Kerby-Miller, *The Memoirs of Scriblerus*, pp. 18 ff. Sherburn wished to date Pope's letter to Gay as October 1, 1712, but Kerby-Miller says the weight of evidence favors October 13, 1712. In his edition of Pope's *Correspondence*, Sherburn places the letter in 1713, a date originally assigned to it by Elwin-Courthope and recently accepted by Professor Donald F. Bond in his edition of *The Spectator* (Oxford: Clarendon Press, 1965), IV. 114.

171

is a folly. You every day give better hints than all of us together could do in a twelvemonth; and to say the truth,
Pope who first thought of the hint has no genius at all to
it, in my mind. Gay is too young; Parnell has some ideas
of it, but is idle; I could put together, and lard, and strike
out well enough, but all that relates to the sciences must be
from you."[64]

A little earlier than Whiston's lecturing at Button's, Swift
spoke of him with respect. In *The Story of St. Alban's
Ghost*, published in 1712, he mentioned difficulties he had
encountered in getting manuscripts. He added: "I wish I
could have had time to have distinguished by an asterism
the circumstances delivered by tradition only, which I was
advised to do by my worthy friend, the Rev. Mr. Whiston,
who, had he not been employed otherways, might have
been a very proper person to have undertaken such a performance."[65] This seems a very liberal attitude on Swift's
part, since he was writing in 1711-12 very soon after Whiston's banishment. Swift here showed no concern about
Whiston's trial for heresy nor his earlier "wicked Works."[66]

[64] Quoted from Swift, *Correspondence*, II. 162-63, by Kerby-Miller,
p. 57. He analyzes the letters in detail, suggesting various reasons for
the attitude of the older man toward the younger. He does not stress
the fact that, if Gay was too young, Pope was nearly three years
younger. We suggest, in addition, that Pope might have been oppos-
ing some of Arbuthnot's scientific satire, and Swift was here ruling,
"all that relates to the sciences must be from you."

[65] *The Works of Jonathan Swift*, ed. Sir Walter Scott (1883), V.
417.

[66] Rae Blanchard, p. 426 of her edition of *The Englishman*, wrote:
"Whiston was the object of Swift's dislike: 'He hated Wh——n like
a Toad,' he said of himself." She was quoting from *Part of the
seventh epistle of the First Book of Horace Imitated*, ll. 35-38:

> In State-Opinion a-la- Mode,
> He hated Wh——n like a Toad,
> Had giv'n the Faction many a Wound,
> And Libell'd all the Junta round.

Harold Williams in his commentary (*The Poems of Jonathan Swift*
[Oxford: Clarendon Press, 1937], I. 171) interprets the reference correctly, we think, as to Thomas, first Marquis of Wharton, and notes
that Swift continued to attack Wharton. Certainly the last couplet
makes little sense, if applied to Whiston.

Arbuthnot's early references to Whiston were casual and showed no personal animosity. The first reference was in his *Examination of Dr. Woodward's Account of the Deluge*, London, 1697. Woodward was, of course, Arbuthnot's whipping-boy, fossil experts as both prided themselves. Whiston is mentioned, in passing, as "a late ingenious Writer" in the Burnet controversy. Our next reference is secondhand, in a letter from Bishop William Nicolson to Edward Lhuyd, January 31, 1701, also referring to the diluvists: "Whether Dr. Burnet's roasted egg, Dr. Woodward's hasty pudding, or Mr. Whiston's snuff of a Comet, will carry the day, I cannot foresee. Dr. Arbuthnot has well observed, that a successful theory must be built on many nice enquiries, not forwardly advanced on the encouragement of a few likely phenomena."[67]

The satire on Whiston in the *Memoirs of Martinus Scriblerus* falls into two main topics: his theories of a comet and the Deluge, and his proposal for a method of determining the longitude. The Whiston satires may well have been written during the early months of 1714, when the shortlived club was in its halcyon period just before the death of Queen Anne, since each of these enthusiasms of Whiston reached a climax at just this time. Whiston was involved with other diluvists in *Martinus Scriblerus* to whom "we owe . . . all the new Theories of the Deluge," and was the particular target of Martin's invention of "Tide-Tables, for a Comet, that is to approximate towards the Earth," and of millenarian prophecy: "Ages must be numbered, nay perhaps some Comet may vitrify this Globe on which we tread, before we behold a Castor and Pollux resembling the beauteous Lindamira and Indamora."[68] Swift and Arbuthnot, both born in 1667, were old enough to remember the Burnet controversy and such works as Whiston's *A New Theory*, originally published in 1696,

[67] These references are from Lester M. Beattie, *John Arbuthnot: Mathematician and Satirist* (Cambridge: Harvard University Press, 1935) , pp. 194, 206, 226.

[68] *Memoirs*, ed. Kerby-Miller, pp. 166, 167, 169, 306, 329-30, 341.

which, as we have seen, had appeared in a second edition in 1708. Early in 1714, while the Scriblerians were meeting as a club, Whiston produced another version of his *A New Theory* under dramatic circumstances. To this we shall return in another connection.

Perhaps thanks to Pope, the Whiston satire in the *Memoirs of Martinus Scriblerus* was on the whole better natured than that on some other projectors, although both Swift and Arbuthnot had become increasingly irritated in various ways by Whiston. In 1712 he had approached Swift with his scheme for discovering the longitude, presumably in the hope that Swift, now at the height of his political power, might give him assistance. Swift wrote to Stella on March 28, 1711/2: "Do you know what the Longitude is? a Projector has been applying himself to me to recommend him to the Ministry, because he pretends to have found out the Longitude. I believe He has no more found it out, than he has found out mine (———). However I will gravely hear what he says, and discover him a Knave or Fool."[69] The next day Swift wrote to Archbishop King about the "projector," adding: "He has given in a petition to the Queen by Mr. Secretary St. John. I understand nothing of the mathematics; but I am told it is a thing as improbable as the philosopher's stone, or perpetual motion."[70]

The fact that Whiston, after all his talk, really had a bona fide proposal for the Commons and later published it,

[69] *Journal to Stella*, ed. Harold Williams (Oxford: Clarendon Press, 1948), II. 527. Williams annotates the bracketed four-letter word, "Swift has blotted out a word which is not in doubt."

[70] *Correspondence of Jonathan Swift*, ed. F. Elrington Ball (London: 1910), I. 324-25. Many years later, in 1727, Swift in the *Holyhead Journal (Prose Works*, ed. Temple Scott [London, 1907], XI, 400-401), wrote of another "projector" who insisted that he had found the way to determine longitude, and had sent letters "to all the Mathematicians in London 3 months ago." Swift quoted himself as saying in his reply: "I had too much of the Longitude already, by 2 Projectors, whom I encouraged, one of which was a cheat and the other cut his own throat." That projector Swift called "Whelden"; we have been unable to find him under any spelling in standard reference books. By this time Swift might well have considered Whiston a cheat. Whether Ditton cut his own throat literally or metaphorically, we have not been able to determine.

irritated Arbuthnot particularly, since it spoiled his plans for a devastating satire possibly already written. He wrote Swift on July 17, 1714: "Whiston has at last published his project on the longitude; the most ridiculous thing that ever was thought on. But a pox on him! he has spoiled one of my papers of Scriblerus, which was a proposal for the longitude, not very unlike his, to this purpose: that since there was no pole for East and West, that all the Princes of Europe should join and build two prodigious poles, upon high mountains, with a vast light-house to serve for a pole-star. I was thinking of a calculation of the time, charges, and dimensions. Now you must understand, his project is by light-houses, and explosion of bombs at a certain hour."[71] Swift replied: "It was a malicious satire of yours upon Whiston, that what you intended as a ridicule, should be any way struck upon by him for a reality." In the *Memoirs* the Scriblerians went no further with the Whiston project than to say: "To build *Two* Poles to the *Meridian*, with immense Light-houses on the top of them; to supply the defect of Nature, and to make the Longitude as easy to be calculated as the Latitude. Both these he could not but think very practicable, by the Power of all the Potentates of the World."[72]

Arbuthnot, however, was able to use part of his Whiston parody in another Scriblerian paper, a satire on the many sorts of projects with which civic and national authorities were deluged, a pamphlet *To the Right Honourable The*

---

[71] *Correspondence*, II. 186; *Memoirs*, ed. Kerby-Miller, p. 343.

[72] Swift, *Correspondence*, II. 197; *Memoirs*, ed. Kerby-Miller, p. 168. In the Beineke collection of Whiston Pamphlets at Yale is a small booklet, *Longitude To be found out with A new Invented Instrument. Both by Sea and Land . . . Written by R. B., Secretary to the Honourable Sir Francis Wheeler* (London, 1715). Basically serious, it begins with satiric references to "Mr. Ditton and Mr. Whiston; the first of which Gentlemen I do not know, but as for the other, People say he is a little beside himself, or rather, if he has any such Thing as Brains they are really crackt. They might as well have propos'd a Method of building half-way Houses on the Ocean from London to all Places as we trade to." The author appended to his book a copy of the letter Whiston and Ditton wrote to *The Englishman*, December 7, 1713.

Mayor and Aldermen of the City of London: *The Humble Petition of Colliers, Cooks, Cook-Maids, Blacksmiths, Jackmakers, Braziers, and Others* (1716) .[73] The pamphlet asserts that "certain Virtuosi disaffected to the Government," who call themselves "Catoptrical Victuallers, by gathering, breaking, folding, and bundling up the Sun-Beams, by the help of certain Glasses," intend to procure a monopoly for cooking in the future, all to be performed by their scientific burning-glasses. Not only would such a patent reduce to beggary hundreds of workers in many trades, but it would "oblige Cooks, and Cook-maids to study Opticks and Astronomy," or, more probably "throw the whole Art of Cookery into the Hands of Astronomers and Glassgrinders . . . to the great detriment of the Health of His Majesty's good Subjects." The "Petitioners humbly pray" that either the City will prohibit such a project or impose a high tax on users of the sun-beams, "reserving the sole right and privilege of the Catoptrical Cookery to the Royal Society, and to the Commanders and Crew of the Bomb-vessels, under the direction of Mr. Whiston, for finding out the Longitude, who by reason of the remoteness of their Nations, may be reduced to Streights for want of firing."

Inevitably the Whiston-Ditton proposals led to sharp criticism by other aspirants for the rich prize[74] and to satire which continued well down in the century. Indeed as late as 1760-61, Smollett twice alluded to Whiston in *Sir Launcelot Greaves* as "a mad astronomer" who "swore he was within three vibrations of finding the longitude at sea."

[73] *Miscellanies . . . by Dr. Arbuthnot, Mr. Pope, and Mr. Gay* (London, 1742) , III. 176-80. Kerby-Miller mentions this, p. 339.

[74] The British prize was not awarded until 1753, when part of it went to a German, Tobias Mayer, who brought out tables of the moon's motions relative to the fixed stars which were accurate enough for approximate determination of the longitude at sea. Halley had devoted much time during his appointment as Astronomer Royal at Greenwich to daily observations of the moon, in part in the hope of finding a method, but he was not successful. The problem was finally solved, by the construction of accurate marine chronometers, in part by John Harrison of Yorkshire, more especially by a Frenchman, Pierre la Roy in 1763. See Humphrey Quill, *John Harrison* (London: John Baker, 1966). GSR

As G. S. Rousseau has shown,[75] the scene in which this occurs is copied from Hogarth's *A Rake's Progress*, Plate 8, which is in part a satire on Whiston. Hogarth's engraving was made in 1732. Some "replies" to Whiston were serious, some vituperative, others as light and passing as Prior's couplets in *Alma*:

> Circles to square, and Cubes to double,
> Would give a Man excessive Trouble;
> The Longitude uncertain roams,
> In spight of Wh——n and his Bombs.[76]

But we shall limit ourselves here to the Scriblerians, apart from the *Memoirs of Martinus Scriblerus*. In the letter Gay and Pope wrote to Caryll in April 1715, Whiston is mentioned as "so celebrated of late for his discovery of the longitude, in an extraordinary copy of verses which you heard when you were last in town." This is repeated, without the last clause, in the joint letter to Congreve, April 7, 1715. The "extraordinary copy of verses" was an "Ode for Musick on the Longitude," later published in Swift's and Pope's *Miscellany* in 1735. Until very recently the "Ode" had been attributed to Gay, largely on the basis of a statement supposedly made by Pope to Spence: "The little copy of verses on Ditton and Whiston in the third volume of the Miscellanies was writ by Pope." Professor James M. Osborn has shown[77] that Spence's memory was incorrect, and that

---

[75] "Doctors and Medicine in the Novels of Tobias Smollett," Ph.D. diss., published on microfilm (Princeton University, 1966), pp. 119-21. Smollett's satire of Whiston is found on pp. 258-59 and 226 of *Sir Launcelot Greaves* (London, 1761). Whiston was not identified by Hogarth's editor and moralizer, John Trusler; he was, however, recognized by Peter Quennell in *Hogarth's Progress* (London: Collins, 1955), pp. 135-37. Further comments on the background of this engraving are found in Ronald Paulson, *Hogarth's Graphic Works*, 2 vols. (New Haven: Yale University Press, 1965), I, 169-70. GSR

[76] Canto III, lines 366-69, *The Literary Works of Matthew Prior*, ed. H. Bunker Wright and Monroe K. Spears (Oxford: Oxford University Press, 1959), I. 499-501.

[77] James M. Osborn, " 'That on Whiston' by John Gay," *Papers of the Bibliographical Society of America* (1962), Vol. 56, 73-78. Professor Osborn's position is well summarized in his conclusion: "Thus

the work Pope attributed to Gay was not the "Ode" but *A True and Faithful Narrative*.

The "Ode for Musick, on the Longitude" is scatological verse, consisting of a quatrain of recitative, followed by two quatrains and a chorus of ritornelle. The easy, vulgar rhymes are largely the four-letter ones we would expect for the surnames of "Whis-ton" and "Dit-ton." Gay's spirit need feel no regret at losing all credit for the ode. The mantle, we are inclined to think, should fall on Swift[78] as Professor Osborn's last sentences imply, and as Swift's semi-deletion of a four-letter word from his letter to Stella about Whiston may also suggest. Swift, as we well know, had no objection to scatology.

The transfer of authorship from Gay to Swift is less than a fair exchange since Professor Osborn returns to Gay *A True and Faithful Narrative*, long attributed to Swift.[79]

---

the preservation of Spence's original notes of his conversation with Pope late in July 1739 has two consequences for the reputation of John Gay. They enable us to remove from him a set of unsavory verses, and to restore to him the delightful prose satire, the *True and Faithful Narrative*, which can now stand with his other suave but incisive burlesque writings. The 'Ode for Musick, on the Longitude' is thus left without an author. Any one of the coffee-house wits (whether Scriblerian or not) was capable of writing this lowly jingle, but students of the scatological strain in Swift may be the only claimants. At least no future writer on John Gay should be plagued further with the problem." In his revised edition (1964) of *Minor Poems of Alexander Pope*, p. 415, the late Professor John Butt notes that these verses were attributed to Parnell in a letter of 23 December 1714 from Sir R. Cox to E. Southwell (BM Add. Mss. 38,157). So far as the dating of the "Ode" is concerned, Osborn suggests that it was written at the time of Gay's and Pope's letter to Caryll. But that is not possible, since they say that Caryll had heard the verses when last in town. Caryll left London on February 21, 1715 (*Correspondence*, I. 282n6). The verses must have been composed before that date.

[78] The "Ode" was attributed to Swift in *The Charmer* by David Nichol Smith in his edition of the *Letters of Thomas Burnet to George Duckett* (Roxburghe Club, 1914). In a note discussing the longitude proposal of Whiston-Ditton, he says (p. 257): "Their failure inspired Swift's 'Ode for music. On the Longitude.'"

[79] Professor Tuveson naturally so discussed it in "Swift and the World-Makers," pp. 67-69; so too Marjorie Nicolson, *Mountain Gloom and Mountain Glory*, pp. 247-48. It was published in the 1735 edition of the *Miscellanies* as by Pope and Gay. References here are to *A Sup-*

Gay was aware from his own experience at Button's and possibly elsewhere that Whiston had proved a spellbinder, capable of holding any kind of audience. The one he invents for him is very different from that "numerous and noble Audience" Whiston described as attending his lecture at the Censorium or the groups of intelligentsia at Button's or Will's. To give a true and faithful account of "What pass'd in London during the general Consternation of all Ranks and Degrees of Mankind: on Tuesday, Wednesday, Thursday, and Friday last" Gay assumed the *persona* of a London draper, one of a group, presumably regular attendants at Whiston's lectures. On Tuesday, October 13, 1714, "Mr. Whiston held his lecture near the Royal Exchange, to an Audience of fourteen worthy citizens, his Subscribers and constant Hearers." The fourteen regular auditors (Gay fabricates a name for each) represented fourteen different trades, haberdasher, corn-chandler, fishmonger, and so on. In addition, "there were five chance auditors for that night only" (these proved to be apprentices, also given names, who had paid a shilling apiece). According to the draper, James Peters, Whiston began by prayers and devotions, more fitting for that occasion, as it proved, than they might have been at Button's or the Censorium. And then —Professor Tuveson well reminds us that various of the diluvists were millenarians, world-enders as well as worldmakers—the excitement began: "Friends and fellow-citizens, all speculative science is at an end; the period of all things is at hand; on Friday next this world shall be no more. Put not your confidence in me, brethren, for tomorrow morning, five minutes after five, the truth will be self-evident; in that instant the comet shall appear, of which I have heretofore warned you. As ye have heard, believe. Go hence and prepare your wives, your families and friends for the universal change."

All things began with a comet; so shall they end, according to Millenarian Whiston. Nothing more convinced the

plement to Dr. Swift's Works: Miscellanies (Edinburgh, 1763), pp. 255-76.

179

draper that Whiston believed his own prophecy than the fact that he "returned a shilling apiece to the youths that had been disappointed of their lecture." "Within a few hours, word of the prediction spread throughout all London." The draper describes the consternation that fell upon the city, mounting to a climax when "faithful to her time" the comet appeared: "for at three minutes after five by my own watch, I saw it." Here Gay takes a sly dig at the alibi Halley and Whiston had found for their error of one minute in the beginning of the total eclipse: "He indeed foretold that it would be seen at five minutes after five, but as the best Watches may be a minute or two too slow, I am apt to think his Calculation just to a minute." All London was to watch an eclipse, but now watched a comet. As astronomer, Whiston proved exact to a minute; as millenarian, he was not so successful. The comet came and passed, "Friday came, and the people covered all the streets . . . they drank, they whor'd, they swore, they lied." London went back to normalcy.

The satires of the Scriblerians were usually occasional, and ordinarily we can discover the occasion that provoked them. But no comet had been seen in England for some time, nor had one been predicted for the near future. Whiston's chief fame at this time rested on his proposals for the longitude. While his theory of the flood's originating in a comet was known, even the second edition of *A New Theory* was six years old. Was there any reason for Gay's specifically associating with Whiston in 1714 the idea of a cometary end of the world? We think there was. Earlier in that year had occurred the long delayed trial of Whiston for heresy. Just at the time the Scriblerians were holding meetings, Whiston had produced, under dramatic circumstances, still another version of his cometary theory. We shall let him tell one particular episode in his own words: "During the Meetings of the Court of Delegates about me, and on the very Day they solemnly met, and determined that I must answer to the Accusation of Heresy; when I was in the greatest Danger that ever I was in through my whole Life; I was so

180

little concern'd at what they were doing with me, that I then first publish'd, and presented to several of my Judges, instead of a Petition for Mercy, as at first they supposed it to be, a single Sheet, wet from the Press, intituled, *The Cause of the Deluge Demonstrated*."[80]

In that little publication, which Whiston added to later editions of *A New Theory*, and also to his *Astronomical Principles of Religion*, published in 1717, Whiston went further than in *A New Theory*. He identified the comet, collision of which with the earth had caused the Deluge, with the comet seen in England in 1680. Its period 575 years, this would also have been the comet seen in 44 B.C., the year after the assassination of Julius Caesar, attested by Seneca, Suetonius, Plutarch and Pliny. "It was a remarkable one," wrote Whiston, "and visible all over the World. The common People believ'd, that it signify'd the Reception of the Soul of *Caesar* into the Number of the immortal Gods." This, Whiston declared, was the only comet listed in Halley's Tables that "can come near enough to our Earth in their Ascent from the Sun to cause the Conflagration." Presumably at its next appearance this comet would destroy the earth. In his conclusion Whiston suggests an attractive analogy between his comet and the phoenix:[81]

Whether the Story of the Phoenix, that celebrated Emblem of the Resurrection in Christian Antiquity; (that it returns once after 5 Centuries, and goes to the Altar and City of the Sun, and is there burnt; and another arises out of its Ashes, and carries away the Remains of the former, &c.) be not an Allegorical Representation of this Comet; (which returns once after 5 Centuries, and goes down to the Sun, and is there vehemently heated, and its outward Regions dissolv'd; yet that it flies off again, and carries away what remains after that terrible burning, &c.) and whether the Conflagration and Renovation of things, which some such Comet in its Ascent from the Sun may bring upon the Earth, be not hereby prefigur'd. I will not here be positive; but I own that I don't know of any Solution of this famous piece of *Egyptian* Mythology and Hieroglyphicks, as this seems to be, that can be compared with it.

Reminiscences in *A True and Faithful Account* of Swift's Bickerstaff Papers are too obvious to need development. Such reminiscences occur also in a slightly later Scriblerian paper, *God's Revenge against Punning,* included with deletions in the *Miscellanies,* originally printed on both sides of a single sheet, published November 7, 1716. Sherburn in *The Early Career of Alexander Pope*[82] thought it "very likely either by Pope or Arbuthnot," offering no evidence for the latter and for Pope only one sentence in a letter to Martha Blount. Norman Ault[83] grappled with two versions of the paper in detail, wishing to attribute it to Pope, but reaching no more certain conclusion than that the testimonies he had collected, "together with the complete lack of any other author, would appear to justify at least the temporary inclusion of *God's Revenge against Punning* in the Pope canon." Like Sherburn, Norman Ault refers to Pope's letter to Martha Blount, August 7, 1716: "Mr. Gay has had a fall from his horse, and broken his fine Snuffbox," and also another sentence, deleted before the paper was published in the *Miscellanies:* "A Devonshire Man of Wit, for only saying in a jesting manner, *I got uppun a Horse,* instantly fell down and broke his Snuff-Box and Neck, and lost the Horse." Ault adds: "It is perhaps needless to say either that Gay was a Devonshire man, or that his accident, or at least the breaking of the snuff-box, was a piece of information unlikely to be known outside

---

[82] P. 182. In the *Correspondence,* however, I. 370n., in connection with a long letter of Pope to Lady Mary, 10 November 1716, toward the end of which Pope refers to "two little pieces" he encloses, Sherburn says that the printed one might have been *God's Revenge.* This, said Pope, "has made much noise." He added: "I am wrongfully suspected to be author of it."

[83] *Prose Works,* I. cx-cxiv.

the immediate circle of his friends, of whom Pope was perhaps the most intimate." While little of Ault's evidence
would apply to Arbuthnot, we venture to suggest that all of
it would apply to Gay, who was certainly aware of his own
accident and capable of having fun about it.[84] *God's Revenge against Punning* is in a way a little sequel to *A True
and Faithful Narrative,* as well as to the Bickerstaff papers.
As Swift had satirized astrological prognostications, the
Narrative satirized astronomical predictions. So, too, *God's
Revenge.* Looking back over Restoration history, the author recalls the Great Plague and the Great Fire, sent for
the "Chastisement of a Sinful People." Scarcely had the nation recovered from these disasters than "other Abomina-
tions rose up in the land." Although the "happy Revolution" corrected some abuses, "still the Nation so greatly
offended, that Socinianism, Arianism, and Whistonism triumph'd in our Streets, and were in a manner become universal." In view of the profound effect that Whiston's lectures seem to have had on Pope's imagination from 1713 to
1715, it would seem strange that only a year later he should
return to his earlier position on the "wicked Works" and
deliberately include "Whistonism" here. Gay, on the other
hand, had already had his fun with Whiston in the earlier
satire.

At this point the author launches into an account of recent astronomical phenomena, two real, one exaggerated
or invented: "And yet still, after all these Visitations, it has
pleased Heaven to visit us with a Contagion more Epidem-
ical, and of consequences more Fatal (Punning) : This was
foretold to Us, First, By that unparallel'd Eclipse in
1714;[85] Secondly, By the dreadful Coruscations in the Air

[84] William Henry Irving, *John Gay: Favorite of the Wits* (New
York: Russell and Russell, 1962) , pp. 144-45, has no doubt that the
pamphlet was Gay's. Among other evidence he mentions the fact that
the copy of the pamphlet in the British Museum is ascribed to Gay in a
contemporary hand, the same hand that ascribed another paper to him.

[85] The date 1714 must have been a typographical error, since
neither Gay nor Pope could have made a mistake about so recent
a phenomenon. When Pope prepared it for publication in the *Miscellanies* in 1732, the incorrect date was repeated. It is not strange

this present Year: and thirdly, By the Nine Comets seen at once over Soho-Square, by Mrs. Katherine Wadlington, and Others." The eclipse and the aurora we recognize. Possibly the nine[86] comets are an exaggeration of that other celestial phenomenon which appeared during the *annus mirabilis* 1715-16, the reappearance of a nova, visible to the naked eye, which many laymen thought a comet. As the author of the article in the *Philosophical Transactions* in 1715 had prophesied, it had been visible in 1716 and showed most brightly around September 10, a month before *God's Revenge* appeared.

God's Revenge against Punning apparently inspired the pseudonymous E. Parker, Philomath to a series of prophecies for the New Year which appeared in December 1716, as *Mr. Joanidion Fielding. His True and Faithful Account of the Strange and Miraculous Comet Which was Seen by the Mufti at Constantinople, As appears by the Daily Courant of Month.*[87] It would seem that E. Parker, who

---

that the exact year of the eclipse should no longer have been clear in Pope's memory. I myself remember vividly Halley's comet, which I saw in 1910, but seventeen years later, I should have had to be reminded of the date. MHN

[86] The phenomenon of multiple suns, moons, and other celestial appearances had been observed for centuries, and causes discussed from Aristotle's *Meteorologica* down through the ages. Such multiplicity was a literary convention. See S.K. Heninger, Jr., *A Handbook of Renaissance Meteorology* (Durham: Duke University Press, 1960), pp. 135-38, for literary passages, particularly from Shakespeare. A paper by Whiston on mock suns (perihelia) is given in *Phil. Trans.*, XXXI, No. 369 (1721), 212-15. Writing from Rutland, Whiston reported observing for several days two mock suns, first appearing on the morning after an aurora borealis. Another paper on a later observation of perihelia is by George Whiston, "An Account of four Mock-Suns, seen at Kensington, March 1st, 1726-27," *ibid.*, XXXIV, No. 398, 257-59.

[87] Sherburn mentions this little satire, *Early Career*, pp. 161, 182-83. Kerby-Miller (p. 46n126) considers this the work of some of the Scriblerians, although he mentions it only in passing. The same author may have written *The Complete Key to the New Farce*, when *Three Hours after Marriage* was performed. We are much indebted to Mrs. Louise Clubb, who read the pamphlet for us in the Folger Library, and sent us a Xerox reproduction. She was also good enough to read some reels of microfilm, catalogued under *Daily Courant* for

had also satirized *Three Hours after Marriage*, attributed *God's Revenge* to Pope, whose name is included among
the prophecies: "If the Pope be not Eat up by Pun-aises,
for Anathema's that he never denounc'd, he shall at least
be Tickled to Death, or receive a Phillip from St. Ambrose." Whiston's name also appears: "Mr. Whiston's
Scheme of Primitive Christianity shall not prevail this Year;
so that it will be more for his Profit to meddle only with
the Inspiration of the Air-Pump at White Hall." The
"Strange and Miraculous Comet, which was Seen by the
Mufti at Constantinople," Parker's point of departure,
was a real comet, as the *Daily Courant* reported in No. 4703
for Thursday, November 15, 1716, from the Paris news-
letter:

> Paris, Nov. 21. They write from Malta, that an English
> ship arrived there from the Isles of the Archipelago re-
> ports that there has been seen at Constantinople for eight
> Days, a Comet, hairy, with a long Tail; which appeared
> soon after Sun-rising, and extended itself from North to
> South. This has very much frighted those People, who
> are not used to such Appearances in the Heavens.

Parker visualizes the Mufti of Constantinople as he sat pen-
sively musing on his pleasant seat on the banks of the Hel-
lespont. His "Favorite Mute" came to him, exclaiming:
"Behold, thou High Priest of Allah, how the Light streameth
out of Darkness, and the Firmament blazeth as a Topaz."

> At this the High-Priest of Mahomet lifted his Eyes from
> the Ground, and lo! he beheld a palish Light, like
> the Crescent of the Imperial Turbant; it soon shot it-
> self forth into the Form of a Comet, whose Body appeared
> two Degrees Diameter; and its Tail in the Form of a Para-
> boloid, shot up within 20 Degrees of the Zenith; so that
> it appeared like the One-ey'd Polyphemus, in a Full-
> bottom'd Periwig.

---

the year 1716, which also included occasional snippets from other
gazettes.

Consternation throughout the land continued for some time, together with all sorts of attempts to explain the phenomenon and to anticipate malign or benign effects. The explanation offered by the Sannadrim was the one that satisfied the Emperor: "that it only denoted the Arrival of a British Ambassadress of marvellous Beauty, with a long Train of Attendants." Mr. Wortley Montagu had become Ambassador to Turkey in August 1716;[88] the "British Ambassadress" was, of course, Lady Mary Wortley Montagu, although the Montagus arrived in Constantinople too late to see the comet. In listing many of the extraordinary appearances in the heavens, which had preceded the comet over Constantinople, "Mr. Joanidian Fielding" says, among others which he personally had or had not observed: "I did not see the late Coruscations, which Mr. Whiston rightly judges to be the Fire-works of Aerial Spirits, being intent upon burning my erroneous Catalogue of the Fixed Stars." That he was probably writing with a copy of *God's Revenge* before him is indicated in two passages: "I did not see the famous total Eclipse of the Sun in 1714, being 17 Minutes too late." Here he picked up the typographical error we have already mentioned, and added: "A Friend of mine did see the Nine Comets at Mrs. Wadlington's in Soho-Square, when he was going to celebrate a Geocentrick Conjunction." To his reference to the total eclipse, he added gratuitously: "I did see Mr. Halley (whom indeed I never had a good Opinion of) flying in a fiery Chariot over Greenwich-Park."

During the supposed "Age of Reason," science was gradually triumphing over superstition, but still had far to go. The spectacular celestial phenomena of the years 1714, 1715, 1716 were completely understood, even when they had not been anticipated, by members of the Royal Society in Crane Court. But such a group of tradesmen as Gay invented for *A True and Faithful Narrative* could hardly have

[88] The Montagus arrived in Adrianople, then capital of Turkey, on March 24, 1717; they went to Constantinople in late May of 1717 (Robert Halsband, *The Life of Lady Mary Wortley Montagu* [Oxford: Clarendon Press, 1956], pp. 68-73).

been blamed for accepting the Whistonian prophecy that the comet foretold the end of the world. Even more sophisticated Londoners at Button's or Will's, might well have echoed Horatio's words to Hamlet:

> In the most high and palmy state of Rome,
> A little ere the mightiest Julius fell,
> The graves stood tenantless and the sheeted dead
> Did squeak and gibber in the Roman streets,

when they realized that that death had been followed by the appearance of the same comet some of them, or their fathers, might have seen in 1680. Indeed "stars with trains of fire and dews of blood" reflected "disasters in the sun." Not only that but

> the moist star
> Under whose influence Neptune's empire stands
> Was sick almost to doomsday with eclipse.

Like Gloucester, many Englishmen must have felt in 1716: "These late eclipses in the sun and moon portend no good to us. . . . We have seen the best of our times."

IV

If Pope had never mentioned Whiston's lectures, and if the passages in the letter to Caryll, like the very similar sentences in *Guardian* No. 169, had appeared elsewhere in Pope's writing, historians would undoubtedly have built up a strong case for purely literary sources for Pope's cosmic imagination. Nor should such background be forgotten. Whiston was a competent and obviously stimulating lecturer on astronomy, but he was no man of letters. There is little question that the astronomy Pope learned from him mingled in his imagination with literary passages he had read and was to read. Let us look at phrases in the letter to Caryll of August 14, 1714, some of which we deliberately omitted, together with another letter to Caryll, a little more than a month later, on September 20.[89] In his August letter Pope had suggested the distraction of his thoughts, one moment "above the stars, with a thousand systems round about me, looking forward into the vast abyss of eternity, and losing my whole comprehension in the boundless space of the extended Creation . . . the next moment I am below all trifles . . . Good God! what an Incongruous Animal is Man?"

The lesson of the New Philosophy was not new but one that the Psalmist had known:

> When I consider the heavens, the work of thy fingers, the moon and the stars, which thou hast ordained; what is man, that thou art mindful of him?

So, too, Shakespeare, who was hovering in Pope's mind as he wrote, though the line he quoted was from the vision in *The Tempest*, not, as we might have expected, from Hamlet's turning from the "brave o'erhanging firmament, this majestical roof fretted with golden fire," to "what a piece of work is a man . . , this quintessence of dust." Pope wrote:

> Sickness and pain is the lot of one half of us, doubt and fear the portion of the other! What a bustle we make about passing our time, when all our space is but a point? What aims and ambitions are crowded into this little instant of our life, which (as Shakespear finely words it) is *rounded with a sleep*? Our whole extent of being no more in the eyes of him who gave it, than a scarce perceptible atom of duration.[90] Those animals whose circle of

[89] *Correspondence*, I. 190-91, 20 September (1713). Sherburn says in his note: "Much of this letter was printed (1735-42) as addressed to Edward Blount under the improbable date of 10 Feb. 1715/6. . . . The Caryll transcript gives no year, but Elwin suggested 1713 on the slight grounds of Pope's being with Jervas and busy at painting." The very close parallels with the earlier letter to Caryll and with the *Guardian* No. 169, September 24, 1713, seem to us to offer still stronger evidence for 1713.

[90] Pope's use of "atom" here seems at first unusual, implying the

living and date of perception is limited to three or four hours, as the naturalists assure us, are yet as long-lived and possess as wide a scene of action as man, if we consider him with an eye to eternity. [In the 1734-42 edition, Pope expanded this to: "with a view to all Space, and all Eternity."] Who knows what plots, what achievements a mite may perform, in his kingdom of a grain of dust, within his life of some minutes? And of how much less consideration than even this, is the life of man in the sight of that God, who is from ever, and for ever!

Who that thinks in this train, but must see the world and its contemptible grandeurs lessen before him at every thought?

Perennial though the lesson has been from the Psalmist to Shakespeare, never had it come home more poignantly to man than after Galileo discovered a new universe of incomprehensible distances, which nevertheless Newton had reduced to order in the most universal of all laws, governing the planets, but no less the fall of a feather. Such had been the New Astronomy Whiston had described to his auditors at a coffee-house. Before writing this letter and some of the sentences in *Guardian* No. 169, Pope may well have been reading the greatest chapter in Pascal's *Pensées*, with its pondering on the astounding contradictions in Nature: the earth but a point in comparison with the vast circuit of the sun, that a minute point compared with the stars in the firmament:

---

concept of "time" rather than the usual one of "space." We pondered whether he had picked up such spatial and temporal combination from Whiston, but have decided that he was here using "atom" in a sense which was already becoming antiquated in his day and is now obsolete. *OED* lists a number of such temporal uses under III, most of them going back to early times when "an atom of time" implied the "twinkling of an eye"; "atom," indeed, had once suggested the smallest possible measure of time, an hour being equal to 22,560 atoms. Pope's other uses of "atom" are in usual spatial conventions: *Correspondence*, I. 148; *Rape of the Lock*, V. 83; *Fourth Satire of Donne Versified*, 243; *Essay on Man*, I. 89, III. 10.

189

If his Sight be limited here, let his Imagination, at least, pass beyond. He may sooner exhaust the power of conceiving, than Nature can want a new store to furnish out his Conceptions. The whole Extent of Visible Things, is but one Line or Stroke in the Ample Bosome of Nature. No Idea can reach the immeasurable Compass of her Space. We may grow as big as we please with Notion: But we shall bring forth meer Atoms, instead of real and solid Discoveries. This is an infinite Sphere, the Centre of which is every where, and the Circumference no where. In a word, 'tis the greatest amongst all the sensible Marks and Characters of the Almighty Power of God: and let our Imagination lose itself in this Reflexion.

And then, after pondering on "What is Man with regard to this Infinity about him?" Pascal abruptly opposes the minute to the vast:

But, to shew him another Prodigy no less astonishing; let him turn his thoughts on the smallest of those things which fall within his Knowledge. Let a Mite, for instance, in the contemptible minuteness of its Body present him with parts incomparably more minute: with jointed Legs, with Veins in those Legs, Blood in those Veins, Humours in that Blood, Drops in those Humours, Vapours in those Drops. . . . And when he has gone as far as his Mind can reach, let the concluding Atom be the Subject of our Discourse. He will probably suppose, that this is the remotest Extreme, the last Diminutive in Nature. But even in this, where he finds himself obliged to stop, I shall undertake still to open before him a new Abyss of Wonders.

Whether in the cosmic universe or the universe of the minute, man beholds a plurality of worlds, stretching from one seeming infinity to another; at one moment he is lord of all things, his body "a Colossus, a World," at another less than the mites so small that his unaided eyes cannot see them.

190

How early Pope knew the *Pensées*—long recognized as one source for the prelude to Book II of *An Essay on Man*[91] —we cannot tell. In his letters he mentioned it only once, many years later, again in a letter to Caryll, who had suggested it presumably in connection with the *Essay on Man*,[92] "Your recommendation of Pascal's *Pensées* is a good one, (tho' I've been beforehand with you in it)." But even earlier than the letter of August 1713 Pope had read some of Pascal's work, since he quoted him, again to Caryll, on July 19, 1711: "I beg you to pardon the length of this letter. I had not time enough (as Mons. Pascal said of one of his) to make it shorter." The reference here is to Pascal's *Provincial Letters*. Well before the letter to Caryll about Whiston, the *Pensées* had been readily available to Pope, both in French and in English.[93]

As the earlier letter to Caryll is reminiscent of Pascal, so *Guardian* No. 169 and the letter of September to Caryll show striking parallels to Fontenelle's *Entretiens sur la Pluralité des Mondes*, the most brilliant popularization of the Cartesian cosmogony ever written, readily available in both French and English editions[94] well before Pope men-

[91] Cf. Maynard Mack's note in his edition of the *Essay*, pp. 53-55.
[92] *Correspondence*, III. 173, February 6, 1730/1.
[93] The *editio princeps* appeared in 1669, followed by at least four other editions before the end of the century. The first English translation was by John Walker in 1688. The next by Basil Kennet was more readily available since it went through at least five editions in the eighteenth century—1725 (2), 1737, 1751, 1752—after the first edition of 1704. Our quotations are from that edition, *Thoughts on Religion, and Other Subjects*, by Monsieur Pascal (London, 1704). The name of the translator does not appear on the title page: on the copy in the Firestone Library, Princeton University, is written in a contemporary hand, "By Basil Kennett, D.D. President of C. C. C. Oxon." In this edition the passage is in Chap. XX, pp. 186-90. In modern translations it is usually Chap. II.
[94] The *Entretiens sur la Pluralité des Mondes* had been published in 1686. The earliest English translations appeared in the year 1688: *A Plurality of Worlds . . . translated into English by Mr. Glanvill* (other editions, 1695, 1702, 1719); *The Theory or System of several new Inhabited Worlds lately discover'd, and pleasantly described,* translated by Aphra Behn (other editions, 1700, 1718). The year before Pope's letter to Lady Mary it appeared again as *Conversations on a Plurality of Worlds. Translated from the last Paris edition by Mr.*

191

tioned Fontenelle's name in a letter to Lady Mary Wortley Montagu on November 10, 1716[95] with a figure drawn from the *Entretiens*. Remembering his recent farewells when she had set out on her travels, Pope looks forward to the future: "I shall at least be sure to meet you in the next world, if there be any truth in Our new Doctrine of the Day of judgment"—presumably a passing allusion to Whiston's millenarian theories. He continued: "Since your Body is so full of fire, and capable of such Solar motions as your Letter describes, your Soul can never be long going to the Fixed Stars (where I intend to settle) Or Else you may find me in the milky way, because Fontanelle assures us, the Stars are so crowded there that a man may stand upon one and talk to his friend on another. From thence, with a good Telescope, what do you think one should take such a place as this world for? I fancy for the Devil's Rookery, where the Inhabitants are ready to deafen and destroy one another with eternal Noise and Hunger." Geoffrey Tillotson takes for granted that Pope had read the *Entretiens* before he published the expanded edition of *The Rape of the Lock* in 1714. Discussing the sylphs, he says[96] that Pope was "more

---

W. Gardiner (London, 1715). There were at least five later editions of the Gardiner translation, that of 1728 containing Addison's "Oration in Defense of the New Philosophy." We quote from the Glanvill edition of 1702.

[95] *Correspondence*, I. 369-70. The passage we quote was omitted from the 1737-42 edition of the letter, but is in the holograph original in the Morgan Library. Pope was paraphrasing a passage in the Glanvill translation, "The Fifth Evening," p. 138: "So near together are the Vortex's of the Milky Way, that the People in one World, may talk, and shake hands with those of another." It is possible that the Fontenelle work had been in Pope's memory also in the preceding letter to Lady Mary (October 1716, *Correspondence*, I. 363-65) when Pope spoke of "a Fair one born under the same Planet with Astolfo's wife." Fontenelle had related in some detail Astolfo's voyage to the moon ("Second Evening," pp. 52-56), based on Ariosto's *Orlando Furioso*. Pope's reference to "Astolfo's wife" was evidently a euphemism, since Lady Mary might well have resented being associated with a notorious mistress.

[96] *The Rape of the Lock*, p. 381. Pope had, of course, known Fontenelle's *Discours sur la nature de l'églogue* when he wrote his *Discourse on Pastoral Poetry*, published in 1717, but written much

scientifically interested than de Villars in the cosmic conditions of the sylphs and his fancy builds scrupulously on contemporary science as it was brilliantly presented in Fontenelle's *Pluralité des Mondes*." Pope's letter to Cromwell on
November 25, 1710, containing a suggestion of Cromwell's
visiting the Milky Way, rather similar to that in the letter
to Lady Mary, suggests that Pope may have known the
Fontenelle work even before that date.

Similarities between the *Conversations* and Pope's astronomical passages in 1713 are most obvious in Pope's
Guardian (No. 169) paper. In describing the "great Shew
of Nature" on the first evening, the Philosopher had compared Nature to an opera. The audience does not see the
stage as it really is: "All the Wheels and Movements are
hid, to make the Representation the more agreeable; Nor
do you trouble yourself how or by what means the Machines
are moved, tho certainly the Engineer in the Pit is affected
with what does not touch you. . . . The Machines
of the Theatre [are] nothing so curious as those of Nature."
In the *Guardian* paper, thunder, lightning, rainbow,
comets are "Decorations of this mighty Theatre," and the
changing heavens "so many successive Scenes." A little later
Pope parallels Fontenelle's spectators in the audience by
his comments on "the Drama of Nature, its Artificial Structure, and those admirable Machines," and thinks of a man
who on earth observes the flux of celestial phenomena as
one who "hath secur'd to himself an easie and convenient
Seat, where he beholds with Pleasure all that passes on the
Stage of Nature." In a passage central to the whole conception of the *Guardian* essay Pope wrote: "In fair weather,
when my Heart is cheered, and I feel that Exaltation of
Spirits which results from Light and Warmth, joined with
a beautiful Prospect of Nature, I regard my self as one
placed by the Hand of God in the midst of an ample Theatre, in which the Sun, Moon, and Stars, the Fruits also, and

---

earlier—he himself said—in 1704. On the problem of dating see
Aubrey Williams' Introduction to the *Discourse* in his edition of
Pope's *Pastoral Poetry*, pp. 13-15, and Ault, *Prose Works*, I. cxv.

193

Vegetables of the Earth, perpetually changing their Positions, or their Aspects, exhibit an elegant Entertainment to the Understanding, as well as to the Eye." This may be a *locus classicus* in the history of the development of a long literary tradition, going as far back as Homer, the theme of *theatrum mundi*. The perennial figure has suffered a change: the world is still a *theatre*, but it has grown tremendously in the speaker's mind, far more "ample" than it had ever been, the human spectator now the center not only of a finite world, but of an indefinite universe. As it is not finite, so it is not static as it had once been; the whole universe moves and changes, not by chance but according to laws of order. The "spectator" is no longer confined within an opera house or theatre; he is the microcosmic center of a vast macrocosm. Pope's figure of the *theatrum mundi* developed fully only after he had discovered indefinite space, the vast universe and the "glaring comets," through the Whistonian astronomy.

Ironically enough, the literary historian seeking the source of Pope's cosmic reflections, and unaware of his attendance at Whiston's lectures, might not have felt it necessary to go even as far afield as Pascal and Fontenelle, but could have limited himself to Addison, who was well acquainted with both the French writers. Addison too had been enthralled by the implications of the New Philosophy. When he was only twenty-one he had delivered an *Oration in Praise of the New Philosophy*[97] at the Sheldonian Theatre at Oxford in which he showed the impact on his imagination of the new telescopic and microscopic universes. Admirer of Des-

---

[97] The original Latin text is given by A.C. Guthkelch in Joseph Addison, *Miscellaneous Works* (London: G. Bell and Sons, Ltd., 1914), II. 466-69. The translation in our text is by Richard Rawlinson, in Richard Hurd's edition of *The Works of the Right Honourable Joseph Addison* (London: H. G. Bohn, 1856), VI. 607. Another translation by W. Gardiner appeared in the second edition of a translation of Fontenelle's *Plurality of Worlds* (London, 1728). As I have suggested in *Mountain Gloom and Mountain Glory*, p. 302n., I suspect that Addison "lifted" a good deal of this exercise from Fontenelle. In this particular passage, if we read "Copernicus" with Fontenelle rather than "Descartes," we find a neat paraphrase of the French author. MHN

cartes as he was at that time, he had attributed to him the shattering of the walls of the world: "This philosopher scorned to be any longer bounded within the straits and crystalline walls of an Aristotelic world; no, his delight is to search the regions beyond, to discover new suns, and new worlds, which lay hid among the stars." From the telescope Addison turned to the microscope: "Here we have not only new heavens opened to us, but we look down on our earth; this philosophy affords us several kinds of animals; where, by the help of the microscope, our eyes are so far assisted, that we may discern the productions of the smallest creatures while we consider with a curious eye the animated particles of matter, and behold with astonishment the reptile mountains of living atoms."

In the *Spectator* Addison treated these ideas on various occasions. The penultimate essay among "The Pleasures of the Imagination," No. 420, echoes much that Addison had written in his Sheldonian "Oration," in the passage beginning, "But among this Sett of Writers, there are none who more gratifie and enlarge the Imagination, than the Authors of the New Philosophy, whether we consider their Theories of the Earth or Heavens, the Discoveries they have made by Glasses, or any other of their Contemplations on Nature." As Fontenelle's Philosopher plucked a green leaf for his Marchioness, Addison was "not a little pleased to find every green Leaf swarm with Millions of Animals, that at their largest Growth are not visible to the naked Eye." Then he passed to the cosmic universe. "When we survey the whole Earth at once, and the several Planets that lye within its Neighbourhood, we are filled with a pleasing Astonishment, to see so many Worlds hanging one above another, and sliding round their Axles in such an amazing Pomp and Solemnity. If, after this, we contemplate those wide fields of *Ether*, that reach in height as far as from *Saturn* to the fixt Stars, and run abroad almost to an Infinitude, our Imagination finds its Capacity filled with so immense a Prospect, and puts it self upon the Stretch to comprehend it. But if we yet rise higher, and consider the fixt Stars as so many vast Oceans of Flame, that are each of them attended with a different Sett of Planets, and still discover new Firmaments and new Lights, that are sunk farther in those unfathomable Depths of *Ether*, so as not to be seen by the strongest of our Telescopes, we are lost in such a Labyrinth of Suns and Worlds, and confounded with the Immensity and Magnificence of Nature."

The theme of the immensity of Nature is continued in *Spectator* No. 465: "The Supream Being has made the best Arguments for his own Existence, in the Formation of the Heavens and the Earth." Addison quotes the "very beautiful Strokes of Poetry" of the Psalmist "in that exalted Strain: *The Heavens declare the Glory of God: And the Firmament sheweth his handy Work. . . .*" Concluding that "such a bold and sublime Manner of Thinking furnishes very noble Matter for an Ode," he adds the three stanzas of what has become his most familiar poetry, "The Spacious Firmament on high. . . ."

The themes are continued in *Spectator* No. 519, "Contemplations on the World of Life, by which I mean all those Animals with which every Part of the Universe is furnished." Here again, "Every green Leaf swarms with Inhabitants," and again Addison turns from the microscopic to the telescopic universe, using among his arguments "the Author of the *Plurality of Worlds*" for belief in "the Peopling of every Planet." Again he describes a God of Plenitude who has expressed his "exuberant and overflowing Goodness" in the creation of a plurality or infinity of worlds, filling "the whole Chasm of Nature" with "diverse kinds of Creatures," rising in degrees and order from the lowest to highest. In *Spectator* No. 565 he developed these themes after a walk which began at sunset and continued when night had fallen. Looking up to the heavens, he was conscious of the vastness of the cosmic universe, "the infinite Hoste of Stars, or to speak more Philosophically, of Suns." "I still enlarged the Idea, and supposed another Heaven of Suns and Worlds rising still above this" and so on to whatever the imagination may grasp of infinity.

Here, even more than in the preceding essays, he is poignantly aware of the insignificance of man in the new cosmic universe: "Whilst I pursued this Thought, I could not but reflect on that little insignificant Figure which I my self bore amidst the Immensity of God's Works. . . . I could not but look upon my self with secret Horror as a Being, that was not worth the smallest Regard of one who had so great a Work under his Care and Superintendency. I was afraid of being overlooked amidst the Immensity of Nature, and lost among that infinite Variety of Creatures, which in all Probability swarm through all these immeasurable Regions of Matter."[98]

There are close parallels in Fontenelle, and Addison, as in Pascal—as, indeed, in many physico-theologists of this telescopic-microscopic age—for Pope's pondering in the earlier Caryll letter on the extremes of Nature. In the conversation of the third evening, Fontenelle turned from the possibility of inhabitants in the moon, planets, or stars of this vastly expanded cosmos, to the world of minute life: "There be as many kinds of invisible as visible Creatures; we see from the Elephant to the very hand-worm . . . and yet, counting from that minute Creature, there are an infinity of lesser Animals, which were they perceptible, would be as little in comparison with a Mite, as a Mite is of an Ox."[99]

Pope's dual response to the vastness of the cosmic universe in the two Caryll letters—at once enthralled and appalled—may again be paralleled in Fontenelle and Pascal, who offer closer analogies than most of the physico-theologists of the later seventeenth and earlier eighteenth centuries, since those usually sang only paeans of praise to the

[98] Many of these ideas are developed also in the last of the *Spectator* papers, No. 635, which is not by Addison but by Henry Grove. Quotations from Addison are from the edition of *The Spectator*, ed. Donald F. Bond (Oxford: Clarendon Press, 1965).

[99] *A Plurality*, p. 89. The passage continues for several paragraphs, and includes a frequently quoted passage, during which the Philosopher plucks a leaf, which becomes in his interpretation "a great World, of a vast extent" with mountains and abysses, as they may seem to the imperceptible mites that inhabit them.

197

Deity who has expressed Himself in the superabundance of infinity and diversity. In the conversation of the fifth evening, Fontenelle achieved his dual effect by contrasting the response to infinity and vastness of the Marchioness and the Philosopher:

> You have made the Universe so large, *says she*, that I know not where I am, or what will become of me. . . . I protest it is dreadful.
>
> Dreadful, Madam, *said I*; I think it very pleasant, when the Heavens were a little blue Arch, stuck with Stars; me-thought the Universe was too strait and close, I was almost stifled for want of Air; but now it is enlarg'd in heighth and breadth, and a thousand and a thousand Vortex's taken in; I begin to breath with more freedom, and think the Universe to be incomparably more magnificent than it was before.

Writing earlier than Fontenelle and much earlier than the most exuberant physico-theologists, Pascal turned from the infinity of worlds in the cosmos to that other infinity of the minute:

> He that shall take this Survey of his own Nature, will, no doubt, be under the greatest Consternation to find himself hanging, as it were, in his material Scale, between the two vast Abysses of Infinite and Nothing; from which he is equally removed. He will tremble at the Sight of so many Prodigies; and turning his Curiosity into Admiration, will, I believe, be more inclined silently to contemplate them, than presumptuously to search their Depths.
>
> For what is Man amongst the Natures which encompass him? In one View he appears as Unity to Infinity, in another as All to Nothing: and must therefore be the Medium between these Extremes; alike distant from that Nothing whence he was taken, and from that Infinity in which he is swallow'd up.

V

Before continuing to discuss the effect on Pope's imagination of Whiston's astronomical lectures and Pope's reading of seventeenth- and eighteenth-century expositions of astronomy by such men of letters as Pascal, Fontenelle, Addison, and others, we pause to consider the persistence in Pope's vocabulary of the word "vortex," an indication of the influence of Fontenelle's *Conversations* on him. The word "vortex" had entered the English vocabulary only after Descartes published his cosmogony.[100] Although by Pope's time the idea of vortices had become involved with the Newtonian theory of gravitation, Pope used the word, we think, with Cartesian connotations. Whiston, so far as we have observed, never used "vortex," determined as he was that Newtonianism should replace Cartesianism, yet all Pope's uses of it were later than his attendance at the first Whiston lecture, and the most important passage in which it occurs differs markedly from astronomical passages in *An Essay on Man*, which are strongly Newtonian and Whistonian.

Pope would have found no sympathy from Swift for his interest in Descartes-Fontenelle. One of the lesser known works of the latter, to be sure, was suggested by Voltaire as a possible source for Swift's *A Tale of a Tub*, and Swift listed Fontenelle's *Dialogues of the Dead* among books he had read in Sir William Temple's library.[101] But Swift's

---

[100] Descartes' theories of the origin of the earth and other planets from fiery matter cast off by the sun, producing a universe of vortices, were developed in Books III and IV of *The Principles of Philosophy*. He was said to have prepared this before the condemnation of Galileo in 1632, but withheld the work until 1644, when it was published at Amsterdam and immediately condemned by the Sorbonne. *OED* quotes the first English usages of the word in 1652 and 1653, both by Henry More. The first reads: "that there are infinite numbers of Atoms or Particles, different in magnitudes and figures . . . and that they are mixed in the Universe after the manner of Vortices."

[101] A.C. Guthkelch and D. Nichol Smith, eds., *A Tale of a Tub*

attitude toward Descartes remained consistently critical throughout his works. In the *Battle of the Books*,

> *Aristotle* observing *Bacon* advance with a furious Mien, drew his Bow to the Head, and let fly his Arrow, which miss'd the valiant *Modern*, and went hizzing over his Head; but *Des-Cartes* it hit. . . . The Torture of the Pain, whirled the valiant *Bow-man* round, till Death, like a Star of superior Influence, drew him into his own *Vortex*.[102]

A little later in the battle, "Homer . . . took *Perrault* by mighty Force out of his Saddle, then hurl'd him and *Fontenelle*, with the same Blow dashing out both their Brains." In "A Digression of Madness," Descartes appeared briefly: "Cartesius reckoned to see before he died, the Sentiments of all Philosophers, like so many lesser Stars in his Romantick System, rapt and drawn within his own Vortex."[103] In *A Voyage to Laputa* Gulliver expressed "a desire to see those ancients, who were most renowned for wit and learning" and "proposed that Homer and Aristotle might appear at the head of all their commentators." After Gulliver had given Aristotle some account of what Scotus and Ramus had made of him, he "then desired the Governor to call up Descartes and Gassendi," and prevailed on these Moderns to expound "their Systems to Aristotle": "This great Philosopher freely acknowledged his own Mistakes in Natural Philosophy . . . and he found, that Gassendi, who had made the Doctrine of Epicurus as palatable as he could, and the Vortices of Descartes, were equally exploded. He predicted the same Fate to Attraction, whereof the present Learned are such Zealous Asserters."[104]

(Oxford: Clarendon Press, 1958), pp. xxxviii-xxxix. Voltaire referred to Fontenelle's *Histoire de Mréo et de Eénegu* which Swift could have read in Temple's library. The list of his reading is given in *ibid.*, p. lvi.

[102] *Ibid.*, pp. 244, 246.

[103] *Ibid.*, p. 167.

[104] *Gulliver's Travels*, in *Prose Works* (Oxford: Clarendon Press, 1941), Chap. VIII, pp. 180-81.

Pope's first use of the word "vortex" occurs in the *Preface to the Iliad* in 1715. Discussing Homer's "vast Invention," which Pope described as "the great and peculiar Characteristick which distinguishes him from all other Authors," Pope said: "This strong and ruling Faculty was like a powerful Planet, which in the Violence of its Course, drew all things into its Vortex."[105] In a later edition Pope changed "Planet" to "star," a change that may or may not have had any significance. Gilbert Wakefield thought that it was "altered without reason, probably at the instigation of some friend, pretending to more philosophy than he professed."[106] While the word "Planet" had been technically more correct, the words *planet* and *star* were often used interchangeably by laymen in the seventeenth and eighteenth centuries, the planets the "wandering," the others the "fixed" stars.[107] In addition to such uses of the word with astronomical overtones, Pope, like others, used it figuratively, as when he wrote to Digby of Arbuthnot's brother as "a Philosopher all of Fire; so warmly, nay so wildly in the Right, that he forces all others about him to be so too, and draws them into his own *Vortex*." Writing Swift about his visit to England, he is glad that Swift is "getting into Our Vortex." The figure appears briefly in a letter to Gay: "I am within Ear-shot of Reports, within the Vortex of Lyes and Censures."[108]

We should not have labored these passing figures of speech were it not for the fact that the idea of vortices seems to have been important in one of the most extended pas-

---

[105] Ault, *Prose Works*, I. 226.

[106] In his edition of *The Iliad of Homer* (London, 1806), I. x, Wakefield added: "The Cartesian hypothesis presumed, that the planets were borne along by the vortices; the secondary around the primary, and the primary around the sun."

[107] To Pope, as to most laymen, "star" was a catch-all term, as when he used it for "comet" in *The Temple of Fame*, I. l. 453; "Stars with blazing Hair," and *The Rape of the Lock*, V. ll. 127-28: "A sudden Star, it shot thro' liquid Air,/ And drew behind a radiant *Trail of Hair*."

[108] Digby, September 1, 1724; Swift, October 15, 1725; Gay, September 11, 1730; *Correspondence*, II. 253, 331; III. 131.

sages of the *Fourth Dunciad* (IV, 73-102), the attraction of Dulness for her sons. Pope called attention to the basic metaphor in the Argument: "All her Children, by a wonderful attraction, are drawn about her; and bear along with them divers others." Both the Argument and the lengthy notes of Pope and Warburton make abundantly clear their desire that the reader should understand the implications. "It ought to be observed," reads the note at the beginning of the passage in the 1742 edition,[109] "that here are three classes in this assembly." "In this new world of Dulness," reads "PW" in 1743, "each of these three classes hath its appointed station, as best suits its nature, and concurs to the harmony of the System."[110]

Pope could have found just what he needed for this section—even to the tripartite structure in the "Fourth Evening" of Fontenelle's *Conversations*, when the Philosopher was explicating Cartesian vortices to the Marchioness:[111]

That then which we call a Whirlpool, or Vortex, is a Mass of Matter, whose Parts are seperated or detach'd one from another, yet have all one uniform Motion, and at the same time, every one is allow'd or has a particular Motion of its own, provided it follows the general Motion. . . . You know the Planets are born up by the Celestial Matter . . . which flows as far as from the Sun to the fix'd Stars, turns round, and bears the Planets along

[109] *Dunciad*, ed. James Sutherland, 3rd ed. rev. (1963), pp. 348-51. We are aware of the problems involved in both text and notes of the *Dunciad* as a result of Warburton's collaboration with Pope during the period of composition and revision of the fourth book. So far as this passage is concerned, there is nothing in the notes to the 1742 edition that Pope could not have written, since the scientific ideas concerned were basically simple and within the competence of an amateur, particularly one who had as much background as did Pope. The first two PW notes of 1743 are slightly more technical, the third much more so. It seems possible that Warburton might have developed these.

[110] *Ibid.*, p. 349.

[111] *A Plurality of Worlds*, ed. cit., pp. 107-109. The paragraphing here is ours. The original is one paragraph. In the "Fifth Evening," p. 136, occurs another passage on vortices which also implies a tripartite structure.

with it, making them all turn after the same manner round the Sun. . . . This is the great Vortex, of which the Sun is Lord. . . .

Yet at the same time, the Planets make little particular Vortex's, in imitation of that of the Sun, each of them in turning round the Sun, doth at the same time turn round it self . . . this then is the particular Vortex of the Planet. . . .

And if by chance, a lesser Planet falls into the Vortex of a greater Planet, it is immediately born away by the greater, and is indispensably forc'd to turn round it, tho' at the same time, the great Planet, the little Planet, and the Vortex which encloses 'em, all turn round the Sun.

In the *Fourth Dunciad*, as if at the call of a trumpet, "the young, the old who feel her inward sway," are inevitably drawn into the vortex of which Dulness is the center:

> None need a guide, by sure Attraction led,
> And strong impulsive gravity[112] of Head:
> None want a place, for all their Centre found,
> Hung to the Goddess, and coher'd around.
> Not closer, orb in orb, conglob'd are seen
> The buzzing Bees about their dusky Queen.

[112] Sutherland (IV. 348n76) annotates these two lines, 75-76, by reference back to Book II. 315-18, which in *Dunciad B* read:

> Not so bold Arnall; with a weight of skull,
> Furious he dives, precipitately dull.
> Whirlpools and storms his circling arm invest,
> With all the might of *gravitation* blest. (Italics ours.)

Parallel lines had appeared in *Dunciad A*, 293-96, there attributed to Welsted rather than to Arnall. Although the lines seem similar, there is, we think, a real difference, in that in the two earlier versions the "might of gravitation" does not imply either Cartesian or Newtonian conceptions. The earlier version uses "gravitation" in a sense of "gravity" now obsolete, defined in *OED* as "the quality of heavy weight, ponderability, the tendency to downward motion, regarded in ancient physics as a property inherent in certain bodies (opposed to *levity*, or the upward tendency ascribed, e.g., to the element of fire)." Pope had written in *The Temple of Fame*, 428-29: "As Flames by Nature to the Skies ascend, / As weighty Bodies to the Center tend . . . ." Cf. Donald Davie, *The Language of Science and the Language of Literature, 1700-1740* (London and New York: Sheed and Ward, 1963), pp. 29-31.

Pope's note at this point indicates that the first group consists of "men absolutely and avowedly dull, who naturally adhere to the Goddess." The "PW" note to the 1743 edition goes a step further: "The *first* drawn only by the strong and simple impulse of Attraction, are represented as falling directly down into her; as conglobed into her substance, and resting in her centre."

The first group of dullards, then, are inevitably, by the laws of nature, in the sphere of attraction of the Queen of Dulness. Among the second group, Pope stresses in his text, dunces who "in College or in Town" sneer at each other "in toupee or gown"—men of fashion in their periwigs, scholars in their academic regalia. These, the earlier note indicates, are in the sphere of attraction not *inevitably*, but "*involuntarily* drawn to her, tho' not caring to own her influence."[113]

> The gath'ring number, as it moves along,
> Involves a vast involuntary throng,
> Who gently drawn, and struggling less and less,
> Roll in her Vortex, and her pow'r confess.
> Not those alone who passive own her laws,
> But who, weak rebels, more advance her cause.

"The *second*," reads the "PW" note in 1743, "tho' within the sphere of her attraction, yet having at the same time a different motion, they are carried, by the composition of these two, in planetary revolutions round her centre, some nearer to it, some further off."

It would seem that, for a final understanding of the third group, we must turn to the "PW" note,[114] rather than to the text or the note of 1742. This is the longest and most technical of all the explanations:

> The *third* are properly *excentrical*, and no constant members of her state or system: sometimes at an immense distance from her influence, and sometimes again almost on

113 IV. 81-86; italics ours.
114 IV. 91-100; the italics are in the text.

the surface of her *broad effulgence*. Their use in their Perihelion, or nearest approach to Dulness, is the same in the moral World, as that of *Comets* in the natural, namely to refresh and recreate the Dryness and decays of the system.

Since this note was written for the edition of the *Dunciad* published in October 1743, it is possible that comparison of the third group of dullards to a comet approaching perihelion might have come to the mind of Pope or Warburton because of the recent death in 1742 of Edmund Halley, who had most fully advanced the theory of the periodicity of comets.

We suspect that this note was Warburton's contribution, even though Pope would have seen and evidently accepted it. There is no suggestion of such an elaborate idea in the verse description of the third group, "Nor absent they, no members of her state, / Who pay her homage in her sons, the Great;" nor are there overtones of gravitation, attraction, or vortices anywhere in the passage or the original note: "The third of such, as, tho' not members of her state, yet advance her service by flattering Dulness." If Pope had wanted an analogy with comets, he could have found better ones in Fontenelle,[115] whose Cartesian comets were not inevitably restrained by universal gravitation, but merely "Planets, which belong to a Neighbouring Vortex" and come to us as occasional visitors, somehow seeming casually to pop in and out of our sphere as the third group of dullards—according to the note—seem to have been intended to do. Warburton's note grew more and more technical, but Pope's text remained the same. Indeed, when we see the three groups again, they are no longer planets,

[115] *Plurality of Worlds*, pp. 144-45: "the Neighbouring Worlds sometimes send Visitors to us, and that in a very magnificent and splendid manner: There come Comets to us from thence, adorn'd with bright shining Hair, Venerable Beards, or Majestick Tails. . . . Comets are nothing but Planets, which belong to a neighbouring Vortex, they move toward the out-side of it. . . . To continue the Circular Motion it is necessary that they enter into another Vortex, which we will suppose is ours, and that they cut through the outsides of it."

comets, or satellites, carried around their center, but street-paraders on a Lord Mayor's Day: "There march'd the bard and blockhead, side by side, / Who rhym'd for hire, and patroniz'd for pride." From this digression we return to the effect of astronomical implications on Pope's imagination.

VI

"Good God! what an incongruous Animal is Man?" Pope had written to Caryll in August 1713 after attending the first Whiston lecture. "What is Man altogether but one mighty inconsistency?" Pope's immediate response, as imagination turned from regions above the stars with a thousand systems round, to the "scarce perceptible world of the Minute," was similar to that of Pascal, Fontenelle, Addison: "Who that thinks in this train, but must see the world and its contemptible grandeurs lessen before him at every thought? 'Tis enough to make one remain stupified in a poise of inaction, void of all desires, of all designs, of all friendships." So too when on September 20 of that year he returned from a solitary moonlight walk in St. James Park, he was "full of the reflections of the transitory nature of all human delights."[116] "Giving my thoughts a loose," as he put it, he pondered an afterlife, when men might range "the starry walks above, and gaze on this world at a vast distance, as now we do on those." The pleasure we may hope to enjoy in that life will be nobler than is possible here. "The happiness of minds can surely be nothing but knowledge," but that will be perfect knowledge. "What we call science here, and study, is little better: the greater number of arts to which we apply ourselves, are mere groping in the dark." Even our apparent solicitude to know in advance about a future life makes us "but curious impertinents in the case of futurity." In such a mood, the sister arts that had been occupying the mind of the young poet

116 *Correspondence*, I. 190-91.

suffered a temporary eclipse. If even that "high Science, Divinity" seemed suspect, what of the "lighter arts?" "I really make no other use of poetry now," he wrote, "than horses do of the bells that gingle about their ears (tho' now and then they toss their heads as if they were proud of 'em)."

This mood of despondency over human learning and poetry Pope repeated to Caryll in July 1714, though without cosmological overtones, in a paragraph concluding: "Our schemes of government, our systems of philosophy, our golden words of poetry, are but so many shadow images and airy prospects, which arise to us but so much the livelier and more frequent as we are more overcast with the darkness, wrapt in the night, and disturbed with the fumes of human vanity."[117] It occurs again, with momentary cosmological overtone, in a letter of Pope's to Sir William Trumbull:[118] "I sincerely wish my self with you, to contemplate the wonders of God in the firmament, rather than the madness of man on the earth. But I never had so much cause as now to complain of my poetical star, that fixes me at this tumultuous time, to attend the gingling of rymes and the measuring of syllables." Repetition is so much a pattern with Pope in his correspondence that such passages as these would be of little significance were it not for another version of the Caryll letter of September 20, 1713, which, according to Professor Sherburn, Pope "fabricated" and printed as addressed to Edward Blount on February 10, 1716.[119] Here he repeated, as if still true nearly two years later, the account of his emotional response on the moonlight walk. The Blount letter concludes with two paragraphs not paralleled in the original to Caryll. The last opens with a sentence about "people who have Sense enough to consider the beautiful order of Nature in her Variations." Referring to a passage supposedly quoted by Blount, Pope continues: "I think it was a generous thought,

117 *Ibid.*, I. 235-37.
118 *Ibid.*, I. 323-25, December 16, 1715.
119 *Ibid.*, I. 329-31; see Sherburn's note, pp. 329-30.

and one that flow'd from an exalted mind, that it was
not improbable but God might be delighted with the various methods of worshipping him, which divided the whole
World." If the last paragraphs were from a letter actually
written by Pope to Blount, may they not conceivably reflect
the first version of "A Prayer to God," which Pope was writing about this time,[120] which twenty-three years later became the "Universal Prayer"? In the early version, Pope
included a stanza suggesting the vastness of the cosmic
system:

> Yet not to Earth's contracted Span,
> Thy Goodness let me bound;
> Or think Thee Lord alone of Man,
> When thousand Worlds are round.

He added another such stanza as his conclusion to the "Universal Prayer":

> To Thee, whose Temple is all Space,
> Whose Altar, Earth, Sea, Skies;
> One Chorus let all Being raise!
> All Nature's Incence rise!

There is more than a suggestion of the new vastness,
which Pope had discovered, in *The Temple of Fame*
(1715), on which he was engaged shortly after the Whiston
lectures. There is nothing of such feeling in the Chaucerian
original which Pope was adapting. Introductory lines 11-20
set the mood:

> I stood, methought, betwixt Earth, Seas, and Skies;
> The whole Creation open to my Eyes:
> In Air self-ballanc'd hung the Globe below,
> Where Mountains rise, and circling Oceans flow;
> Here naked Rocks, and empty Wastes were seen,
> There Tow'ry Cities, and the Forests green:

---

[120] Sherburn, *Early Career of Alexander Pope*, p. 61, showed that the
poem was written, not just before publication in 1738, as had always
been surmised, but in 1715. Cf. Ault, *Minor Poems*, pp. 149-50. In a
letter to Ralph Allen, September 8 [1736], Pope enclosed a copy of "A
Prayer to God," dated 1715. See *Correspondence*, IV. 31-33.

Here sailing Ships delight the wand'ring Eyes;
There Trees, and intermingl'd Temples rise:
Now a clear Sun the shining Scene displays,
That transient Landscape now in Clouds decays.

The same general impression is felt in later lines (89-92) :

There might you see the length'ning Spires ascend,
The Domes swell up, the widening Arches bend,
The growing Tow'rs like Exhalations rise,
And the huge Columns heave into the Skies.

On the South Wall of the Temple Pope adds to various Chaucerian characters a group of astronomers (ll. 109-12) :

a long Majestic Race
Of *Ægypt's* Priests the gilded Niches grace,
Who measur'd Earth, describ'd the Starry Spheres,
And trac'd the long Records of Lunar Years.

Still again (ll. 244-47) the poet suggests the effect of vastness upon his "aking Sight":

These massie Columns in a Circle rise,
O'er which a pompous Dome invades the Skies:
Scarce to the Top I stretch'd my aking Sight,
So large it spread, and swell'd to such a Height.

One word in another passage, some lines of which were quoted earlier, may serve as transition to a consideration of other attitudes, particularly with regard to Nature, which Pope seems to have derived from his astronomical studies:

The Wall in Lustre and Effect like Glass,
Which o'er each Object casting various Dies,
Enlarges some, and others multiplies.
Nor void of Emblem was the mystic Wall,
For thus Romantick Fame increases all.

(ll. 132-36)

This is Pope's first use, in prose or poetry, of the word "romantic," a word rare in his poetry but increasingly familiar in letters. Edwin Abbott,[121] who did not include this one, listed only three uses of "romantic" in Pope's poetry, one in a minor poem, *The Bassett Table*, which is no longer admitted to the canon. The use in *Dunciad*, III. 9-12 is quite different from that we shall find in the letters:

> the Fool's Paradise, the Statesman's scheme,
> The air-built Castle, and the golden Dream,
> The Maid's romantic wish, the Chymist's flame,
> And Poet's vision of eternal Fame.

Another in *An Epistle to a Lady* (line 16), "If Folly grows romantic, I must paint it," is also in the older deprecatory tradition. Pope's first use of the word in a letter is not in the sense in which we shall find it elsewhere in his correspondence. He was writing to Lady Mary Wortley Montagu on November 10, 1716: "The more I examine my own mind, the more Romantick I find myself. . . . Let them say I am Romantick, so is every one said to be that either admires a fine thing, or praises one. 'Tis no wonder such people are thought mad, for they are as much out of the way of common Understanding as if they were mad, because they are in the Right."[122] In the postscript to the same letter, the word occurs again: "To give you a convincing proof how Romantic I am, if you pass thro Italy next Spring . . . It is very possible I may meet you there." In the omitted passage, Pope ponders the human tendency to follow an absent idol with zeal even warmer than in the presence, and declares that he considers Lady Mary "as a glorious, tho' remote being." Here the word is used with sexual connotations. Curiously enough the word does not

---

[121] *Concordance to the Works of Alexander Pope* (New York: Appleton and Co., 1875). It should be remembered that Abbott did not index the prose, the letters, or the translations, of which *The Temple of Fame* is one.

[122] *Correspondence*, I. 367-70. See also I. 365 and I. 406. There is another use of the word in a letter to Lady Mary, written in the autumn of 1717 (*ibid.*, 439-42): "I fancy myself, in my romantic thoughts & distant admiration of you, not unlike the man in the Alchymist that has a passion for the Queen of the Faeries." In the same letter he says that "our Romance is like to have a more fortunat Conclusion."

seem to appear where we might most expect it, in *Eloisa to Abelard* (1717), on which Pope was engaged at this time. This is a "romantic" poem in the earlier sense of the word,[123] since it was based on old romances. It is also, in the older and the later sense of both words a "Gothic romance," "romantic" most of all in the passion and fervor of the emotions depicted, and in its melancholy. As Pope wrote Martha Blount, presumably in March 1716: "The Epistle of Eloise grows warm, and begins to have some Breathings of the Heart in it, which may make posterity think that I was in love."[124]

After the first occasions of the word in his letters, Pope's use of it is—with one exception—in connection with natural scenery. In September 1717 he went on a ramble that finally led him to Oxford. He had spent one evening walking by moonlight in Hampton Court. "I can easily believe," he wrote the Blount sisters on September 13,[125] "no lone House in Wales, with a Mountain & a Rookery, is more contemplative than this Court; and as a proof of it, I need only tell you Mrs. L[epell] walk'd all alone with me three or 4 hours, by moonlight." At the end of the letter, Pope added: "On Thursday I went to Stonor, which I have long had a mind to see since the romantic description you gave me of it. The Melancholy which my Wood, and this Place [Oxford], have spread over me, will go near to cast a cloud

---

[123] Cf. Logan Pearsall Smith, "The History of Four Words," *Society for Pure English* (Oxford: Clarendon Press, 1924), XVII. 12: "The word *romantic* then, from the general meaning of 'like the old romances,' came to be used as a descriptive term for the scenes which they describe, old castles, mountains and forests, pastoral plains, waste and solitary places. In the earlier instances of the adjective the literary reference is more or less explicit; but by the eighteenth century, it had come to express more generally the newly-awakened, but as yet half-conscious, love for wild nature, for mountains and moors, for 'the *Woods*, the *Rivers*, or *Sea-shores*,' which Shaftesbury mentions as sought by those who are 'deep in this *romantick* way.'"

[124] *Correspondence*, I. 338-39.

[125] *Ibid.*, I. 426-31. The last sentence Pope lifted bodily—omitting only the reference to Mrs. L—into a letter to Lady Mary, dated only [1718] (*ibid.*, I. 470). As Sherburn says: "This sort of echoing is not infrequent in the letters to Lady Mary and Martha Blount of this period."

upon the rest of my letter, if I don't make haste to conclude it here." The romantic melancholy reaches a height in the prose-poetry of his letter from Oxford to the Blount sisters:[126]

> I came from Stonor . . . to Oxford the same night. Nothing could have more of that Melancholy which once us'd to please me, than that days journey: For after having pass'd thro' my favorite Woods in the forest, with a thousand Reveries of past pleasures; I rid over hanging hills, whose tops were edgd with Groves, & whose feet water'd with winding rivers, listening to the falls of Cataracts below, & the murmuring of Winds above. The gloomy Verdure of Stonor succeeded to these, & then the Shades of the Evening overtook me, the Moon rose in the clearest Sky I ever saw, by whose solemn light I pac'd on slowly, without company, or any interruption to the range of my thoughts. About a mile before I reachd Oxford, all the Night bells toll'd in different notes; the Clocks of every College answerd one another: & told me, some in a deeper, some in a softer voice, that it was eleven a clock.

The mood of pensive though not somber melancholy continued during Pope's stay "among those old walls, venerable Galleries, Stone Portico's, studious walks & solitary Scenes of the University," where, "rolld up in books & wrapt in meditation," he lay "in one of the most ancient, dusky parts of the University . . . as dead to the world as any Hermite of the desart." His vanity was touched by the respect he received and by "seeing myself seated with dignity on the most conspicuous Shelves of a Library."

The violence of Nature is emphasized in a letter of August 1718,[127] again to Martha Blount, in which the word "romantic" is not used, though Pope described "a Romance under a Beechen Shade," when "a terrible Storm of Thunder & Lightning" left untouched "the most proud & extrava-

---

[126] *Ibid.*, I. 429-31.
[127] *Ibid.*, I. 479-82. A letter from Gay about the same event is given pp. 482-83. James Thomson wrote verses about the death of the lovers.

gant Heap of Towers in the nation," but "miserably reduced to ashes . . . a Cock of Corn in the next field," instantly killing two lovers who had taken shelter there. Except for suggestions in this letter, the new Nature Pope was
discovering was not the elemental fury that often moved
Mallet and Thomson. Nor was his transfer of the
"Aesthetics of the Infinite" to the grander aspects of Nature—mountains and oceans.[128] Perhaps we can best explain
this difference by referring to two letters, one using the
word "romantic" in connection with scenery, written not by
Pope but to him. On May 1, 1714 George Berkeley wrote
Pope from Leghorn,[129] after reading *The Rape of the Lock*,
reminding him of a "half-form'd design" of coming to Italy.
He continued:

> What might we not expect from a Muse that sings so
> well in the bleak climate of *England*, if she felt the same
> warm Sun and breath'd the same Air with *Virgil* and
> *Horace*? . . . I know not whether it might not be worth a
> Poet's while, to travel, in order to store his mind with
> strong Images of Nature.
> Green fields and groves, flow'ry meadows and purling
> streams, are no where in such perfection as in *England*:
> but if you wou'd know lightsome days, warm suns, and
> blue skys, you must come to *Italy*: and to enable a man
> to describe rocks and precipices, it is absolutely necessary
> that he pass the Alps.

Three years later, on October 22, 1717, [130] Berkeley wrote
Pope from Naples, describing the island Inarime from
which he had recently returned, as "an Epitome of the
whole Earth, containing within the compass of eighteen
Miles, a wonderful variety of Hills, Vales; ragged Rocks,
fruitful Plains, and barren Mountains, all thrown together

128 See Marjorie Nicolson, *Mountain Gloom and Mountain Glory*,
particularly Chaps. VII and VIII.

129 *Correspondence*, I. 221-22.

130 *Ibid.*, I. 445-47. No reply of Pope is extant, probably because the
letter was written on the day of Pope's father's death, and for a
time Pope was diverted from both poetry and landscape.

in a most romantic Confusion." Such "noble Landscape,"
he said, "would demand an Imagination as warm, and numbers as flowing as your own, to describe it." Throwing in
for good measure, "barren Spots . . . naked Rocks . . . a
terrible *Volcano* . . . the finest Prospect in the World,"
Berkeley might have been writing a prescription for the
descriptive poetry written a little later by Mallet and
Thomson and aped by Savage and other versifiers, following a new pattern.

Pope's travels led him no farther than Bristol and Bath
—on one brief occasion to York—in one direction, Southampton in another. He was never to cross the ocean or the
Alps, never to share the experience of Burnet, Dennis,
Shaftesbury, Addison, Thomson, all of whom in their various ways, transferred the "Aesthetics of the Infinite" from
God and Space to the greatest objects in the terrestrial
world. Pope was too honest a poet to pretend a response
to emotions he had not experienced, as did Savage and
other third-rate versifiers. His landscape is not "sublime" in
the sense in which the word was to be used in his lifetime,
though, as we shall see, he was conscious of "a prodigious
Beauty," such as he described in letters to which we turn,
all but one including the word "romantic." It is significant,
we think, that all the letters in which the word is associated
with landscape were addressed to Martha Blount, to whom
alone he wrote in these moods.

Probably in 1724[131] Pope visited Lord Digby at Sherborne, from which he wrote Miss Blount a description of
the great estate. "The Gardens," he wrote, "are so Irregular.
. . . Their beauty rises from this Irregularity." It was "a
little triangular wilderness . . . a Line of Wilderness with
wild winding walks." Everywhere he was conscious of ruins:
"venerable Ruins of an Old Castle . . . a Bridge . . . built
in the same ruinous taste . . . the Ruin of another Arch or
two . . . venerable broken Walls," and still other "Ruins,
to compleat the Solemnity of the Scene." "A Hill of ven-

---

[131] *Ibid.*, II. 236-40. The letter had formerly been dated as of 1722,
but Sherburn considers 1724 more probable.

erable Wood overarchd by nature" rose to "a vast height." Water was all about: "a natural River . . . a Canall . . . a natural Cascade with never-ceasing murmurs." "You lose your eyes upon the glimmering of the Waters under the wood, & your ears in the constant dashing of the waves." In the "Deep Scene" Pope felt "a prodigious Beauty." The effect of the whole was "inexpressibly awful & solemn," the views "more romantick than Imagination can form them."

If the letter was written in 1724 Pope was then engaged upon his edition of Shakespeare, which appeared in 1725. A passage from the Preface[132] is in a different way significant of Pope's increasing taste for such landscape as he saw at Sherborne: "I will conclude by saying of Shakespear, that with all his faults, and with all the irregularity of his *drama*, one may look upon his works, in comparison of those that are more finished and regular, as upon an ancient majestic piece of Gothic architecture, compared with a neat modern building: the latter more elegant and glaring, but the former is more strong and more solemn. It must be allowed, that in one of these there are materials enough to make many of the other. It has much the greater variety, and much the nobler apartments; though we are often conducted to them by dark, odd, and uncouth passages. Nor does the whole fail to strike us with greater reverence, though many of the parts are childish, ill-placed, and unequal to its grandeur." Here too we have "irregularity" and "variety," with a feeling for ruins of another sort. Shakespeare shows the lavishness of Nature, pouring himself forth with profusion. The impression he produces is "strong and solemn," arousing "reverence" in the beholder. And here too we find the growing tendency of the century to appreciation of the Gothic.

A letter to Martha Blount from Bath, written on September 4, 1728,[133] contains only passing references to scenery, but the word "romantic" occurs. On his journey Pope "lay

---

[132] *Works of Alexander Pope*, ed. Whitwell Elwin and William John Courthope (London: John Murray, 1871-89), X. 549.
[133] *Correspondence*, II. 513-14.

one night at Rousham, which is the prettiest place for water-falls, jetts, ponds inclosed with beautiful scenes of green and hanging wood, that ever I saw." He stayed also with the family of Sir William Codrington, and found: "Their house is pretty enough, the situation romantic, covered with woody hills tumbling upon one another confusedly, and the garden makes a valley betwixt them, with some mounts and waterfalls." More extensive are details in the letter to Miss Blount of August 11 [1734], which has recently been published for the first time.[134] "I think it my Duty, to a Person of your Romantic Taste," Pope began, "to give you an account of an Adventure & Discovery, made by Ld Peterborow & me last week." Planning a trip to the Isle of Wight, they were caught by ebb tide, so turned their course "& got in to a neck of Land on the Southside." "When we came to the Shore, we were both struck with the beauty of it, a rising Hill very deeply hung with Woods, that fell quite in to the Water, & at the Edge of the Sea a very old min'd Castle" with "Towers, & the high crumbling Battlements, overgrown with Ivy." Peterborough went in one direction, Pope in another, seeking the best place for their picnic lunch. "Thro' a glade of Trees," Pope saw a building that "provd [to be] an old Barn, where was nothing but Emptiness & open doors, but very cool & shady: Round it were very high Oaks . . . on the slope of the Hill, you saw the Sea opening in a hundred broken views." In the meantime Peterborough had made a much more important discovery, "a Ruin of a large Monastery," Netley Abbey, of which he had never heard. The shell of the church was not much smaller than Westminster, "a whole side of windows entire, to the number of eight great arches; the End window over the Altar vastly high, & the whole wrought finely with old Gothic ornaments." The "Quire of the church" was filled with "fallen Fretworks, & window frames

---

134 By G.S. Rousseau, *PQ*, XLV (1966), 409-18. Professor Sherburn mentioned the letter in *Correspondence*, III. 427, as being in the hands of a dealer who refused to grant permission to publish it. It is now owned by Mr. Robert Taylor of Princeton, who permitted its publication.

of Stone, mixed with high heaps of Rubbish, & great Trees of Elder &c. growing among them." Recalled to their ship by the sailors, since the tide was ebbing, "the night coming on apace, with a beautiful Moon," they looked back to shore to see "the Woods stretched a great way to the Tops of very high hills, & at the side of one of the Woods we saw a large plain very highly seated." Pope concludes the letter "with a story, which is necessary to a Romance," of a carpenter who "dream'd that his brains were beaten out by pulling down the Great window" of the church, only to have the dream come true.

Two later letters to Martha Blount, November 19 and 24, 1739,[135] describing Bristol, may be considered one, since the second continues the first, and Pope sent them at the same time, according to the postmarks. Here alone, among the descriptive letters, we do not find the word "romantic," possibly because Pope was in great physical discomfort during his Bristol stay. There is more color in this letter than in the others, in which the color green is emphasized. Here again we find the repetition of "vast": "a vast Extent of Houses," "a vast Rock," "a vast depth below." Pope suggests that the Bristol scene should be painted rather than merely described, because "it is so unlike any Scene you ever saw." Between Bath and Bristol he had found "steep rising Hills cloathd with Wood at top, and sloping toward the stream in Green Meadows, intermixt with white Houses, Mills & Bridges. . . ." Looking in the opposite direction from his house Pope saw that "a vast Rock of 100 foot high, of red, white, green, blue & yellowish Marbles, all blotch'd & variegated strikes you quite in the face, & turning on the left, there opens the River at a vast depth below, winding in & out, & accompanied on both sides, with a Continued Range of Rocks up to the Clouds, of a hundred Colours, one behind another, & so to the end of the Prospect quite to the Sea. But the Sea nor the Severn you

---

[135] *Correspondence,* IV. 200-202; 204-205. A different use of "romantic" will be found in *Correspondence,* IV. 232. Writing to the Earl of Orrery about his letters to Swift, Pope described Mrs. Whiteway as "so poetically mad, so romantically impertinent."

do not see, the Rocks & River fill the Eye, and terminate the View. . . ." From his room he watched the tide rising and filling the bottom "between these scenes of Rocks." He could also see "huge Shaggy Marbles, some in Points, some in Caverns, hanging all over & under them in a thousand shapes." This seems to have been Pope's first sight of the stalactites and marbles of which he was to make so much in his later grotto, various of the materials for which came to Twickenham from Bristol.

In the second part of the letter, Pope described to Miss Blount a pathway of turf on the top of high rocks. "It looks too frightful to approach the brink, & look down upon the River; but in many parts of this Down the Vallyes descend gently, & you see all along the Windings of the Stream, & the Opening of the Rocks, which turn, & close in upon you, from space to space. . . ." A tower stands close to the edge of the highest rock:

> All the Banks one way are Wooded, in a gentle slope for near a mile high quite green; the other bank all inaccessible rock, of a hundred colours & odd shapes, some hundred foot perpendicular. I am told that one may ride ten miles further on an Even Turf, on a Ridge, that on one side views the River Severn & the banks steeper & steeper quite to the Open Sea, & on the other side a vast Woody Vale as far as the Eye can stretch.

In this study of Pope's use of the word "romantic" we are making no attempt to kidnap him to the movement of "Romanticism," a tendency that has gone on for more than three quarters of a century in the case of various neo-classical writers.[136] We have found in Pope's letters suggestions

---

[136] Such a tendency began with William Lyon Phelps, *The Beginnings of the English Romantic Movement* (Boston: Riverside Press, 1893). In 1912 Raymond D. Havens attracted much attention by his "Romantic Aspects of the Age of Pope," *PMLA*, XXVII, 297-324. A.O. Lovejoy's famous essay "On the Discrimination of Romanticisms" again raised the issue, as did his "Nature as Aesthetic Norm" and other articles on the eighteenth century collected in *Essays in the History of Ideas* (Baltimore: The Johns Hopkins University Press, 1948). In 1934 Samuel W. Stevenson published "'Romantic' Tendencies in Pope,"

of a new kind of landscape description which reached one climax with the publication of Thomson's complete *Seasons,* Akenside's *Pleasures of Imagination,* and Young's *Night Thoughts.* Earlier than any of these—on his journey to Oxford—Pope had experienced the pleasing melancholy aroused in moonlight by "hanging hills . . . winding Rivers . . . falls of Cataracts . . . gloomy Verdure . . . solemn light." Throughout the rest of his life he was capable of feeling the charm of "venerable Ruins . . . towers & crumbling Battlements." Rocks and rivers "filled" his eye, "as far as Eye could stretch." A hundred broken views led the poet to feel the "irregular beauty," the "prodigious Beauty" of "an inexpressibly solemn scene." Yet after *The Temple of Fame* and *Eloisa to Abelard* Pope's poetry remained neo-classical. Shortly before Thomson, Akenside, and Young published their "Romantic" poems, Pope published the complete *Dunciad.*

To what extent Pope might have become a Romanticist had it not been for the pressure exerted by Swift and Bolingbroke that he stoop to truth and moralize his song, we cannot tell. It must be remembered that the "romantic" aspects of Nature we have discussed were all in letters, and in letters to one person, a woman. Here he showed that like Thomson, Akenside, and Young he could and did transfer to Nature in the terrestrial globe the sense of vastness he had felt in Space, even though his experience, unlike theirs, had not included the grandest aspects of external Nature— mountains and ocean.[137]

ELH, I. 126-55. B. Sprague Allen discussed Pope's taste in gardening and other aspects of art and architecture in *Tides in English Taste,* 2 vols. (Cambridge: Harvard University Press, 1937). More recently the question of Pope's "Romanticism" has been raised by Frederick Bracher, "Pope's Grotto: the Maze of Fancy," *HLQ,* XII (1949), 141-62, and A. Lynn Altenbernd, "On Pope's 'Horticultural Romanticism,'" *JEGP,* LIV (1955), 470-77; G.K. Hunter, "The 'Romanticism' of Pope's Horace," *Essays in Criticism,* X (1960), 390-414.

[137] In *Mountain Gloom and Mountain Glory,* p. 328, I said, discussing Berkeley's letter and Pope's attitude toward Nature: "It is useless to wonder whether Pope would have shared the enthrallment of Burnet and Dennis had he seen the Alps, or whether, like Evelyn,

Berkeley and Whiston were involved in Pope's imagination in a quite different way—in their interest in millenarianism.[138] Pope's first reference to the doctrine important in Whiston's thinking had been in the first letter to Lady Mary in which he used the word "romantic." "I shall at least be sure to meet you in the next world," he wrote, "if there be any truth in Our new Doctrine of the Day of judgment." The sentence was followed by the Fontenelle passage, quoted earlier, in which Pope proposed a lovers' tryst upon two stars in the Milky Way. He returned to the subject in letters to Robert Digby and to Swift in October 1725.[139] Writing to Digby, he reflected in passing another enthusiasm of Whiston's—primitive Christianity: "You are all of one Heart and one Soul, as was said of the Primitive Christians: 'Tis like the Kingdom of the Just upon Earth; not a wicked Wretch to interrupt you; but a Set of try'd, experienc'd Friends, and fellow Comforters, who have seen Evil Men and Evil Days, and have by a superior Rectitude of Heart set yourselves above them, and reap your Reward. Why will you ever, of your own accord, end such a Millenary Year in *London*? transmigrate (if I may so call it) into other Creatures, in that Scene of Folly Militant, when you may reign for ever at *Hom-lacy* in Sense and Reason Triumphant?"

To Swift he wrote a few days later on October 15, 1725: "I have often imagined to myself, that if ever All of us met again, after so many Varieties and Changes, after so much of the Old world, and of the Old man in each of us, had

---

he would have swept aside the rubbish of the world in a brilliant metaphor. Pope did not follow Berkeley's advice, nor did he continue his enthusiasm for those aspects of the new science that were breaking down world barriers and the basis of neoclassical ethics and aesthetics." Although I referred to Professor Sherburn's article on "The Great Shew of Nature," I was not then aware of the lasting effect of Whiston's lectures, nor had I read the *Correspondence* in any detail. MHN

[138] Professor Sherburn has discussed Pope's interest in millenarianism in "Pope and 'The Great Shew of Nature,'" pp. 311-15. He did not note the passage in the letter to Lady Mary.

[139] *Correspondence*, II. 329-31.

been alter'd; after there has been a New Heaven, and a
New Earth, in our Minds, and bodies, that Scarce a single
thought of the one any more than a single atome of the
other, remains just the same: I've fancy'd, I say, that we
shou'd meet like the Righteous in the Millennium, quite
in peace, divested of all our former passions, smiling at all
our own designs, and content to enjoy the Kingdome of
the Just in Tranquillity. But I find you would rather be
employ'd as an Avenging Angel of wrath, to break your
Vial of Indignation over the heads of the wretched pityful
creatures of this World."

In the letter to Digby he laughingly threatened to "come
upon you with such irresistable Arguments another Year,
as may carry you all with me to the *Bermudas*, the Seat of
all Earthly Happiness, and the new *Jerusalem* of the Righteous." This sentence he annotated in the edition of 1735:
"About this time the Rev. Dean Berkley conceiv'd his Project of erecting a Settlement in Bermuda for the Propaga-
tion of the Christian Faith, and of Sciences in America."
It is in this letter that Pope mentioned "Reflecting Telescopes," which in the edition of 1735 he annotated,
"These Instruments were just then brought to perfection."
Astronomy seems to have been hovering in Pope's mind,
since his letter to Swift five days later on October 15, 1725
rejoices that Swift will soon be "getting into Our Vortex,"
and describes Lord Bolingbroke as "one, who was once a
powerful Planet . . . who has now (after long experience
of all that comes of shining) learn'd to be content with
returning to his First point, without the thought or ambition of shining at all." Pope adds toward the conclusion:
"Dean Berkley is well, and happy in the prosecution of his
Scheme."

The most obvious effect of astronomy on Pope is of course
in *An Essay on Man*, the first epistles of which were published in 1733, six years after the death of Sir Isaac Newton.
In the year of the death, Pope had been approached by
John Conduitt, Newton's literary executor, asking Pope's
aid in assisting Conduitt to draft a dedication to the Queen

of an edition he was preparing of Newton's *Chronology of Ancient Kingdoms Amended*.[140] Pope urged less fulsome praise of the Queen who apparently overshadowed Newton: "Your Real Subject, (I mean both Sir Isaac Newton & her Majesty) will shine of themselves; and a Shortness, a Dignity, and Plainness, will become them. . . . It takes very much from the Praise of Sir I. N. and I fear unjustly, to imagine Any Prince's Reign can *Make* Newtons, however it might *incourage*, or *admire* them." Pope concluded his letter: "I am sincerely of opinion that your Dedication is very just, and decent, and well-judg'd. I could wish it were Inlarged with some Memoirs & Character of him, as a private Man: I doubt not his Life & Manners would make as Great a Discovery of Virtue, & Goodness, & Rectitude of Heart, as his Works have done of Penetration and the utmost Stretch of human knowledge."

If Pope turned directly to Newton during his period of preparation for the astronomical passages in *An Essay on Man*, two recent editions would have been readily available to him. In 1729 Andrew Motte had published the first English translation of the *Principia*;[141] in 1730 appeared the fourth edition of the *Opticks*,[142] now considered the definitive edition. Passages quoted by various modern commentators to show similarities between Pope's poem and Newton are usually from the *Opticks* rather than the *Principia* for reasons made clear by Professor I. Bernard Cohen:[143]

> In order to understand the extraordinary appeal that the *Opticks* had in the 18th century, we must compare it to the *Principia*—in scientific, philosophic, and speculative content; literary style; and the approach of

[140] *Correspondence*, II. 457-59; Conduitt's letter and Pope's reply are both given.

[141] This may conveniently be found in the edition of *Sir Isaac Newton's Mathematical Principles of Natural Philosophy and his System of the World*, ed. Florian Cajori, 2 vols. (Berkeley and Los Angeles: University of California Press, 1962).

[142] This also is conveniently found in *Opticks: or a Treatise of the Reflections, Refractions, Inflections & Colours of Light*, ed. I. Bernard Cohen (New York: Dover Publications, 1952).

[143] *Ibid.*, pp. xix-xx.

the author to the subject. On such a comparison, an important difference between the two books is immediately apparent. The *Opticks* invites and holds the attention of the non-specialist reader while the other, the *Principia*, is as austere and forbidding to the non-specialist as it can possibly be. Of course, the general reader of the *Opticks* would be more interested in the final section of "Queries" than in the rest of the work, just as the general reader of the *Principia* would be drawn to the General Scholium at the end of Book Three; but whereas in the *Opticks* such a reader could enjoy almost 70 pages, in the *Principia* there would be but four. The latter would discuss for him the mechanism of universal gravitation and give him a hint of the direction of Newton's thinking about this important problem; but the former would allow the reader to roam, with great Newton as his guide, through the major unresolved problems of science, and even the relation of the whole world of nature to Him who had created it.

On occasion in *An Essay on Man* Pope seems to have written with the *Opticks* before him but he also had assistance from William Whiston, both from the lectures and from published books. We shall here quote from *Astronomical Principles of Religion, Natural and Reveal'd*,[144] because it was written so shortly after the coffee-house lectures and is our closest approach to what Pope probably heard at that time. As the title indicates, it combines astronomy and religion, reading the Newtonian hypothesis into religion. Although Whiston was not a man of letters in the limited sense of that term, Pope might have been pleased that he introduced as a prefatory poem Milton's great "Hymn to the Creator" in Book V of *Paradise Lost* and

[144] In 1715 Whiston had published *Astronomical Lectures, Read in the Publick Schools at Cambridge; by William Whiston . . . Whereunto is added a Collection of Astronomical Tables; being those of Mr. Flamsteed, Corrected; Dr. Halley; Monsieur Cassini, and Mr. Street. For the Use of Young Students in the University. And now done into English* (London, Printed for R. Senex, 1715). Many of the lectures are dated as having been delivered at Cambridge in 1701-1703.

223

quoted Milton again in his "Recapitulation." Pope may not have equally admired Whiston's taste in concluding with Sir Richard Blackmore's "Hymn to the Creator" in Book VII of *The Creation*. The *Astronomical Principles of Religion* is divided into two main parts: the first five sections are devoted to technical description of various aspects of the cosmic system: the sun and planets, comets and fixed stars, diurnal and annual motion, the known laws of matter and motion, the law of gravitation. Several charts, diagrams and other illustrations are given, all intelligible to the layman. The second part of the volume deals with "Important Principles of Natural Religion, Demonstrated from the foregoing Observations." The *Astronomical Principles* is the work of a deeply devout man who begins his Preface:

> Before I come to treat of this Noble Subject, THE ASTRONOMICAL SYSTEM OF THE UNIVERSE, with its wonderful Consequences, as it is now discovered to us by the good Providence of God, and the laborious Searches of this and the last Age; and chiefly, by the surprizing Sagacity and Penetration of the Illustrious Sir Isaac Newton; I think it proper to premise two Enquiries, as of great Consequence in way of Preparation to the receiving real Advantage by this Treatise; and without Satisfaction wherein, all such Discourses will be of little Effect with many of its Perusers: I mean the Enquiry about that Temper of Mind, which is necessary for the Discovery of Divine Truth; and the Enquiry into that Degree of Evidence, that ought to be expected in Divine Matters. . . .
>
> As to the former of these Enquiries . . . it can certainly be no other than what the Light of Nature, and the Consciences of Men influenc'd thereby, dictate to us . . . such as Seriousness, Integrity, Impartiality, and Prayer to God; with the faithful Belief, and ready Practice of such Truths and Duties, as we do all along discover to be the Word and Will of God. . . .

We pause over comments of two recent critics of *An Essay on Man*. Professor Martin Kallich, discussing "The Conversation and the Frame of Love: Images of Unity in Pope's *Essay on Man*"[145] says of the "frame":

> What emerges as the central integrating image is an astronomical vision of Nature as a huge frame originally constituted by God: a dynamic machine shaped as a vast circle, the macrocosm or "gen'ral frame" (I. 264), enfolding an infinite series of smaller circles. . . .
>
> Pope may actually be imagining an enormous mechanical loom in which all the loose ends of the strings are drawn tightly together and made equal, or he may also be imagining an enormous orrery, an elaborate mechanical representation of the solar system made up of discs and spheres designed to illustrate the motions of the planets and moons. . . .

The orrery may have been in Pope's mind, since such instruments were familiar in his day, but we venture to suggest as a probable model, Whiston's "Copernicus," which he had designed for the solar eclipse of April 22, 1715 which he demonstrated to his pupils and which some of them undoubtedly bought. As we have suggested, Pope, who was deep in the study of eclipses for the spectacular event, may have owned one. The "Copernicus," as we have said, was made up of many circles, an outside immovable one, a movable one within, and ten *annuli*, circular rings that revolved one within another, some removable, but, when inserted, firmly connected with the frame, revolving as freely as the others. Designed for an eclipse, the "Copernicus" could be used to demonstrate many other cosmic phenomena, and so Whiston seems to have used it in his lecture and demonstration courses. Here was as graphic a cosmology as could be fashioned from simple materials. Whether Pope bought a "Copernicus" or not, he had certainly seen one, and it is possible that the instrument was close to him when he was working over the first Epistle of *An Essay on Man*.

[145] *Papers on Language and Literature*, II. i (Winter 1966), 21-37.

In his essay, "Pope and the Great Chain of Being,"[146] Professor F.E.L. Priestley makes what seems to us an important point. In its traditional sense, the Great Chain of Being is not the dominant doctrine in Epistle I of *An Essay on Man*. Pope is not thinking of the Great Chain in terms of plenitude or continuity and indeed denies some of its presuppositions. Professor Priestley says: "The context here is primarily that of the astro-theologian. The 'amazing Whole' is that of earth, planets, suns, 'world on world,' held in a system of orderly motion. When Pope describes the way in which, in the 'amazing Whole,' 'each system in gradation' rolls, he is clearly using 'gradation' in a quite different sense from that of the Great Chain. The 'dread Order' he here pictures as being broken is that observed by the astronomer."[147] Mr. Priestley goes on to show that "there is no ontological, or any other kind, of necessity about this order." Newton, like many other thinkers of the age, held that the order of motion of the heavenly bodies was an order established by the fiat of God; another order might have been imposed on the system. "The catastrophe Pope describes so vividly is precisely the same as that which Newtonians like Whiston ascribe to the suspension or withdrawal from the Universe of the 'continued exercise' of the Divine and Immaterial Power upon which its order depends."[148]

In his *Astronomical Principles* Whiston said: "If that Power of Gravity were suspended, all the whole System would immediately dissolve; and each of the Heavenly Bodies would be crumbled into Dust; the single Atoms commencing their several Motions in such several strait Lins, according to which the projectile Motion chanc'd to be at the Instant when that Influence was suspended or

[146] In *Essays in English Literature from the Renaissance to the Victorian Age, Presented to A.S.P. Woodhouse* (Toronto: University of Toronto Press, 1964), pp. 213-28. Ed. Millar MacLure and F.W. Watt.
[147] *Ibid.*, p. 221.
[148] Priestley here quotes a passage from Whiston's *Sermons and Essays* (London, 1709), p. 209. We quote corresponding ones from *Astronomical Principles of Religion*, pp. 82, 111.

withdrawn . . . God, the Creator of the World, does also exercise a continual *Providence* over it, and does interpose his general, immechanical, immediate *Power*, which we call the *Power of Gravity*, as also his particular immechanical *Powers of Refraction, of Attraction, and Repulse, &c.* in the several particular Cases of the Phaenomena of the World; and without which all this beautiful *System* would fall to pieces, and dissolve into Atoms."

Professor Priestley shows that the order Pope is developing is conceived of by Pope in Newtonian terms, by comparing with Pope's familiar passage beginning, "All are but parts of one stupendous whole," a passage from the *Opticks*, one section of which was not in the original but added in the edition of 1718. He continues: "The way in which this passage of the Epistle echoes Newton's passages in the *Opticks* and in the General Scholium of the *Principia* has often been noted, but I do not think the significance has been brought out. The significance is, as I have said, that the Newtonian doctrine represents a quite different context of thought from the Great Chain, with a quite different concept of cosmic order, of the origin of cosmic order, and of the principles underlying that order. And also quite different possibilities of interpreting man's attitude to the order. Since the Newtonian order is based upon divine choice, and could have been otherwise, it is possible for man to challenge the divine Will, and, as it were, criticize the divine arrangements, which is hardly the case in the Great Chain theory, where things could not possibly have been otherwise. At least there is a difference between challenging the inevitable and challenging a voluntary act."[149]

We shall leave the reader to read for himself the interesting discussion of Pope's *a posteriori* logic in *An Essay on Man* and his condemnation in *The Dunciad* of those who

> nobly take the *high Priori* Road,
> And reason downward, till we doubt of God.

There is little question that the magnificent first Epistle of *An Essay on Man* would never have been written had

[149] *Ibid.*, p. 223.

Pope not heard Whiston's coffee-house lectures. As we know from his early letters, what most impressed him was the astounding extent of cosmic space, the worlds on worlds that make one universe. One of many passages from *Astronomical Principles* will suggest how the teacher interpreted such conceptions for his pupils.[150] Whiston had been giving a mathematical estimate of the size of the universe, and concluded three lines of digits with

> three Sextilions, or three Millions of Millions of Millions of Millions of Millions of Millions of Cubical Miles. An amazing Space this, and as to any Power of Imagination, scarcely to be distinguish'd from Infinite Space it self!

The reader carries away from the *Astronomical Principles of Religion* two dominant conceptions: the vastness of the universe and its essential order and harmony. Whiston says in his recapitulation:

> We have taken a short imperfect View of the vastly numerous, the vastly great, and vastly distant Systems of the Fixed Stars, or to us new Systems of Worlds quite remote from this our Planetary and Cometary World: In comparison of all which Systems of Worlds, our own entire System, with its Sun, and all its Planets and Comets, must be but inconsiderable; probably not the 10,000th, perhaps not the 100,000th, or 1,000,000th Part of the Whole. . . . So immensely numerous, and immensely great and glorious is the entire System; and so inconsiderable are we poor Worms, creeping upon this little little Earth, if compared thereto; even *as Nothing, yea less than Nothing, and Vanity*! And here we have plainly lost our selves in the amazing *Length* and *Breadth* and *Heighth* of the Grand System, and of that Power, Wisdom, and Goodness, which shines forth in every Branch thereof.[151]

Particularly in the first Epistle, and occasionally throughout *An Essay on Man*, we are conscious of "vast immensity,"

---

150 *Ibid.*, pp. 121-22.   151 *Ibid.*, pp. 253-54.

the "amazing," the "stupendous whole," of "worlds unnumber'd." "My foot-stool earth, my canopy the skies," as
imagination stretches "Far as the solar walk and milky
way." Meteors flame lawless through the void, only to destroy themselves. Atoms or systems may be "into ruin
hurl'd, / And now a bubble burst, and now a world (I.
89-90)." Yet we are always conscious, too, that "worlds on
worlds compose one universe," that "All are but parts of
one stupendous whole, / Whose body Nature is, and God
the soul (I. 267-68)." Overwhelming though the universe
seems to the limited imagination of man, Order is everywhere: "The gen'ral ORDER, since the world began, /
Is kept in Nature, and is kept in Man (I. 171-72)." Order
is everywhere in the cosmos; only "presumptuous Man" in
his little world seeks to violate it:

> And if each system in gradation roll,
> Alike essential to th' amazing whole;
> The least confusion but in one, not all
> That system only, but the whole must fall.
> Let Earth unbalanc'd from her orbit fly,
> Planets and Suns run lawless thro' the sky,
> Let ruling Angels from their spheres be hurl'd,
> Being on being wreck'd, and world on world,
> Heav'n's whole foundations to their centre nod,
> And Nature tremble to the throne of God:
> All this dread ORDER break—for whom? for thee?
> Vile worm! oh Madness, Pride, Impiety!
>
> (I. 247-58)

Whiston had written:

> . . . the Moral or Living World, does not here always
> seem to agree with the Natural or Astronomical one.
> In the latter there is plainly and every where Marks of
> such Exactness, Harmony, Prudence, Sagacity, Wisdom,
> and Conduct, that not only perfectly Convinces,
> but Amazes and Astonishes us, even all of us, who thor-
> oughly consider the particular Instances . . . of the same,
> in every Part of the Universe: And he must be stupid to

the utmost Degree, who can go to a Course of
Mechanicks, of Anatomy, of Botanicks, and especially of
Astronomy, without the most satisfactory Conviction
in this Case. . . .

But then, how it comes about that we do by no means
perceive the same Exactness and Harmony in the Moral
and Living World, which we everywhere see in the Material and Physical, is a great and noble Problem . . .
I have my self occasionally touch'd upon it in my other
Writings; but acknowledge it to deserve a much larger
and fuller Disquisition.[152]

Pope's poem, for all its cosmic overtones, is, as its title indicates, an essay on *Man*, treating the "great and noble
Problem" Whiston describes, the lack of "the same Exactness and Harmony in the Moral and Living World, which
we see everywhere in the Material and Physical." Pope had
attended "a Course of Astronomy" to become convinced
of the order and harmony of the universe, although it
"amazed and astonished" him. So far as limited and finite
man might speak of the cosmos, he has spoken: his main
theme is the arrogance, the pride, the presumption of man
in defiance of the universal Order—microcosmic Man seeming to challenge the Macrocosm. The conflicting moods of
exaltation and doubt, even momentary despair, about which
Pope wrote John Caryll shortly after the first Whiston
lecture, were never better expressed than in the prelude to
Epistle II with its Pascalian overtones:

> Know then thyself, presume not God to scan;
> The proper study of Mankind is Man.
> Plac'd on this isthmus of a middle state,
> A being darkly wise, and rudely great:
> With too much knowledge for the Sceptic side,
> With too much weakness for the Stoic's pride,
> He hangs between; in doubt to act, or rest,
> In doubt to deem himself a God, or Beast;
> In doubt his Mind or Body to prefer,

[152] *Ibid.*, p. 118.

Born but to die, and reas'ning but to err;
Alike in ignorance, his reason such,
Whether he thinks too little, or too much:
Chaos of Thought and Passion, all confus'd;
Still by himself abus'd, or disabus'd;
Created half to rise, and half to fall;
Great lord of all things, yet a prey to all;
Sole judge of Truth, in endless Error hurl'd:
The glory, jest, and riddle of the world!

Discussing Pope's interest in theories of the millennium, Professor Sherburn wrote: "The *Essay on Man* should have ended with some epic view of a blissful condition; but it does not."[153] A little later, approaching the conclusion of his essay, he said: "Naturally, perhaps, Pope's most significant application of his millennial thinking to poetry is negative—is the millennium transversed." He refers, of course, to the *Fourth Dunciad*. Pope's friend George Berkeley had concluded the poem he originally called "America or the Muses Refuge, a Prophecy":

Westward the Course of Empire takes its Way,
    The four first Acts already past.
A fifth shall close the Drama with the Day,
    Time's noblest Offspring is the last.

The immediate future for man lay in America; at the conclusion of that chapter would come the millennium. Pope's "millennium transversed" was of quite another sort. *The Dunciad* is not basically an astronomical poem, though Pope never ceased using figures drawn from the science. One of his additions in *The New Dunciad* seems symbolically to look forward to the great conclusion (II. 9-12). When "High on a gorgeous seat . . . Great Cibber sate":

His Peers shine round him with reflected grace,
New edge their dulness, and new bronze their face.
So from the Sun's broad beam, in shallow urns
Heav'ns twinkling Sparks draw light,
                    and point their horns.

[153] "Pope and 'The Great Shew of Nature,'" in *Seventeenth Century*, p. 313.

Here is the "reflected" light of moon and planets, here too the phases of Venus in which Pope recalls Milton as well as Galileo.[154] The *Fourth Dunciad* opens with light growing ever less:

> Yet, yet a moment, one dim Ray of Light
> Indulge, dread Chaos, and eternal Night!

The portent of the beginning of the end is again astronomical (ll. 9-16):

> Now flam'd the Dog-star's unpropitious ray,
> Smote ev'ry Brain, and wither'd ev'ry Bay;
> Sick was the Sun, the Owl forsook his bow'r,
> The moon-struck Prophet felt the madding hour:
> Then rose the Seed of Chaos, and of Night,
> To blot out Order, and extinguish Light,
> Of dull and venal a new World to mold,
> And bring Saturnian days of Lead and Gold.

When Dulness mounts her throne, "her head a Cloud conceal'd"; we have a memory of Milton's Satan on his return from Chaos, before another chaos was to occur. As we approach the dread climax, astronomical figures again appear: (ll. 627-40):

> In vain, in vain,—the all-composing Hour
> Resistless falls: The Muse obeys the Pow'r.
> She comes! she comes! the sable Throne behold
> Of *Night* Primaeval, and of *Chaos* old!
> Before her, *Fancy's* gilded clouds decay,
> And all its varying Rain-bows die away.
> *Wit* shoots in vain its momentary fires,
> The meteor drops, and in a flash expires.
> As one by one, at dread Medea's strain,
> The sick'ning stars fade off th' ethereal plain;
> As Argus' eyes by Hermes' wand opprest,

---

[154] Whiston said (*Astronomical Principles*, p. 16): "[Venus] most plainly thro' the Tellescope appears with Phases, and Horned like the Moon." Pope's passage is similar to Milton's (*Paradise Lost*, VII. 364-66) in that both poets use the figure of "urns."

Clos'd one by one to everlasting rest;
Thus at her felt approach, and secret might,
Art after *Art* goes out, and all is Night.

Color has disappeared and light is to follow. Symbolically, this may take us back to that happiest year of his youth when Pope had really discovered both, color in Jervas' studio, light through Whiston's lectures. The effect of astronomy on his mind was profound. He had already become familiar with some of Newton's theories in the *Opticks,* as his early charming prismatic figures show. The more complicated optical figures in his mature poetry may well have been the result of Whiston's expositions. Throughout his life Pope maintained the highest regard for Newton and his teaching. A passage in the *Essay on Man,* sometimes considered a criticism of Newton (II. 19-34) has frequently been misunderstood:

Go, wond'rous creature! mount where Science guides,
Go, measure earth, weigh air, and state the tides;
Instruct the planets in what orbs to run,
Correct old Time, and regulate the Sun . . .
Go, teach Eternal Wisdom how to rule—
Then drop into thyself, and be a fool!
    Superior beings, when of late they saw
A mortal Man unfold all Nature's law,
Admired such Wisdom in an earthly shape,
And shew'd a NEWTON as we shew an Ape.

The lines "indicated a specific irritation at the extremes of adulation to which the Newtonians were going in the years immediately following the death of their idol, when they had so adored him that Newton bade fair to ascend to the throne of Deity, displacing God Himself. It was not Newton, but the Newtonians, whom Pope castigated."[155] The limitations Pope implies in the succeeding lines are limitations of man, as man:

[155] Marjorie Nicolson, *Newton Demands the Muse* (Princeton: Princeton University Press, 1946), pp. 134-35.

Could he, whose rules the rapid Comet bind,
Describe or fix one movement of his Mind?
Who saw its fires here rise, and there descend,
Explain his own beginning, or his end?
Alas what wonder!

No human being could answer such questions. The limitation was Isaac Newton's because he was a man and not the God his followers would try to make him. At the death of the greatest thinker of the modern world, when poems poured profusely from the press, Pope had been content with a couplet, the finest of Newton's epitaphs:

Nature, and Nature's Laws lay hid in Night.
God said, *Let Newton be!* and All was *Light*.

Pope had not known Newton but he learned astronomy from a man who had been Newton's pupil and colleague, who became his successor, and who was at that time wholeheartedly devoted to a thinker clearly his idol. The aloofness and austerity of Newton disappear when we read of him in Whiston's earlier works, with their religious and emotional overtones.

The New Astronomy had evoked a response in many men of letters in the seventeenth century. We have seen that Pope's contemporaries, John Gay and John Hughes, who had probably attended Whiston's coffee-house lectures, had written astronomical poems shortly after that event.[156] Gay had been momentarily stimulated to lines on vastness and Space, but was also capable of poking mild fun at Whiston's enthusiasm, if our attribution of some of the Scrib-

---

[156] William Powell Jones, *The Rhetoric of Science: A Study of Scientific Ideas and Imagery in Eighteenth-Century English Poetry* (Berkeley and Los Angeles: University of California Press, 1966), pp. 90-92, discusses astronomical passages in Gay's *Rural Sports* and two of Hughes' poems. He mentions the year 1713 but naturally makes no association with the Whiston lectures, attributing Gay's meditation "to the general physico-theology of the *Spectator*." He adds: "Gay never wrote seriously about science after 1713, but Pope's ideas were later to triumph in *An Essay on Man*." See also, G.S. Rousseau, *PQ*, XLVI (1967), pp. 316-19.

lerian papers is valid. Pope's response to Whiston had been not only intellectual but deeply emotional—and this we think an important point. He found astronomy "romantic" in the sense in which we have found him using the word. Such arousal of emotions was responsible for the fact that when he was writing "romantically," he wrote only to women and momentarily exaggerated his own emotions, first toward Lady Mary, then toward Martha Blount. Indeed at this time he might have become a "Romantic" poet, laboring under new emotions he had never experienced before, had it not been that he set himself the task of translating the *Iliad*, which was to occupy him for several years. His treatment of Homer is not infrequently "romantic." There are elements of such feeling in his grottoes. In the later one we feel what might be called "scientific aesthetics," in the combination of mathematical design, the "geological museum," and the emphasis upon light and color. Insofar as his limited experience permitted, Pope transferred "the Aesthetics of the Infinite" to things in this world, irregular Nature, ruins, caves, grottoes. His enthrallment with Infinite Space and terrestrial Nature had an added dimension—an emotional dimension. George Berkeley may well have been correct in believing that if Pope could have travelled and seen the great variety of Nature, his would have been the "flowing numbers" and degree of "Imagination" to describe what Berkeley aptly called "romantic confusion." Yet the power and emotion of Pope's most majestic lines are all the more intense for their restraint within heroic couplets:

> Lo! thy dread Empire, CHAOS! is restor'd;
> Light dies before thy uncreating word:
> Thy hand, great Anarch! lets the curtain fall;
> And Universal Darkness buries All.

Part Four

Pope and Other Sciences

Pope and Other Sciences

I

The Old and the New

L IKE POETS of any period, Pope frequently used conventional figures that had become scientifically outdated by his time. Thus in "Spring. The First Pastoral," published in 1709, his shepherd sees on a bowl the seasons and the signs of the zodiac (ll. 37-40) :

> Four Figures rising from the Work appear,
> The various Seasons of the rowling Year;
> And what is That, which binds the Radiant Sky,
> Where twelve fair Signs in beauteous Order lye?

In *The Temple of Fame*, we hear (ll. 452-53) of omens that had long presaged the coming of disaster:

> Of Prodigies, and Portents seen in Air,
> Of Fires and Plagues, and Stars with blazing Hair.

Both these passages, it should be remembered, were not only early in the canon of Pope's works, but both appear in an imitation of Virgil on the one hand, Chaucer on the other, and each is entirely appropriate to its context. In *Windsor Forest* (1713), we find the old tradition of the elements in the original Chaos (ll. 11-16) :

> Here Hills and Vales, the Woodland and the Plain,
> Here Earth and Water seem to strive again,
> Not *Chaos*-like together crush'd and bruis'd,
> But as the World, harmoniously confus'd;
> Where Order in Variety we see,
> And where, tho' all things differ, all agree.

Again the context justifies any apparent anachronism, since Pope had just been memorializing the "Groves of Eden" in *Paradise Lost,* and was aware that Milton, with many of his generation, took for granted that at the Word of God the warring elements had settled into harmony. Later lines in the same poem (241-44) introduce other traditional beliefs, scientifically outmoded by the time Pope wrote the words. "Happy the Man," he had been saying, who among other pleasures

> gathers Health from Herbs the Forest yields,
> And of their fragrant Physick spoils the Fields:
> With Chymic Art exalts the Min'ral Pow'rs,
> And draws the Aromatick Souls of Flow'rs.

These lines, too, appear in an adaptation of Virgil's and Horace's praise of country retirement, and indeed were actually by no means antiquated in Pope's own day. Many of the medicinal potions Pope used in his long struggle with illness were herbal recipes, prescribed even by doctors of the newer schools of medicine. The kind of alchemy implied in the second couplet was still practiced by some of Pope's intelligent contemporaries.[1]

To suggest that the youthful Pope was out of step with the science of his day because he used traditional conventions would be as absurd as to attempt to prove that he was, like some of his slightly later contemporaries, basically a "scientific poet," because he could introduce in the same casual manner allusions to the discoveries or theories of Boyle, Hooke, or Newton, as indeed he did in exactly the same early poems. In *Windsor Forest* (ll. 333-34) "Old Father Thames" is reminiscent of mythology with his "shining Horns," but in the next line we are conscious of the effect of the moon on tidal ebb and flow, "the Moon, that guides His swelling Waters, and alternate Tydes." In the

---

[1] In comparison with, for example, Dryden, there is surprisingly little alchemical reference anywhere in Pope's prose or poetry. James Sutherland in his edition of *The Dunciad,* p. 150, suggests that one such reference in *Dunciad A,* III. 10-11, "the golden Dream . . . the Chymist's flame," may be to Steele's unlucky ventures into alchemy.

Temple of Fame (line 431) Pope refers to the magnetized needle of a compass, attracted by the lodestone, "And the touch'd Needle trembles to the Pole."[2] A few lines further, developing a figure of circles resulting from the dropping of a stone into a lake, Pope uses an analogy that went back ultimately to Boyle's and Hooke's discoveries of the nature of "fluid air" and the conveyance of sound:[3]

> Thus ev'ry Voice and Sound, when first *they break*
> *On neighb'ring Air a soft Impression make*;
> Another ambient Circle then they move,
> That, in its turn, impels the next above;
> *Thro undulating Air the Sounds are sent,*
> And spread o'er all the fluid Element.

Any thoughtful reader of the canon of Pope's works becomes aware that he is a deliberately repetitive poet. We see instances of his picking up a couplet or quatrain from an earlier work and embedding it in a different context in a work of his maturity. This is not merely because he jealously refused to let a good couplet remain in limbo. It is chiefly that, as he developed, the significance of an early phrase or line developed with him. An excellent example of this may be seen by comparing the somewhat verbose passage already quoted from *Windsor Forest* on the conflict of the elements in original Chaos with his masterly succinct expression of the same theme in the first Epistle of *An Essay on Man*[4] (ll. 169-72) :

[2] Geoffrey Tillotson, *The Rape of the Lock and other Poems*, II. 284, points out that this line was taken almost verbatim from Dryden.

[3] Lines 442-47. (The italics are ours.) Tillotson, II. 445, p. 285n., quotes a Dryden analogue: "And as the Fountain still supplies her store, / The Wave behind impels the Wave before." Pope's sound analogy and vocabulary are more technical.

[4] The comparison is made by F.E.L. Priestley, "Pope and the Great Chain of Being," *Essays in English Literature: From the Renaissance to the Victorian Age* (Toronto: University of Toronto Press, 1964) , p. 227. Professor Priestley calls attention to the repetition of the idea of "strife." See also William Powell Jones, *The Rhetoric of Science* (Berkeley and Los Angeles: University of California Press, 1966) , pp. 139-43.

> But ALL subsists by elemental strife. . . .
> The gen'ral ORDER, since the whole began,
> Is kept in Nature, and is kept in Man.

A still more interesting example of the development of earlier lines into more scientific and much finer poetic expression may be found in the couplet in *An Essay on Man* (I. 199-200) : "Or quick effluvia darting thro' the brain,/ Die of a rose in aromatic pain?" Various critics since Edmund Gosse have suggested that Pope's source here was *The Spleen* of the Countess of Winchilsea, in which there are two couplets with rather similar implication. While the Countess may have contributed something, we suggest that Pope's original source was in Alexander Pope, again in lines that have been quoted: "With Chymic Art exalts the Min'ral Pow'rs, / And draws the Aromatick Souls of Flowers." In *Windsor Forest*, however, Pope associated "the Aromatick Souls of Flowers" with alchemy, "the Chymic Art." Sir Thomas Browne's "ghost of a Rose" in *The Garden of Cyrus* went back to a literary tradition at least as old as Pliny.[5] Pope's brilliant couplet was for many years associated with another literary tradition.[6] We agree with Samuel Monk that the Pope couplet is "scientific" in the best meaning of the word,[7] and that Pope drew the figure from Robert Boyle's "effluviums," corpuscles adapted by Boyle from Epicurean philosophy to atomic science. With characteristic modesty Mr. Monk developed only briefly his discovery that Pope had been impressed by accounts given by Boyle in his *Essays of the Strange Subtilty, Great Efficacy, and Determinate Nature of Effluviums*[8] of the effects of sensations aroused by the smell of flowers in causing faintness and sometimes convulsions in those who, as we would say today, are "allergic" to such sensations.

[5] *The Works of Sir Thomas Browne*, ed. Geoffrey Keynes (London and New York: Oxford University Press, 1929) , IV. 125.

[6] Gordon Keith Chalmers, "Effluvia, the History of a Metaphor," *PMLA*, LII (1937) , 1,050.

[7] "Die of a Rose," *Huntington Library Quarterly*, XXI (1958), 359-61.

[8] *The Works of the Honourable Robert Boyle*, ed. Thomas Birch (London, 1772) , III. 680-81. The *Essays* first appeared in 1673.

Most of all, Boyle added accounts of men and women who were overcome by the smell of roses. In his letters Pope occasionally played with figures of speech contrasting sweetness of odor, which might become cloying, and "stinks" that might or might not prove salutary correctives. On this theme he wrote Swift on December 14, 1725: "Praise is like Ambergrize; a little unexpected Whiff of it . . . is the most agreeable thing in the world; but when a whole lump of it is thrust to your nose, it is a Stink, and strikes you down." On at least two occasions, he versified the idea, in the *Epistle to Bathurst* (ll. 234-36) :

> As Poison heals, in just proportion us'd:
> In heaps, like Ambergrise, a stink it lies,
> But well-dispers'd, is Incense to the Skies;

and again in his *Imitation of Horace*, addressed to Hugh Bethel (ll. 29-30) :

> By what *Criterion* do ye eat, d'ye think,
> If this is priz'd for *sweetness*, that for *stink*?

Pope's "quick effluvia darting through the brain" are as technical as Boyle's effluviums, their effects only slightly more drastic than the states of some victims Robert Boyle had scientifically described.

II

The Small in Nature

No poet as late as Pope's generation needed technical training to teach him to coin figures from the very small in Nature. Perhaps some of Pope's persistent interest in "the poetry of little things" went back, in part at least, to his own smallness. He wrote his friend John Caryll on January 25, 1711,[9] early in their correspondence: " 'Tis certain the

[9] *Correspondence*, I. 114.

greatest magnifying glasses in the world are a mans own eyes, when they look upon his own person; yet even in those, I appear not the great Alexander Mr Caryll is so civil to, but that little Alexander the women laugh at." Many years later he wrote in the *Epistle to Cobham* (ll. 15-16) :

> There's some Peculiar in each leaf and grain,
> Some unmark'd fibre, or some varying vein.

But Pope's eyesight was such that he could rarely have detected for himself minute peculiarities in leaf or grain. Rather, he drew many of his reiterated figures for the small from traditions, familiar from the author of *Proverbs* down to Sir Thomas Browne, which said in effect: "What Reason may not go to school to the wisdom of Bees, Ants, and Spiders?" Pope's many insect references are largely to the nonmicroscopic. The earliest in "Phryne"[10] had to do with one of the seeming miracles of Nature that has always fascinated human beings, insect metamorphosis:

> So have I known those Insects fair,
> (Which curious *Germans* hold so rare,)
>   Still vary Shapes and Dyes;
> Still gain new Titles with new Forms;
> First Grubs obscene, then wriggling Worms,
>   Then painted Butterflies.

Lines on "equivocal generation" in *An Essay on Criticism*[11] go back at least as far as Ovid:

> Those half-learn'd Witlings, num'rous in our Isle,
> As half-form'd Insects on the Banks of *Nile*;
> Unfinish'd Things, one knows not what to call,
> Their Generation's so *equivocal*.

Read in their context, these lines, too—with the double play of meaning in "equivocal"—deal with metamorphosis, though devolutionary rather than evolutionary. They occur in a verse paragraph beginning:

10 In *Minor Poems*, VI. 50, lines 19-24.
11 Lines 40-43. See note, *Pastoral Poetry and An Essay on Criticism*, p. 243, for the Ovidian analogy.

Some have at first for *Wits*, then *Poets* past,
Turn'd *Criticks* next, and prov'd plain *Fools* at last.

The same idea is implied in *To a Lady*:[12]

So morning Insects that in muck begun,
Shine, buzz, and fly-blow in the setting-sun.

Few minor motifs are more reiterative in Pope's writing at various periods of his life than insects and maggots. He wrote to Caryll on August 14, 1713: "Who knows what plots, what achievements a mite may perform, in his kingdom of a grain of dust, within his life of some minutes?"[13] Complaining of the hot weather, he wrote Arbuthnot on July 11, 1714: "This is not a Time for us to make others live, when we can hardly live ourselves; so Scriblerus (contrary to other Maggotts) must lye dead all the Summer, & wait till Winter shall revive him."[14] Ironically enough, he used the figure, with very different undertones, in a letter to Hugh Bethel, February 20, 1744, three months before his death: "I live like an Insect, in hope of reviving with the Spring."[15]

Deft as he was, Pope could play upon this theme in many moods, laughing, satiric, serious. He overdid the figure in an early minor poem, "To Mr. John Moore,"[16] though he doubtless justified the exaggeration by his subtitle, "Author of the Celebrated Worm-Powder," since Moore was a notorious quack. Bookworms, glowworms, slowworms, muckworms, silkworms—they are all here in profusion. Particularly:

Man is a very Worm by Birth,
   Vile Reptile, weak, and vain!
A while he crawls upon the Earth,
   Then shrinks to Earth again. . . .
The Fops are painted Butterflies,
   That Flutter for a Day;

---

[12] *Epistles to Several Persons*, p. 52, ll. 27-28.
[13] *Correspondence*, I. 186.   [14] *Ibid.*, I. 233.
[15] *Ibid.*, IV. 499.   [16] *Minor Poems*, pp. 161-62.

First from a Worm they take their Rise,
And in a Worm decay.

In his major works, however, Pope handles the many insect-figures deftly and usually succinctly. Sometimes they emphasize the ephemeral:

Ye tinsel Insects! whom a Court maintains,
That counts your Beauties only by your Stains,
Spin all your Cobwebs o'er the Eye of Day!
The Muse's wing shall brush you all away.[17]

In an extended passage in *Dunciad I*[18] on stylistic matters, poems and plays emerge from an original Chaos, "Hints, like spawn, scarce quick in embryo lie," whimsical fancies like "Maggots half form'd in rhyme exactly meet, / And learn to crawl upon poetic feet." Largely Pope used insect figures to stress insignificance, particularly in man. In one instance in the *Epistle to Burlington*[19] memories of the relativity of small and great seem to have hovered in Pope's mind from *Gulliver's Travels*. The specious magnificence of Timon's Villa is introduced:

Greatness, with Timon, dwells in such a draught
As brings old Brobdingnag before your thought.

The true insignificance of the villa owner is emphasized by an insect-figure:

Who but must laugh, the Master when he sees,
A puny insect, shiv'ring at a breeze!

This couplet was wickedly rewritten by Lady Mary Wortley Montagu and Lord Hervey to describe Pope himself:

17 *Epilogue to the Satires, Dialogue II* in *Imitations of Horace*, p. 325, ll. 220-23. Cf. another such use, *Dunciad*, IV, ll. 421-23:
Of all th' enamel'd race, whose silvery wing
Waves to the tepid Zephyrs of the spring,
Or swims along the fluid atmosphere. . . .

18 Lines 53-82.
19 *Epistles to Several Persons*, p. 147, ll. 103-104. The couplet by Lady Mary is given, p. 148n.

> Who but must laugh, this Bully when he sees,
> A little Insect shiv'ring at a Breeze?

Lines on the small, familiar to most readers from *An Epistle to Dr. Arbuthnot,* were first published in 1727 in "A Fragment of a Satire":

> Pretty, in Amber to observe the forms
> Of Hairs, or Straws, or Dirt, or Grubs, or Worms:
> The *Thing,* we know, is neither rich nor rare,
> But wonder how the Devil it got there.

Based on a poem by William Dingley, "Upon a Bee Entom'd in Amber," this quatrain follows still another classical tradition.[20] A somewhat similar amber-figure had been used by Tacitus in the *Germania,* and Pliny in the *Natural History,* but Dingley's source—and hence Pope's—was Martial, *Epigrams,* IV. 32, a common schoolboy exercise throughout the seventeenth century.

No reader of Pope needs to be reminded of his most exquisite adaptation of the small in the Rosicrucian "machinery" of the revised *Rape of the Lock,*[21] with the "Denizens of Air," summoned by the Sylph: "Transparent Forms, too fine for mortal Sight, / Their fluid Bodies half dissolv'd in Light." Their minuteness is seen in the passage on punishments designed for those who broke the rules, who should

> Be stopt in *Vials,* or transfixt with *Pins;*
> Or plung'd in Lakes of bitter *Washes* lie,
> Or wedg'd whole Ages in a *Bodkin's* Eye. . . .
> Or Alom-*Stypticks* with contracting Power
> Shrink his thin Essence like a rivell'd Flower.

Pope did, however, introduce microscopical figures into both his prose and his poetry, although these too came to him less from personal observation than from literary tradi-

---

[20] *Minor Poems,* p. 284. See W. Lee Ustick and Hoyt H. Hudson, "Wit, 'Mixt Wit' and the Bee in Amber," *HLQ,* VIII (1935), 103-30.
[21] *The Rape of the Lock,* II. 61-62; 126-32.

247

tion.[22] Again, it is probable that Pope's eye problems
made it difficult if not impossible for him to observe at
first hand as did many of his immediate predecessors and
contemporaries. It is significant that on the one occasion on
which he referred to a real instrument it was his mother
rather than Pope himself who made the observation. Writing to John Caryll on February 18, 1718,[23] he mentioned a
"seasonable acquaintance" with "Mr. Hatton," a clock-
maker, who "is likewise curious in microscopes and showed
my mother some of the *semen masculinum*, with animascula
in it." Pope's most charming microscopical adaptations appear in "Verses on *Gulliver's Travels*," written in Scriblerian mood, and published by Swift in the second edition.[24]
In "The Words of the King of Brobdingnag, As he held
Captain Gulliver between his Finger and Thumb," Pope
followed in the train of various writers of the late seventeenth century when the microscopical fad was at its
height.[25]

> In Miniature see *Nature's* Power appear;
> Which wings the Sun-born Insects of the Air,
> Which frames the Harvest-bug, too small for Sight,
> And forms the Bones and Muscles of the Mite!

[22] See Marjorie Nicolson, *The Microscope and English Imagination*,
in *Science and Imagination* (Ithaca: Cornell University Press, 1956),
esp. pp. 170-82, for analogous passages and also passages on vermin.

[23] *Correspondence*, I. 465. Animalcules in semen had first been
observed by Antony von Leeuwenhoek, who reported his observations
to the Royal Society in November 1677. His Latin report was published in *Phil. Trans.*, XII, No. 142 (December-February 1677-78),
1,046 ff. Others of his reports appeared: *ibid.*, XIII, No. 145 (March
1683), 74-81; No. 152 (October 1683), 347-55.

[24] We are here accepting the attribution of these poems to Pope by
Norman Ault, in *Minor Poems*. See also "The 'Gulliver' Poems," in
New Light on Pope, pp. 231-42. Ault suggests the possibility that Gay
collaborated in "The Lamentation," but apart from that attributes all
five to Pope.

[25] *Minor Poems*, p. 280, ll. 1-8. The microscope for observing the
circulation of the blood had been developed in the late seventeenth
century, the most famous example extant today being the double
microscope of John Marshall, 1693. See R.T. Gunther, *Early Science
in Oxford* (Oxford: Printed for the Oxford Historical Society at the
Clarendon Press, 1923), I. 285-289 for description and illustration.

Here view him stretch'd. The Microscope explains,
That the Blood, circling, flows in human Veins:
See, in the Tube he pants, and sprawling lies,
Stretches his little Hands, and rolls his Eyes.

The "Sun-born Insects of the Air" momentarily recall the
passage in *The Rape of the Lock*, in which the sylphids
"to the Sun their Insect-Wings unfold." Like many others,
Pope not only recalls various insects, "too small for human
sight," but is aware that seventeenth-century microscopists
had demonstrated the circulation of blood in mites as well
as in men—and Gulliver here is both man and mite. Like
various predecessors, too, Pope used the microscope to point
a moral for over-proud human beings who think themselves
lords of the universe:

Fond of his Hillock Isle, his narrow Mind
Thinks Worth, Wit, Learning, to that Spot confin'd;
Thus Ants, who for a Grain employ their Cares,
Think all the Business of the Earth is theirs.
Thus Honey-combs seem Palaces to Bees;
And Mites imagine all the World a Cheese.

When Pride in such contemptuous Beings lies,
In Beetles, Britons, Bugs and Butterflies,
Shall we, like Reptiles, glory in Conceit?
Humility's the Virtue of the Great.[26]

In "The Lamentation of Glumdalclitch, for the Loss of
Grildrig," Pope follows a lengthy tradition of satire upon
virtuosi and demi-virtuosi who spent their lives collecting
minutiae and studying the most minute forms of life discovered by the microscope, such as "eels in vinegar." Satiric though it may be, there is something touching about
the lines of the lament in which Glumdalclitch remembers
how she had used such "eels" for the diversion of her tiny
charge, letting him fish in the vinegar-cruet she had prepared for his fish pond:[27]

[26] *Minor Poems*, pp. 280-81, ll. 25-34.
[27] Whether written by Pope or another Scriblerian, the "Verses on

"Was it for this (she cry'd) with daily Care
Within thy Reach I set the Vinegar?
And fill'd the Cruet with the Acid Tide,
While Pepper-Water-Worms thy Bait supply'd;
Where twin'd the Silver Eel around thy Hook,
And all the little Monsters of the Brook.
Sure in that Lake he dropt—My *Grilly's* drown'd"—
She dragg'd the Cruet, but no *Grildrig* found.

"The eye of a critick," Pope wrote as early as his *Thoughts on Various Subjects*,[28] "is often like a microscope, made so very fine and nice, that it discovers the atoms, grains, and minutest particles, without ever comprehending the whole, comparing the parts, or seeing all at once the harmony." He versified the sentence many years later in *The Dunciad*:

The critic Eye, that microscope of Wit,
Sees hairs and pores, examines bit by bit;
How parts relate to parts, or they to whole,
The body's harmony, the beaming soul,
Are things which Kuster, Burman, Wasse shall see,
When Man's whole frame is obvious to a *Flea*.

Pope's most familiar microscopical reference is, of course, in couplets in *An Essay on Man*:[29]

The bliss of Man (could Pride that blessing find)
Is not to act or think beyond mankind;
No pow'rs of body or of soul to share,
But what his nature and his state can bear.
Why has not Man a microscopic eye?
For this plain reason, Man is not a Fly.

Gulliver's Travels" bears out the "metaphor of the telescope" as a clue to the interpretation of the first two books, suggested by Des Fontaines and Walter Scott, and developed, with reference to both telescope and microscope, by Marjorie Nicolson, *Science and Imagination*, pp. 196-99.

28 Quoted by Sutherland in *The Dunciad*, pp. 365-66n. The lines quoted from *The Dunciad*, are IV. 233-38. On the proper names, in which two foreign and one British scholar are satirized, see Sutherland's note and the Biographical Appendix.

29 I. 189-96.

Say, what the use, were finer optics giv'n,
T' inspect a mite, not comprehend the heav'n?

In the great passage on the vast chain of being, a little later in the same epistle,[30] Pope brings together microscope and telescope:

> See, thro' this air, this ocean, and this earth,
> All matter quick, and bursting into birth.
> Above, how high progressive life may go!
> Around, how wide! how deep extend below!
> Vast chain of being, which from God began,
> Natures aethereal, human, angel, man,
> Beast, bird, fish, insect! what no eye can see,
> No glass can reach! from Infinite to thee,
> From thee to Nothing!

III
Grottoes and Geology

On New Year's Day 1742 Pope wrote Hugh Bethel about the *New Dunciad*, on which he was working: "Whenever I publish this poem, An Army of Virtuosi, Medalists, Ciceronis, Royal Society-men, Schools, Universities, even Florists, Free thinkers, & Free masons will incompass me with fury. It will be once more, *Concurrere Bellum atque Virum.*" Pope was evidently engaged upon two sections in the *Fourth Dunciad* in which "collectors" of various sorts were his targets. In the first (ll. 397ff.) :

> Then thick as Locusts black'ning all the ground,
> A tribe, with weeds and shells fantastic crown'd,
> Each with some wond'rous gift approach'd the Pow'r,
> A Nest, a Toad, a Fungus, or a Flow'r.

In a following scene (ll. 565-70) Her Majesty prepares to assign honors to members of her court:

[30] Lines 233-41.

Next bidding all draw near on bended knees,
The Queen confers her *Titles* and *Degrees*.
Her children first of more distinguish'd sort,
Who study Shakespeare at the Inns of Court,
Impale a Glow-worm, or Vertù profess,
Shine in the dignity of F.R.S.

Satire on "collectors" had been old when Pope was young, and by the period of *The New Dunciad* was stereotyped. The "Florists" might have had reason to resent the satiric descriptions of subjects who vied with each other to present to the Queen rare blossoms they had grown for her delectation, but other "collectors" were not treated as savagely as Pope's letter to Bethel would lead us to expect. The Royal Society, indeed, comes off lightly, since these are mere passing references to a once time-honored theme of satire. There is no such animus or bitterness here as there had been in Samuel Butler's reiterated satires on what had then been a new organization, struggling for life.[31] The third book of *Gulliver's Travels* had been a climax of satiric depiction of "Gresham College," in preparation for which Swift had used the *Philosophical Transactions* to advantage, even though Dr. Arbuthnot, like many later critics, considered the third book the least brilliant. By the 1740's the Royal Society was respected enough that Pope was wise to limit himself to passing remarks. Sir Nicholas Gimcrack, the "collector" par excellence, was forgotten now, even though Pope and others had earlier read his "Will" in the *Tatler*.[32]

[31] Butler's several satires on the Royal Society are discussed in Marjorie Nicolson, *Pepys' Diary and the New Science* (Charlottesville: The University Press of Virginia, 1965), pp. 139-57.

[32] In connection with these passages, James Sutherland, in his edition of *The Dunciad*, p. 398, refers to a *Tatler* satire in 1710, and includes only one other sentence of satire on the Royal Society from *The Champion*, April 29, 1740, where mention is made of "such as we generally say can hardly write or read, or in other Words, a Man *barely* qualified to be a Member of the R—— S——y." He adds: "At this period peers and gentlemen with little or no scientific knowledge were frequently elected to the Society." That had been true from the beginning and remained true down through the eighteenth century.

Pope's satire on virtuosi in *The New Dunciad* is not so drastic as it might have been had he introduced corresponding passages into the earlier Dunciads, when "collecting" might have seemed to him more a subject for satire than it had become in his mind by 1742. This was certainly at least in part the result of the fact that Pope was honest enough with himself to realize that he too had fallen under the virtuosi-spell and had himself become a "collector," as his note on "a wilderness of Moss" indicates: "Of which the Naturalists count I can't tell how many hundred." Mr. Sutherland adds here:[33] "In *A Plan of Mr. Pope's Garden*, [by] J. Searle, 1745, 'Moss of many sorts,' both living and petrified, is several times mentioned." The grotto which became Pope's major enthusiasm in the early 1740's changed radically from the one he had developed between 1722 and 1725.[34] Sometime during the intervening period, Pope had discovered the charm of geology.

Grottoes, caves, caverns were not new in either landscape gardening or poetry in the eighteenth century. Adapted from more exotic lands, they became at home in English landscaping in the sixteenth and seventeenth centuries, but around the turn of the eighteenth century, they were transformed. "In the 'grotto fad' that peppered English estates with artificial retreats, the new geology merged with old literary conventions to produce something that distinguishes eighteenth-century caves and caverns from those of their predecessors. Responding to Nature, they yearned for Art: responding to Art, they realized that Nature's caverns put their own to shame. If a 'grot' were natural, it must be im-

[33] *Dunciad*, p. 384n.

[34] Pope's grottoes have been discussed so frequently and competently that it would be a work of supererogation to attempt to repeat much of what has been said. See particularly Benjamin Boyce, "Mr. Pope, in Bath, Improves the Design of his Grotto," in *Restoration and Eighteenth-Century Literature: Essays in Honor of A.D. McKillop*, ed. Carol Camden (Chicago: University of Chicago Press, 1963), pp. 143-53; Richard D. Altick, "Mr. Pope Expands his Grotto," *PQ*, XXI (1942), 427-30; Frederick Bracher, "Pope's Grotto: the Maze of Fancy," *HLQ*, XII (1948-49), 141-62; Maynard Mack, "'The Shadowy Cave': Some Speculations on a Twickenham Grotto," *Restoration and Eighteenth-Century Literature*, pp. 69-88.

proved by Art; if artificial, it must seem to follow Nature."[35]

In his correspondence Pope first mentioned the earlier grotto in a letter to William Broome on July 9, 1722. He wrote to Judith Cowper on November 5, mentioning "my Solitude & Grotto," and added some lines of verse, beginning:[36]

> What are the falling rills, the pendant Shades,
> The morning Bow'rs, the Evening Colonnades?
> But soft Recesses for th' uneasy mind,
> To sigh un-heard in, to the passing Wind.

Three years later he wrote Edward Blount on June 2, 1725:[37] "I have put the last Hand to my works of this kind, in happily finishing the subterraneous Way and Grotto." On September 29 of that year, Swift wrote Pope: "I have been long told by Mr Ford of your great Atchivements in building and planting and especially of your Subterranean Passage to your Garden whereby you turned a blunder into a beauty, which is a piece of Ars Poetica."[38] In Pope's descriptions the earlier grotto, attractive though it may well have been, shows little trace of the interest in geology which strongly marks the later experiment. Behind that remarkably "scientific" grotto lay certain literary traditions that were being established in the eighteenth century as well as Pope's firsthand experience with the "secret places of the earth" in quarries and a growing knowledge of geology.

Pope's first poetic use of the idea that minerals, metals, and gems grow in earth by the influence of the sun's heat occurs as early as *Windsor Forest* (ll. 393-96) where it is involved with other conventional beliefs about natural processes:

[35] Marjorie Nicolson, *Mountain Gloom and Mountain Glory* (Ithaca: Cornell University Press, 1959), pp. 341-42. The following section treats the general theme.

[36] *Correspondence*, II. 125, 141-42.

[37] *Correspondence*, II. 296-97. This letter contains the fullest description of the early grotto. We shall discuss this later in "Color and Light."

[38] *Ibid.*, II. 324-27.

For me the Balm shall bleed, and Amber flow,
The Coral redden, and the Ruby glow,
The Pearly Shell its lucid Globe infold,
And *Phoebus* warm the ripening Ore to Gold.

This is, however, only a reference to a long accepted geological theory, and shows little stirring of the imagination.
A cluster of more extended figures on the subject in
Epistles to Several Persons may well make us consider
whether around the period 1733-35 Pope's imagination had
been stimulated by his reading to consider the theory
more curiously. We find it briefly in the *Epistle to a Lady*
(ll. 289-90) : "The gen'rous God, who Wit and Gold re-
fines, / And ripens Spirits as he ripens Mines." It is more
fully developed in the *Epistle to Bathurst* (ll. 7-12) where
it plays an integral part in developing the argument "Of
the Use of Riches":

> But I who think more highly of our kind,
> (And surely, Heav'n and I are of a mind)
> Opine, that Nature, as in duty bound,
> Deep hid the shining mischief under ground:
> But when by Man's audacious labour won,
> Flam'd forth this rival to, its Sire, the Sun,
> Then careful Heav'n supply'd two sorts of Men,
> To squander these, and those to hide agen.

The figure is best developed in the *Epistle to Cobham*
(ll. 93-103) :

> Court-virtues bear, like Gems, the highest rate,
> Born where Heav'n's influence scarce can penetrate:
> In life's low vale, the soil the virtues like,
> They please as Beauties, here as Wonders strike.
> Tho' the same Sun with all-diffusive rays
> Blush in the Rose, and in the Diamond blaze,
> We prize the stronger effort of his pow'r,
> And justly set the Gem above the Flow'r.

Pope also used the theme briefly in the fourth epistle of

An Essay on Man (IV. 7-10), published in 1734, the same period as the *Epistles*:

> Plant of celestial seed! if dropt below,
> Say, in what mortal soil thou deign'st to grow?
> Fair op'ning to some Court's propitious shine,
> Or deep with di'monds in the flaming mine?

Milton, Pope, Mallet, Thomson, together with many other poets, earlier and later, who repeated what was only gradually becoming a fallacy, could have found authority among reputable scientists, some of whom continued to posit the time-honored belief—going back at least to Aristotle—that minerals and precious stones grow in earth, whether from heat, petrific seeds, or other processes.[39]

During Pope's lifetime certain themes had been coming into literature of which he would have been well aware. The convention of a journey to the nether world, familiar since Homer and Virgil, had experienced a change during the seventeenth century. Robert Burton's descent into "the bowels of the earth" in the "Digression of Air"[40] had begun in time-honored fashion: "I would have a convenient place to go down with Orpheus, Ulysses, Hercules, Lucian's Menippus," but matters attracting the attention of his "long-winged hawk," as he descended from his celestial journey, were scientific rather than literary: "Do stones and metals grow there still?" Most of all, Burton's voyager was interested in fossils: how explain the fact that "fish bones, shells, beams, iron works" are found "many fathoms under ground?" The Scriblerians had turned their satire on some fossil collectors (notably Dr. John Woodward), but that was because Dr. Arbuthnot was as pas-

39 See Frank Dawson Adams, *The Birth and Development of the Geological Sciences* (Baltimore: The Johns Hopkins Press, 1938), Chap. IV, "On the 'Generation of Stones.'" Pope's editors are inclined to dismiss his figures as vulgar errors, but they were still widely accepted, even though Agricola and others had begun to establish new theories.
40 *Anatomy of Melancholy*, ed. Floyd Dell and Paul Jordan-Smith (New York: Farrar & Rinehart, 1927), pp. 412-13.

sionate a collector as was Woodward, on the opposite side in the long controversy about fossil origins. During the late seventeenth and early eighteenth centuries, the imaginary and the cosmic voyage usually included at least a section on "the bowels of the earth," raising geological problems. The Grand Tour of earth and cosmos on which Shaftesbury's Theocles led his pupil, Philocles, in *The Moralists*, is the most familiar example.[41] In imagination Philocles enters into earth's entrails:

> Here, led by curiosity, we find minerals of different natures which, by their simplicity, discover no less of the divine art than the most compounded of nature's works. Some are found capable of surprising changes; others as durable, and hard to be destroyed or changed by fire, or utmost art. So various are the subjects of our contemplation, that even the study of these inglorious parts of nature in the nether world is able itself alone to yield large matter and employment for the busiest spirits of men, who in the labour of these experiments can willingly consume their lives.

The conversion of Philocles to "enthusiasm" is a result of his discovery of the principle of *irregularity* as an integral aspect of Nature:

> And Philocles, the cold indifferent Philocles, is become a pursuer of the same mysterious beauty.
> 'Tis true, said I, Theocles, I own it. Your genius, the genius of the place, and the Great Genius have at last prevailed. I shall no longer resist the passion growing in me for things of a natural kind, where neither art nor the conceit or caprice of man has spoiled their genuine order by breaking in upon that primitive state. Even the rude rocks, the mossy caverns, the irregular unwrought grottos and broken falls of waters, with all the horrid graces of the wilderness itself, as representing

[41] *The Moralists*, in *Characteristics of Men, Manners, Opinions, Times*, ed. John M. Robertson (Indianapolis, Bobbs-Merrill, 1964), II, 116, 125.

Nature more, will be the more engaging, and appear with a magnificence beyond the formal mockery of princely gardens.

Thomas Yalden had initiated a new kind of descriptive poetry in a poem written about 1698, "To Sir Humphry Mackworth,"[42] in which he turned the cosmic poem to new uses, capitalizing on growing popular interest in geology, and insisting that the mining regions of the British Isles were as legitimate themes for poetry as more familiar aspects of topography, long celebrated:

> Downward, my Muse, direct thy steepy flight,
> Where smiling shades and beauteous realms invite . . .
> Through dark retreats pursue the winding ore,
> Seek Nature's depth, and view her boundless store;
> The secret cause in tuneful measures sing,
> How metals first were fram'd, and whence they spring.

The two poets most responsible for establishing a "new" kind of nature poetry in the 1720's and 1730's were David Mallet and James Thomson, both of them among Pope's personal acquaintances. Pope's references to them in his letters begin around 1730. All three poets devoted some time and energy to trying to help Richard Savage help himself. Pope's messages to Thomson do not suggest intimacy, but as time went on David Mallet became one of Pope's closest friends, one of the confidants to whom he unburdened himself, and, as we have seen, the person who has told us much of what we know of Pope's last illness and death. During the 1720's Mallet and Thomson worked closely together on their major poems, Mallet on *The Excursion*, published in 1728, and Thomson on the various descriptive poems which he published seriatim, and brought into the

42 In Alexander Chalmers, *Works of the English Poets* (London, 1810), XI, 74-75. On the general subject, see Robert A. Aubin, "Grottoes, Geology, and the Gothic Revival," *Studies in Philology*, XXI (1934), 408-16. Mr. Aubin developed some of this material in *Topographical Poetry in XVIIIth Century England* (New York: The Modern Language Association of America, 1936).

first collected edition of *The Seasons* in 1730. They shared a common theme: "a description of the grand works of Nature raised and animated by moral and sublime reflections." Therefore, as Thomson advised Mallet,[43] they "ought to leave no great scene unvisited. Eruptions, earthquakes, the sea wrought into a horrible tempest, the abyss amidst whose amazing prospects, how pleasing must be that of a deep valley covered with all the tender profusion of Spring." Mallet paid passing attention to the heat of the sun awakening minerals and metals in the bowels of the earth:[44]

> Fairest of beings! first-created light!
> Prime cause of beauty! for from thee alone,
> The sparkling gem, the vegetable race,
> The nobler worlds that live and breathe, their charms,
> The lovely hues peculiar to each tribe,
> From thy unfailing source of splendor draw!

His chief interest in "the secret places of the earth," however, was as a breeding place for storms, tempests, earthquakes, volcanic eruptions, all "fermenting in their womb, / Pregnant with fate."[45]

> And now, within the bosom of the globe,
> Where sulphur stor'd and nitre peaceful slept,
> For ages in their subterranean bed,
> Ferments th' approaching *tempest.*

Thomson, too, treated such themes:[46]

> The infuriate hill that shoots the pillared flame;
> And, roused within the subterranean world,
> The expanding earthquake, that resistless shakes
> Aspiring cities from their solid base,
> And buried mountains in their flaming gulf.

[43] Quoted by Peter Cunningham, "James Thomson and David Mallet," *Miscellanies of the Philobiblon Society* (1857-58), IV. 30. See also Alan Dugald McKillop, *The Backgrounds of Thomson's Seasons* (Minneapolis: University of Minnesota Press, 1942), p. 129.
[44] *The Works of David Mallet, Esq.* (London, 1759), I. 97.
[45] *Ibid.*, pp. 74, 84.   [46] "Summer," ll. 1096-1100.

As *The Seasons* grew under his hand, the scientific passages became more and more technical, as various studies of their genesis and development have shown. Thomson was reading widely in scientific literature, particularly in geology, and was quite capable of apposing two, three, or more scientific theories in the same passage, evidently trying to represent each one fairly. By the edition of 1744 some of these passages had inevitably become cumbersome because of their over-fidelity to scientific truth. But at his best he was surpassed by no other "scientific" poet. Of all poetic attempts at the resolution of light into colors and the return of colors to light—in an attempt at which, as we shall see, Pope had been a pioneer—Thomson's is the finest.[47] Deep in earth's entrails, the warmth engendered by the sun rouses the gems as light, reflected in the diamond, breaks into prismatic colors, passing through red, yellow, green, blue, purple, all gathered together in the "whitening opal" which reflects each one, then begins to return them to the white light from which they were derived.[48]

During the period Pope was enthusiastically developing his "geological" grotto, a group of his fellow poets were writing poetry in which geology played an important part. In 1743 the revised *Dunciad* appeared. In 1744-45 James Thomson published the expanded *Seasons*, Edward Young the *Night Thoughts*, Mark Akenside, *The Pleasures of Imagination*, all differing in various ways, but all showing a basic interest in science, all dealing, to some extent, with geological themes:

> ... search, undismay'd, the dark profound
> Where nature works in secret; view the beds
> Of min'ral treasure, and th' eternal vault
> That bounds the hoary ocean ...
> .... behold the seeds
> Of being, and the energy of life
> Kindling the mass with ever-active flame.[49]

[47] "Summer," ll. 140-59.
[48] See Nicolson, *Newton Demands the Muse,* ed. cit., Chap. II, for other examples of this technique.
[49] Akenside, *The Pleasures of Imagination* (London, 1744), I. 512-19.

Professor Benjamin Boyce, in his study on the grotto to which we have referred in a note, shows that Pope's visit to Bristol and Bath toward the end of 1739 had a profound effect on him, and marks the real beginning of the change in grotto planning. He spent a long period of time on the estate of Ralph Allen, where Allen was then building a Palladian mansion of white stone cut in Allen's quarries on Combe Down, not far from Allen's home. Boyce writes:[50] "A guest for two months in the house of a man whose quarries supplied stone in large amounts to Bath, Bristol, and London, Pope probably would have come to know something about the strata of rock under the surface of the hills around him. Perhaps during this visit he had a look into a quarry; at any rate a few months later he felt able to describe the pillars in his grotto as being "like supporters left in a Quarry" rather than architectural columns. Eventually he must have learned about the crevices in the limestone in Allen's quarries where water ran and stalactites formed. Some of the stones, a visitor reported, were "like the jaspar-agate of Saxony; and some of the stalactites are mixed with the fine particles of the spar and the free stone, some of the strata of the former shoot like crystals and these the workmen call cockles, and are very beautiful for grottos."

Very important for an understanding of the change occurring in Pope's imagination was his acquaintance with Dr. William Oliver, one of the most prominent physicians at Bath, and particularly his introduction of Pope—by correspondence at least—to a kinsman of Oliver's, the Reverend William Borlase, whose *Natural History of Cornwall* was a monument to Cornish geology. Borlase considered himself an amateur, and as an amateur he is usually described, but the Royal Society of London published at least eighteen of his scientific articles in the *Philosophical Transactions*, and elected Borlase to membership in 1750.[51]

[50] "Mr. Pope, in Bath, Improves the Design of his Grotto," ed. cit., pp. 144-45.

[51] This fact is not mentioned by Professor Boyce nor other writers on

In his letter introducing Pope—whose writing Borlase already seemed to have known and greatly admired—Dr. Oliver asked Borlase to arrange for shipment to Pope of "three or four Tun, of the finest Spar, Mendick, Copper and Tin Ore," packed in hogsheads for delivery at Twickenham, and added the explanation: "He has a Mind to make this Passage a beautiful Grotto, adorn'd with all the Several Productions of Nature, which are properly to be found under ground. I must therefore beg of you that you will let our Country have the honour to contribute all it can to the Beauty of this Grotto, where the greatest Geniuses of this Age will often contemplate, and admire the Riches of our native Soil."[52]

Borlase apparently wrote Pope immediately but addressed him at Twickenham. The forwarded letter he had received when he breakfasted with Dr. Oliver at Bath on January 11, 1740,[53] when Oliver showed Pope his own letters from Borlase, together with Borlase's "Account of the Growth of Cornish Crystals." These he had observed during a difficult and dangerous descent into a small cave near the tin mines. Pope found the account so interesting that he seems to have made off with it in his pocket. Through Oliver Pope sent Borlase a "Sketch of his Grotto," where he desired "to place all the Minerals in their several natural Strata."

On his return to Twickenham, Pope wrote Dr. Oliver on February 25[54] a mock-heroic letter (supposedly in reply

---

the subject we have noticed. The first article is a lengthy "Enquiry into the original State and Properties of Spar, and Sparry Productions, particularly, the Spars, or Crystals found in the Cornish Mines, called Cornish Diamonds," *Phil. Trans.*, XLVI (1749), 250-77. This complements and supplements the letters quoted by Mr. Boyce, and also his extracts from the *Quarterly Review*, Vol. 139 (1875), 250-77, 291-303. The *Phil. Trans.* report is based on Borlase's firsthand account of his experience in a mine, and parallels the account Oliver showed Pope.

[52] Mr. Boyce ("Mr. Pope, in Bath," pp. 146-47) quotes from the *Borlase Correspondence* in the Penzance Library.

[53] *Ibid.*, pp 147-48. Borlase's letter to Pope at Twickenham is evidently not extant, since it does not appear in the *Correspondence*.

[54] *Correspondence*, IV. 227.

to a love letter from an unknown lady sent by Oliver), in which he reported the demise of Alexander Pope who had so languished after his return from Bath that "a sudden paralytic took away, first his Verse, & after his Prose side. . . ." He concluded: "Since his Burial (at Twitnam) he has been seen sometimes in Mines and Caverns & been very troublesome to those who dig Marbles & Minerals." The shipment commissioned by Oliver arrived at Twickenham on the morning of March 9, 1740, when, as Pope wrote Borlase, he found that his "bounty, like that of Nature, confounds all choice."[55] Since Pope had been urged by both Oliver and Borlase to request other shipments, he wrote to Borlase: "But as I would imitate rather her Variety, than make Ostentation of what we call her Riches; I shall be satisfy'd if you make your next Cargo consist more of such Ores or Sparrs as are beautiful, & not too difficult to be come at, than of the Scarce & valuable kinds. Indeed the 2 or 300 of Cubes of Mundick which you mention, might find a place luminous enough in one part of my Grotto, and are much the finest Ornaments it can receive. It will want nothing to complete it, but Your Instruction as to the Position, and the Direction of the Sparrs & Ores in the Mine, for I would be glad to make the Place resemble Nature in all her workings, & entertain a Sensible, as well as dazzle a Gazing, Spectator. The Stalactites are appropriated to the roof, & the Marbles (I think) of various colors to the pavement."

At least one other lavish shipment arrived at Twickenham, as a result of which Pope wrote Borlase on June 8,[56] fearing that Borlase had robbed his own collections to enrich Pope's. He sent Borlase an account of his progress: "[The grotto] is now half finished, the ruder parts entirely so; in its present condition it is quite natural, and can only admit of more beauties by the Glitter of more minerals, not the disposition or manner of placing them, with which I am quite satisfy'd. I have managed the Roof so

[55] *Correspondence.* IV. 228-29.
[56] *Ibid.,* IV. 245-46. We omit here a section which will be treated later.

as to admit of the larger as well as smaller pendulous [crystals]; the sides are strata of various, beautiful, but rude Marbles, between which run the Loads of Metal, East and West, and in the pavement also, the direction of the Grotto happening to lie so. . . . [I] have stellifyed some of the Roof with Bristol stone of a fine lustre. I am in hopes of some of the Red transparent Spar from the Lead mines, which would vastly vary the colouring. . . . I wish it were glittering tho' not curious; as equally proper in such an Imitation of Nature, who is not so Profuse as you, tho' ever most kind to those who cultivate her."

During the years 1740-42 Pope's letters are filled with references to his grotto, with request for and acknowledgments of contributions of his friends. On one occasion he ordered six tons of minerals from Allen's estate; on another he acknowledged receipt of a hogshead of scallop shells from Judge Fortescue.[57] One of the contributions he most appreciated was a specimen of stone from the Giant's Causeway, sent him by the great collector, Sir Hans Sloane, whom he thanked on March 30, 1742[58] for "furnishing my Grotto with that surprizing Natural Curiosity" and eagerly hoping that there might be something he could in return offer Sloane "among the Minerals and Fossiles which I have gathered." One phrase frequently used in letters of this period is "my Mine" or "my Mine adventure," for his grotto. The reader will already have noticed the extent to which Pope insists that in his arrangement of the minerals underground he is imitating Nature, the most reiterated phrase of the period. He sent a message to Mrs. Allen, who also had begun to plan a grotto on the Allen estate: "I rejoice extraordinarily that Mrs Allen has begun to imitate the Great Works of Nature, rather than those Bawbles most Ladies affect."[59] His comments to his many friends are subsumed in a letter to Bolingbroke, September 3, 1740, at the beginning of the new venture: "Next to patching up my Constitution, my great Business has been to patch up a Grotto

<hr>

[57] *Correspondence*, IV. 253, IV. 356.
[58] *Ibid.*, IV. 391.
[59] *Ibid.*, IV. 254.

(the same You have so often sate in the Sunny part of under my house,) with all the varieties of Natures works under ground—Spars Minerals & Marbles. I hope yet to live to philosophize with You in this Musaeum, which is now a Study for Virtuosi, & a Scene for contemplation. . . ."[60]

> Thou, who shalt stop, where Thames translucent wave
> Shines a broad Mirror thro' the Shadowy Cave;
> Where lingering drops from Mineral Rocks distill,
> And pointed Crystalls break the sparkling Rill;
> Unpolished Gems no Ray on Pride bestow,
> And latent Metals innocently glow.
> Approach! Great Nature studiously behold.
> And Eye the Mine without a wish for Gold.

Pope has come a long way since those early Scriblerian days of satire on virtuosi and collectors. In his landscape gardening, he is consciously following a Nature marked by variety, diversity, irregularity, which nevertheless is based on natural law. He is at one with Shaftesbury's Philocles, with Mallet and Thomson, with Akenside and Young, in the fascination of the "secret parts of Nature." In his youth, Pope's cosmic imagination had been released and expanded by his study of astronomy. Close to the end of his life, like Burton's "long-winged hawk," his imagination swooped down "to descend & see, what is done in the bowels of the earth." Alexander Pope had discovered the charm of geology which led him to a scientific study of orderly processes within the earth and a greater aesthetic appreciation of Nature than he had felt before.

[60] *Ibid.*, IV. 260-62.

IV
Color and Light

Two modern critics of Pope have dealt in some detail with his poetic use of color and light.[61] Norman Ault believed that Pope was "the first of our poets to explore the possibilities of colour composition in poetry, and the first whose verses might often be called a gallery of pictures in colour." One need not agree entirely with Mr. Ault's interpretation of his statistics of the use of color among poets earlier than and contemporary with Pope, yet there is no question that "Mr Alexander Pope: Painter" is illuminating in its emphasis on Pope's innate love of color and the extent to which his study of painting under Charles Jervas in 1713-14 aided in his poetical use of it. Professor Maynard Mack calls Pope "perhaps the acutest observer of effects of light among the English poets." "Pope's eye," he says, "loved light, and was capable of the most delicate discernments with respect to it." Mr. Mack does not enter into similarities between Milton and Pope in their susceptibility to light, probably inevitable in the case of the poet who became blind and the other who had some reason to fear the same fate. Such physiological and psychological factors do not entirely account for those "delicate discernments" Mack subtly analyzes: "His poems know the difference between effulgence and refulgence; between the 'mild Lustre' of spring mornings and the peculiarly 'Purple Light' of autumn sunsets; between the 'glitter' of ice, the 'Gleam' of

[61] Norman Ault, "Mr Alexander Pope: Painter," in *New Light on Pope* (London: Methuen, 1949), Chap. V, particularly pp. 76-78, 82-100; Maynard Mack, "The Shadowy Cave: Some Speculations on a Twickenham Grotto," in *Restoration and Eighteenth-Century Literature: Essays in Honor of A.D. McKillop* (Chicago: University of Chicago Press, 1963), particularly pp. 74-75. Jean Hagstrum also makes some study of Pope's use of color, in *The Sister Arts: The Tradition of Literary Pictorialism and English Poetry from Dryden to Gray* (Chicago: University of Chicago Press, 1958), esp. Chap. VIII.

water, the flame and 'blaze' of diamonds, the 'shine' of fruits, the 'glow' of flowers. They know how armor 'beams' in lamplight, 'flashes' in firelight. They know how moonlight on foliage yields a yellow radiance, on stone a silver."

If Mr. Ault had continued his statistics of the use of color by poets into the period after 1727, he would have found a much higher proportion of color allusion than among the earlier poets, the result of a new consciousness of both light and color, thanks to the interest aroused in Newton's *Opticks* after his death in 1727. Among some of the poets writing in and after that year, the interest in light was particularly—sometimes preeminently—"Newtonian." We make no such assertion about Pope, even though many of his light and color figures, particularly in his earlier years, were obviously affected by Newton's prism. We do suggest that, added to what Ault calls his "innate love" of color, was a conscious interest in the refraction of light into colors and the return of colors to light, probably enhanced by his experience in Jervas' studio where his eye was trained in close observation of color and light and his hand in attempting to transfer them to canvas. Pope's interest in Newton's spectrum began earlier than his period of study with Jervas, presumably sometime between 1709 and 1711.[62]

Whether Pope had read Newton's *Opticks*, published in 1704, before he coined his first Newtonian figures cannot be determined. His early references are to the simple fact that the prism refracts light into colors and that colors return to light, which he could have picked up in casual conversation, perhaps at a coffee-house. Yet, on the other

[62] There is some overlapping here with Marjorie Nicolson's *Newton Demands the Muse*, although the treatment of Pope here is more extensive and intensive than in that study. Professor Mack does not specifically discuss Newton in his article, but after the passage quoted in the text, he goes on to say of Pope's eyes: "They know the telescope and microscope, the mirror and prism: how the obliquity of the latter can break a ray of light; how the reflections in a mirror may falsify reality or discover it; and how with the right kind of instruments, optical, dioptrical, and catoptrical, one may so manipulate a beam that it enlarges, multiplies, contracts, inverts, to say nothing of coloring, with 'ten thousand dyes' all that we see."

267

hand, the fact that his are the first "Newtonian" figures
we have found in English poetry, preceding most of the
others by many years, poses an interesting problem. Pope
had not yet become a Scriblerian, so that his interest was
not aroused by Dr. Arbuthnot, as it might have been a little
later. Arbuthnot was a fellow member with Newton in the
Royal Society,[63] and had known the principles of the
Opticks even before the work was published. Pope might
have learned of the theories from Addison who had heard
of them as early as his continental visit to Malebranche in
1700, and alluded to them in the *Spectator*, even though
he wrote no one essay about them. Before Pope coined the
more technical figures based on the *Opticks*, he had come
in contact with William Whiston, who instructed his students in the principles of the *Principia*, and may well have
added the simpler ones of the *Opticks*.

During the period of his early uses of prismatic color
and light, Pope reported Swift's adaptation to his own
purposes of Newton's description of observations he had
begun to make as early as his student days in Cambridge,
when he had first installed a prism in his window: "In a
very dark Chamber, at a round Hole, about a third Part of
an Inch broad, made in the Shut of a Window, I placed a
Glass Prism, whereby the Beam of the Sun's Light, which
came in at that Hole, might be refracted upwards toward
the opposite Wall of the Chamber, and there form a
colour'd Image of the Sun."[64] Newton's prism had become
a burning-glass when, writing to Dr. Arbuthnot on July
11, 1714,[65] Pope told of a visit to Swift, and mentioned
among the activities of "the Deane": "As for the methods
of passing his time, I must tell you one which constantly
employs an hour about noone. He has in his window an

[63] On Arbuthnot and Newton see Lester M. Beattie, *John Arbuthnot:
Mathematician and Satirist* (Cambridge: Harvard University Press,
1935), pp. 7-20 and *passim*.

[64] *Opticks: Or A Treatise of the Reflections, Refractions, Inflections
and Colours of Light*, ed. I. Bernard Cohen (New York: Dover Publications, 1952), Prop. II, Theor. II, p. 26.

[65] *Correspondence*, I. 234.

Orbicular Glass, which by Contraction of the Solar Beams into a proper Focus, doth burn, singe, or speckle white, or printed Paper, in curious little Holes, or various figures."

Pope's first lines on Newtonian light and color, which seem to be the earliest in English poetry, are in *An Essay on Criticism*, published in 1711, though much of it was written earlier. In lines 311-17 we find specific reference to the prism:

> *False Eloquence,* like the *Prismatic Glass,*
> Its gawdy Colours spreads on *ev'ry place;*
> The Face of Nature we no more Survey,
> All glares *alike,* without *Distinction* gay:
> But true *Expression,* like th' unchanging *Sun,*
> *Clears,* and *improves* whate'er it shines upon,
> It *gilds* all Objects, but it *alters* none.

Later in the poem (ll. 488-89), describing the process of artistic composition, Pope contrasts with a later period the moment of creation, when a new world leaps out at the poet's command:[66] "When the ripe Colours *soften* and *unite,* / And sweetly *melt* into just Shade and Light." As Donne, in another context, learned that "[Love's] first moment, after noone, is night," so Pope discovered that after the "mellowing Years their full Perfection give," "The *treach'rous Colours* the fair Art betray, / And all the bright Creation fades away!" (ll. 492-93). Another passage in *An Essay on Criticism* shows Pope struggling for a figure of light, and, according to the story told by the manuscript, having his problems with it. As finally printed, the lines (470-73) read:

> When first that Sun too powerful Beams displays,
> It draws up Vapours which obscure its Rays;
> But ev'n those Clouds at last adorn its Way,
> Reflect new Glories, and augment the Day.

[66] Cf. "Epistle to Mr. Jervas" (published 1716) in *Minor Poems,* VI. 156: "Like friendly colours found them both unite, / And each from each contract new strength and light."

Before he arrived at these,[67] Pope had gone through at least two stages, first making the passage more involved by the introduction of a figure on the sun's eclipse, then temporarily settling for

> *Wit*, as the *Sun*, such pow'rful Beams displays,
> It draws up Vapours that obscure its Rays;
> And all those *Clouds* that did at first invade
> The *rising Light*, and interpos'd a Shade,
> When once transpierc'd with its prevailing Ray;
> *Reflect* its *Glories*, and augment the Day.

Pope's one youthful attempt at a resolution of light into the primary colors and their fusion in the rainbow may possibly have served as pattern for a technique that became increasingly popular among poets of dedicatory poems that followed Newton's death. Pope's is not yet so deft as later passages written by James Thomson, particularly his expert refraction of light into colors and resolution of colors into light, mentioned in another connection.[68] Pope's much earlier passage may well have been in Thomson's memory when he wrote the lines in "Summer." Pope would seem to have been a pioneer in the light/color passage in *The Temple of Fame* (ll. 248-57), which had no analogue in the Chaucerian verses he was translating:

> Full in the midst, proud *Fame's* Imperial Seat
> With Jewels blaz'd, magnificently great;
> The vivid Em'ralds there revive the Eye;
> The flaming Rubies shew their sanguine Dye;
> Bright azure Rays from lively Saphirs stream,
> And lucid Amber casts a Golden Gleam.

[67] See Robert M. Schmitz, *Pope's Essay on Criticism* (St. Louis: Washington University Press, 1962), pp. 62-65, for variant readings in the manuscript, and p. 12 for comment on the cancelled lines. We quote the earlier version because Pope here, as so often, seems working for a contrast between light and shade.

[68] Cf. also the color-light figures in Thomson's "To the Memory of Sir Isaac Newton." Other examples of the fusion of Newtonian light and color by Thomson and other poets may be found in *Newton Demands the Muse*, Chap. II.

Here are the primary red, yellow, green and blue. In the following lines, light and colors are combined, then fused in the rainbow:[69]

> With various-colour'd Light the Pavement shone,
> And all on fire appear'd the glowing Throne;
> The Dome's high Arch reflects the mingled Blaze,
> And forms a Rainbow of alternate Rays.

Much more subtle and charming is Pope's adaptation of prismatic color and light in the second version of *The Rape of the Lock* (1714). When the Sylph summons his "Denizens of the Air," we are conscious now of prismatic light, again of color (II. 59-68):

> Some to the Sun their Insect-Wings unfold,
> Waft on the Breeze, or sink in Clouds of Gold.
> Transparent Forms, too fine for mortal Sight,
> Their fluid Bodies half dissolv'd in Light.
> Loose to the Wind their airy Garments flew,
> Thin glitt'ring textures of the filmy Dew;
> Dipt in the richest Tincture of the Skies,
> Where Light disports in ever-mingling Dies,
> While ev'ry Beam new transient Colours flings,
> Colours that change whene'er they wave their Wings.

Among the "little people" called to defend Belinda are some whose natural habitat is far from earth. The colors they have temporarily acquired fall away on their return to the realms of ether (ll. 77-78):

> Some in the fields of purest *Æther* play,
> And bask and whiten in the Blaze of Day.

Still finer "in the key of white," as Norman Ault says, are lines on Nova Zembla, in *The Temple of Fame*, pub-

---

[69] Cf. in the same poem, ll. 132-34:

> The Wall in Lustre and Effect like Glass,
> Which o'er each Object casting various Dies,
> Enlarges some, and others multiplies.

The last line we shall find more fully developed in the *Epistle to Cobham*, ll. 27-28.

lished in 1715. Pope had been working on the lines in 1712, when he wrote John Caryll on December 21, telling him of his "ill state of health ever since the cold weather began." His spirits, he said, "like those in a thermometer mount and fall thro' my thin delicate contexture just as the temper of the air is more benign or inclement."[70] Then follows his account of the preparation he had been making for the Nova Zembla description: "The severity of the cold has turned my studies to those books, which treat of the descriptions of the Arctic regions, Lapland, Nova Zembla and Spitsberg; deserts of snow, seas of ice and frozen skies might administer some odd kind of shivering satisfaction (or as the vulgar have it cold comfort), in the comparison with my own case. This, I say, some people would imagine who are of opinion that the knowledge of others' sufferings alleviate our own: but I never could conceive this sorry and inhuman consolation, nor am one degree the less chill for all I read on these subjects." Pope went on to "put together several beautiful winter pieces of the poets, which have occurred to my memory on this occasion," quoting from Homer, Virgil, Milton, among others, and a couplet by Ambrose Philips:

> All hid in snow, in bright confusion lie,
> And with one dazling waste fatigue the eye.

The Nova Zembla lines (53-60) are "white light," nowhere refracted into color, suggesting the purity of ether and something of the remoteness and vastness of the cosmic system:

> So Zembla's Rocks (the beauteous Work of Frost)
> Rise white in Air, and glitter o'er the Coast;
> Pale Suns, unfelt, at distance roll away,
> And on th' impassive Ice the Lightnings play:

[70] *Correspondence*, I. 165-68. Geoffrey Tillotson in his edition of *The Rape of the Lock and Other Poems*, has added Appendix H, pp. 410-11, in which he suggests possible books that Pope might have been reading.

Eternal Snows the growing Mass supply,
Till the bright Mountains prop th' incumbent Sky:
As *Atlas* fix'd, each hoary Pile appears,
The gather'd Winter of a thousand Years.

An important transition from Pope's earlier figures of light and color to those of his maturity may be found by study of light and color in his translation of Homer. "It seems to have been generally agreed," wrote Norman Ault in "Mr Alexander Pope: Painter,"[71] "that, although Homer excels in descriptions of the various effects of light and darkness, colour-suggestion is not one of the more striking features of his verse. Indeed, some scholars in the past have not hesitated to assert that his epics are lacking in that particular quality; and others have actually called him colour-blind." Neither time nor space permits us to study in detail Pope's translations of Homer's numerous light passages. We content ourselves with only one, famous in Homer, famous in Pope, the great description of night at the end of Book VIII,[72] which Ault called a "moonlight sonata, in the key of blue, in which azure is no sooner sounded than the key is changed with a burst of stars to that of gold, from which the colour-music modulates slowly through yellow and silver back to blue again." Pope himself commented in his translation of the passage: "It is the most beautiful night-piece that can be found in poetry. He presents you with a prospect of the heavens, the seas, and the earth: the stars shine, the air is serene, the world enlightened, and the moon mounted in glory." Pope's translation is, we believe, the finest that has been made:

[71] Ault, *Light on Pope*, p. 92. In the following pages Ault gives several illustrations of Pope's "numerous arbitrary additions of colour to his translation, which the painter-poet seems to have thought necessary to render the old Greek story attractive to his contemporaries."

[72] *The Iliad of Homer, Translated by Alexander Pope, Esq.*, ed. Gilbert Wakefield (London, 1806), II. 470-73; VIII. 685-708. Vols. VII-X of the Twickenham Edition of Pope's *Translations of Homer*, ed. Maynard Mack et al. (London: Methuen, New Haven: Yale University Press, 1967), appeared after our manuscript had gone to press.

The troops exulting sat in order round,
And beaming fires illumin'd all the ground.
As when the moon, refulgent lamp of night!
O'er heav'n's clear azure spreads her sacred light,
When not a breath disturbs the deep serene,
And not a cloud o'ercasts the solemn scene;
Around her throne the vivid planets roll,
And stars unnumber'd gild the glowing pole,
O'er the dark trees a yellower verdure shed,
And tip with silver ev'ry mountain's head;
Then shine the vales, the rocks in prospect rise,
A flood of glory bursts from all the skies:
The conscious swains, rejoicing in the sight,
Eye the blue vault, and bless the useful light.
So many flames before proud Ilion blaze,
And lighten glimm'ring Xanthus with their rays:
The long reflections of the distant fires
Gleam on the walls, and tremble on the spires.
A thousand piles the dusky horrours gild,
And shoot a shady lustre o'er the field.
Full fifty guards each flaming pile attend,
Whose umber'd arms, by fits, thick flashes send,
Loud neigh the coursers o'er their heaps of corn,
And ardent warriors wait the rising morn.[73]

For Pope's introduction of color into Homeric lines, we limit ourselves to what may broadly be called "astronomical" passages. Here a curious fact emerges: into all but one of these Pope introduces one color, and that the primary color, red. With all his deftness at color-shading, Pope does not vary the monosyllabic "red" to other shades of scarlet. Perhaps a passage from Pope's "Preface" to his translation affords one clue:[74]

[73] See G.S. Rousseau, "Seven Types of *Iliad*," *English Miscellany: A Symposium of History, Literature and the Arts*, ed. Mario Praz, XVI (Rome: The British Council, 1965), 143-67, for a comparison of seven translations of the passage.

[74] *Ed. cit.*, I. v-ix. In a study of some two dozen light-passages, we noticed that Pope never lost an opportunity to emphasize in his translation Homeric fire images or figures.

It is to the strength of this amazing invention we are to attribute that unequaled fire and rapture, which is so forcible in Homer, that no man of a true poetical spirit is master of himself while he reads him. What he writes, is of the most animated nature imaginable; every thing moves, every thing lives, and is put in action. . . . The course of his verses resembles that of the army he describes. . . . *They pour along like a fire that sweeps the whole earth before it.* . . . Exact disposition, just thought, correct elocution, polished numbers, may have been found in a thousand; but this poetical fire, this *Vivida vis animi,* in a very few. . . . Nay, where this appears . . . it brightens all the rubbish about it, till we see nothing but its own splendor. This *Fire* is discerned in Virgil, but discerned as through a glass, reflected from Homer, more shining than fierce, but every where equal and constant: In Lucan and Statius, it bursts out in sudden, short, and interrupted flashes: in Milton it glows like a furnace kept up to an uncommon ardor by the force of art: in Shakespear, it strikes before we are aware, like an accidental fire from heaven: but in Homer, and in him only, it burns every where clearly, and every where irresistibly.

Pope is, of course, using "fire" in a broad sense, yet no one who studies his translation can fail to realize how greatly impressed he was with Homer's use of fire in a more literal sense and how carefully he worked over translations of such passages. In a recent study, Professor Cedric H. Whitman,[75] discusses the extraordinary range of observation shown in Homer's images, some occurring only once, others recurring frequently, often in groups. "Only one," he writes, "stretches from beginning to end of the *Iliad,* reflecting the progress of the main action. This is the image of fire." In one form or another, he finds, fire occurs about two hundred times in the *Iliad,* of which "only ten can

[75] *Homer and the Heroic Tradition* (Cambridge: Harvard University Press, 1958), Chap. VIII, "Fire and Other Elements." The passage quoted and paraphrased here is on p. 129.

really be said to be casual uses, unconnected with the main scheme. For the rest, fire itself, or comparisons of things to fire, forms a remarkable pattern of associations, all centering around the theme of heroic passion and death."

To some extent Pope's desire to carry over into his translation the fire he found everywhere in the *Iliad* may be in part responsible for the reiteration of red, not in the original.[76] Book XI, for example, which contains a number of such similes, begins at sunrise (ll. 5-7) :

> When baleful Eris, sent by Jove's command,
> The torch of discord blazing in her hand,
> *Thro' the red skies her bloody sign extends.*

In the original the goddess of discord bore in her hand only "a portent of war." In the same book (XI. 69-70), translating a passage in which thunder is not mentioned, Pope imagines that

> Ev'n Jove, whose thunder spoke his wrath, distill'd
> *Red drops of blood* o'er all the fatal field.

A few lines later (XI. 81-88), in a passage otherwise filled with light, the Homeric "baneful star" becomes red:

> Great Hector, cover'd with his spacious shield,
> Plies all the troops, and orders all the field.
> *As the red star now shows his sanguine fires*
> Thro' the dark clouds, and now in night retires;
> Thus thro' the ranks appear'd the god-like man,
> Plung'd in the rear, or blazing in the van;
> While streamy sparkles, restless as he flies,
> Flash from his arms as light'ning from the skies.

And yet again, when the goddess of Discord appears (XI. 99-102), she is associated with the redness of blood, not suggested in the original:

> Discord with joy the scene of death descries,
> And drinks large slaughter at her *sanguine eyes:*

[76] In the quoted passages, the italics are ours.

Discord alone, of all the immortal train,
Swells the red horrors of this direful plain.

Such "red" adaptations of Homer can be found throughout
Pope's translation, but we shall content ourselves with these
few examples which form a cluster in Book XI.

On several occasions Pope heightens the ominous impression of the original by changing Homer's "star" to a comet.
Gilbert Wakefield to the contrary notwithstanding (as we
shall see presently) Homer never used the word "comet";
if we may trust modern lexicons, *kometes* was not in the
Homeric vocabulary. In Book IV (ll. 434-35) Pope radically changed a passage which in the original implied only
that Zeus showed tokens of ill:

> While dreadful comets glaring from afar
> Forewarn'd the horrours of the Theban war.

This is the only one of the astronomical passages in which
red does not appear. It is found, however, in another
comet-passage in Book IV, lines 99-108:

> Fir'd with the charge, she [Minerva] headlong urg'd
> her flight,
> And shot like lightning from Olympus' height.
> As the *red comet*, from Saturnius sent
> To fright the nations with a dire portent,
> (A fatal sign to armies on the plain,
> Or trembling sailors on the wintry main)
> With sweeping glories glides along in air,
> And shakes the sparkles from its blazing hair:
> Between both armies thus in open sight.
> Shot the bright Goddess in a trail of light.

In his annotation of these lines Gilbert Wakefield wrote:
"Homer says literally: 'Just like a comet, Jove Saturnian
sends,' "[77] though Homer says no such thing.

Because of its warlike connotations, the planet Mars was
of course red in popular parlance. Antares, the brightest

[77] *The Iliad of Homer*, ed. cit., II. 78n.

star in Scorpio, at the heart of the constellation, is still described by modern astronomers as a red star. It was not, however, known to Homer nor to other classical Greeks. According to the Liddell-Scott-Jones lexicon, it was first mentioned in the *Almagest* of Ptolemy. Since little of the constellation Scorpio is visible from Britain, Antares seems never to have played such a part in English literature as did another star—no longer recognized as red by astronomy, but predominantly red in classical literature and so frequently mentioned by Pope. He seems to have found the Dog Star Sirius, in Canis Major, the most forbidding and foreboding of all the signs in the heavens. It was the brightest of all stars, which rose as summer settled into autumn, bringing with it not only sultry weather but disease and pestilence. Throughout his life Pope accepted the traditional theory of the effect of the Dog Star on human beings. In September 1737 he wrote his friend Hugh Bethel: "I beg you will continue to acquaint me of the State of your health . . . and more especially at this [time], when the Autumn is extremely sickly, & great numbers die of sudden Fevers."[78] Sirius was a star with which Homer was familiar. A recent historian of astronomy writes: "Homer mentions some stars by name; in the *Iliad* he speaks of the Evening Star and the Morning Star, the Pleiades, Orion, the Great Bear, and 'the star which rises in the late summer . . . which is called among men Orion's Dog [i.e., Sirius]; bright it shines forth, yet it is a baleful sign, for it brings to suffering mortals much fiery heat' (*Iliad*, XXII. 26-31) ."[79] Sirius, too, in Pope's translation, is associated with the ominous red. On two occasions the Dog Star figure is used of Achilles. When he assumed the helmet Hephaestus had made (XIX. 412-15) it gleamed:

> *Like the red star*, that from his flaming hair
> Shakes down diseases, pestilence and war;

[78] *Correspondence*, IV. 86.
[79] A. Pannekoek, *A History of Astronomy* (New York: Interscience Publishers, 1961) , p. 95.

So stream'd the golden honours from his head,
Trembl'd the sparkling plumes,
                                   and the loose glories shed.

Most ominous was the use of the figure in Book XXII (ll.
35-43) when Priam, filled with dread, watched Achilles
making toward his son:

Him, as he blazing shot across the field,
The careful eyes of Priam first beheld.
Not half so dreadful rises to the sight
Through the thick gloom of some tempestuous night
Orion's dog (the year when autumn weighs)
And o'er the feebler stars exerts his rays;
Terrific glory! for his burning breath
Taints the red air with fevers, plagues, and death.
So flam'd his fiery mail.

In an earlier Sirius passage in which a warrior is described in terms of cosmic light imagery, we may find another clue to Pope's handling of such passages. At the beginning of Book V (ll. 5-14) , Diomedes is described:

High on his helm celestial lightnings play,
His beamy shield emits a living ray;
Th' unwearied blaze incessant streams supplies,
Like the red star that fires th' autumnal skies,
When fresh he rears his radiant orb to sight,
And bath'd in Ocean, shoots a keener light.
Such glories Pallas on the chief bestow'd,
Such, from his arms, the fierce effulgence flow'd:
Onward she drives him, furious to engage,
Where the fight burns, and where the thickest rage.

Here, as Gilbert Wakefield noted in his edition of Pope's
translation,[80] Pope had probably been influenced by Virgil's
imitation of this passage, in which Wakefield felt that Virgil
had surpassed his original. "In Homer's comparison," he

[80] Ed. cit., II. 157n.

said, "there is no other circumstance alluded to but that of remarkable brightness; whereas Virgil's comparison, besides this, seems to foretel the immense slaughter his hero was to make, by comparing him first to a comet, which is vulgarly imagined a prognostic, if not the real cause, of much misery to mankind; and again to the dog-star, which appearing with the greatest brightness in the latter end of summer, is supposed the occasion of all the distempers of that sickly season." Not only did Virgil make Homer's star into a comet, but he added the association of blood-red in "si quando nocte cometae / Sanguinei lugubre rubent." Curiously enough, Pope omitted Virgil's comet, devoting his attention solely to Sirius, but here, as elsewhere, he seems to have remembered "Sanguinei lugubre rubent."

The Dog Star appears elsewhere in Pope's poetical works. In his very early poetry he introduced it into "Summer" in the *Pastorals* (ll. 19-21) :

> The bleating Sheep with my Complaints agree,
> They parch'd with Heat, and I inflam'd by thee.
> The sultry *Sirius* burns the thirsty Plains.

Its introduction into *An Epistle to Dr. Arbuthnot* (ll. 3-6) is in satirical vein as Pope describes his pursuit by would-be poets:

> The Dog-star rages! nay, 'tis past a doubt,
> All *Bedlam*, or *Parnassus*, is let out:
> Fire in each eye, and Papers in each hand,
> They rave, recite, and madden round the land.

The rising of Sirius caused not only sickness but also madness, as, again in satiric mood, Pope suggested to Hugh Bethel a little later, in the letter in which he expressed concern for Bethel's health at this particular season. During his recent visit to Bath, he tells Bethel, he had read in newspapers of an "Epidemic Distemper," and could not guess what it was, unless, he adds cynically, "it were Madness, of which, in my return, I found three Doctors lockd up at Oxford, three old sober Women at Reding, and many young & old in Town. You may be sure there can be no such thing at Hampton Court, but at Twitenham I see many Symptoms, & grievous ones of it, & all about my Neighborhood."[81]

Pope's most somber satiric use of Sirius is in the Prologue to the *Fourth Dunciad* (ll. 9-14) where it marks the beginning of the end:

> Now flam'd the Dog-star's unpropitious ray,
> Smote ev'ry Brain, and wither'd ev'ry Bay;
> Sick was the Sun, the Owl forsook his bow'r,
> The moon-struck Prophet felt the madding hour:
> Then rose the Seed of Chaos, and of Night,
> To blot out Order, and extinguish Light.

Warburton's note on these lines[82] suggests the combination in Pope's imagination of the ominous conjunction of cosmic signs presaging the end of the world:

> The Poet introduceth this, (as all great events are supposed by sage Historians to be preceded) by an *Eclipse of the Sun*; but with a peculiar propriety, as the Sun is the *Emblem* of that intellectual light which dies before the face of Dulness. Very apposite likewise is it to make this *Eclipse*, which is occasioned by the *Moon's predominancy*, the very time when *Dulness* and *Madness* are in *Conjunction*; whose relation and influence on each other the poet hath shewn in many places.

"To blot out Order, and extinguish Light"—but light was not to be extinguished for Pope until close to the end of his life. One of the most charming uses he made of it can be seen in his earlier grotto. The fullest account is the one Pope wrote to Edward Blount on June 2, 1725[83] of "the subterraneous Way and Grotto": "I there found a Spring of the clearest Water, which falls in a perpetual Rill, that echoes thro' the Cavern day and night. From the River *Thames*, you see thro' my Arch up a Walk of the Wilder-

[81] *Correspondence*, IV. 86.   [82] *Dunciad*, p. 340n.
[83] *Correspondence*, II. 296-97.

281

ness to a kind of open Temple, wholly compos'd of Shells in the Rustic Manner; and from that distance under the Temple you look down thro' a sloping Arcade of Trees, and see the Sails on the River passing suddenly and vanishing, as thro' a Perspective Glass. When you shut the Doors of this Grotto, it becomes on the instant, from a luminous Room, a *Camera obscura*; on the Walls of which all the objects of the River, Hills, Woods, and Boats, are forming a moving Picture in their visible Radiations: And when you have a mind to light it up, it affords you a very different Scene: it is finished with Shells interspersed with Pieces of Looking-glass in angular forms; and in the Cieling is a Star of the same Material, at which when a Lamp (of an orbicular Figure of thin Alabaster) is hung in the Middle, a thousand pointed Rays glitter and are reflected over the Place."

Various aspects of the earlier, as well as the later grotto, as we have said, have been studied by critics, but little has been said of Pope's analogies with a "Perspective Glass" and the *camera obscura*. We have seen in "Pope and Astronomy" that the poet knew more about telescopes than most amateurs, and may have used them under Whiston's direction, particularly at the time of the total solar eclipse of 1716. Observation of large aspects of Nature would probably have proved more possible for his eyesight than microscopic minutiae. The only "perspective" aspects of the passing scene he mentions are the ships appearing and vanishing on the Thames. The fact that he uses "as" implies that this is merely figurative. But the allusion to a *camera obscura* for a time raised in our minds a question whether Pope had actually installed such an instrument in the door of his grotto chamber. We have concluded, however, that the effects of the *camera obscura* he wished to produce could have been obtained by the slit in the door which is indicated in Pope's own sketch of the grotto and that of his gardener, John Searle.

How far back in human history the principle of the *camera obscura* had been known, no one can tell. In Pope's time its invention was probably still attributed to Giambattista della Porta who had popularized it in the sixteenth century. Before Porta's birth, however, an account of it had been published by Vitruvius in 1521, and Leon Battista Alberti, the artist, had used something of the kind in an exhibition in 1437. It is entirely possible that Roger Bacon had used such a device, and, indeed, some modern historians find the principle as early as Euclid. One of the most familiar seventeenth-century descriptions was in a letter written by Sir Henry Wotton to Francis Bacon in 1620,[84] describing Kepler's camera, "a little black tent . . . which he can suddenly set up where he will . . . exactly close and dark." John Locke's famous "closet-simile" was based on the principle of the *camera obscura*: "Methinks the understanding is not much unlike a closet wholly shut from light, with only some little opening left, to let in external visible resemblances, or ideas of things without: would the pictures coming into a dark room but stay there, and lie so orderly as to be found upon occasion, it would very much resemble the understanding of a man, in reference to all objects of sight, and the ideas of them."[85]

The *camera obscura* had become increasingly familiar during the early eighteenth century. In one of the essays on "The Pleasures of the Imagination,"[86] Addison had described a scene not unlike that Pope saw on the walls of his grotto room: "The prettiest Landskip I ever saw, was one drawn on the Walls of a dark Room, which stood opposite on one side to a navigable River, and on the other to a Park." A chief reason for the charm of such a scene, he added, was that "it does not only, like other Pictures, give the Colour and Figure, but the Motion of the Things it represents." Pope's friend John Gay had used the analogy of the *camera obscura* in "The Fan," describing the miniature scenes inscribed on a lady's fan:

[84] *Life and Letters of Sir Henry Wotton*, ed. Logan Pearsall Smith, (Oxford: Clarendon Press, 1907) , II. 205-206.
[85] *Essay Concerning Humane Understanding*, Book II, Chap. XI, Sec. 17.
[86] *Spectator*, No. 414.

Thus have I seen woods, hills, and dales appear,
Flocks graze the plains, birds wing the silent air
In darken'd rooms, where light can only pass
Through the small circle of a convex glass;
On the white sheet the moving figures rise,
The forest waves, clouds float along the skies.

Many painters made use of the *camera obscura* and some
taught its use to students. Wotton described Kepler's "draft
of a landscape on a piece of paper, methought masterly
done," although Kepler had said that he had made the
draft "non tanquam pictor, sed tanquam mathematicus."
According to Walter Harte's "Essay on Painting,"[87] the
eighteenth-century painter Vandervaart made use of the
instrument:

So Vandervaart in later times excell'd,
And nature liv'd in what our eyes beheld.
He too can oft (in optics deeply read)
A noon-day darkness o'er his chamber spread:
The transient objects sudden as they pass
O'er the small convex of the visual glass,
Transferr'd from thence by magic's pow'rful call,
Shine in quick glories on the gloomy wall;
Groves, mountains, rivers, men surprise the sight,
Trembles the dancing world, and swims the wavy light.

It would be interesting to know where Charles Jervas stood
on the use of the instrument for students of art. Conceivably in his studio Pope might first have become well
acquainted with the *camera obscura*. Whether or not this
was the case, the charm of the small, the small made
large—such the eighteenth century found in various optical instruments that had become increasingly familiar.[88]

[87] Chalmers, *Works of the English Poets*, ed. cit., XVI. 323.
[88] The most extensive treatment of the instrument we have found is
a set of anonymous verses in the British Museum entitled "Verses,
Occasion'd by the Sight of a Chamera Obscura," printed at London
in 1747 for an optical instrument maker. Had these verses appeared
a little earlier Pope might have been interested in them. In early
days, says the poet, the "miracles" of this "creative Glass" so amazed

By means of the *camera obscura* the world outside was reflected on their walls, the outlines clear and sharp, the colors true, and, best of all, the pictures were in motion with all the charm and variety of Nature herself.

So far as we can tell from Pope's descriptions, the *camera obscura* illusion had disappeared from the more extensive and elaborate grotto he developed in the early 1740's. "I have opened the whole into one Room," he wrote William Borlase,[89] "groin'd above from pillar to pillar . . . by which means there is a fuller Light cast into all but the narrow passage." Some semblance of the original remained, since behind the two largest pillars was a deep recess of stone, "where two Glasses artfully fix'd reflect the Thames . . . almost deceive the Eye to that degree as to seem two arches opening to the River on each side." One earlier device remained in the enlarged grotto, the orbicular alabaster lamp, like a star in the ceiling. From it, even in the earlier days, "a thousand pointed Rays glitter." How much more it must have glittered in a grotto now ornamented with "Stalactites above, and Spars and Cornish Diamonds on the Edges."

Pope's use of figures reflecting the *Opticks* continued in

---

beholders that Friar Bacon, because of his extraordinary skill in optics, was tried as a conjurer. But now that the Augustans have become familiar with the once magical instrument, the poet continues, all men find it delightful:

  Come; lead us to thy Chamber; there unfold
Thy secret Charms, delightful to behold;
How little is thy Cell? How dark the Room?
Disclose thine Eye-lid, and dispel this Gloom!
That radiant Orb reveal'd, smooth, pure, polite;
In darts a sudden Blaze of beaming Light,
And stains the clear white Sheet, with Colours strong and bright;
Exterior Objects painting on the Scroll,
True as the Eye presents 'em to the Soul;
A New Creation! deckt with ev'ry Grace!
Form'd by thy Pencil, in a Moment's Space!
As in a Nutshell, curious to behold;
Great *Homer's Iliad* was inscrib'd of old;
So the wide World's vast Volume, here, we see
To Miniature reduc'd, and just Epitome.

89 *Correspondence*, IV. 246.

the period of his maturity. Sometimes these were simple light/color comparisons, like those in the early poetry, as when he wrote to Aaron Hill, presumably in September 1726:[90] "The Eye of Candour, like the Sun, makes all the Beauties which it sees; it gives Colour and Brightness to the meanest Objects purely by looking on them." Largely, however, the mature figures are more complex, and involve different implications. Like some of the professed Newtonian poets, Pope sometimes used color pejoratively. He could speak of "gawdy Colours . . . without distinction gay"; "treach'rous Colours"; manners that "come discolour'd thro' our Passions," and various others. In such passages, "discolored" color is contrasted with the light of the empyrean, the pure light of Reason. The denigration of color implied in the *Epistle to a Lady*[91] is less a contrast between color and light than old themes of transience and fickleness:

> If Folly grows romantic, I must paint it.
>   Come then, the colours and the ground prepare!
> Dip in the Rainbow, trick her off in Air. . . .
>   Ladies, like variegated Tulips, show,
> 'Tis to their Changes that their charms they owe. . . .
> Some wand'ring touch, or some reflected light,
> Some flying stroke alone can hit 'em right:
> For how should equal Colours do the knack?
> Chameleons who can paint in white and black?

A cluster of Pope's mature figures of color and light appear in the *Epistle to Cobham*, published in 1734. These are more technical than the youthful color-light figures and involve other Newtonian ideas in addition to the prismatic interplay of light and colors. One, already quoted in connection with the belief that precious stones grow in the earth by virtue of the sun's rays, includes the lines (97-98) : "Tho' the same Sun with all-diffusive rays / Blush in the

90 *Ibid.*, II. 404-405.
91 *Epistles to Several Persons*, ll. 16-18, 41-42, 153-56. Jean Hagstrum, *The Sister Arts*, pp. 236-41, analyzes these passages in detail.

Rose, and in the Diamond blaze." Newton had had much
to say of vision and of causes of "imperfect," "confused,"
and "weak" vision. Since Alexander Pope had more reason
than most poets to be conscious of imperfections of vision,
it is not strange that he used "imperfect vision" twice in
the *Epistle to Cobham*, once in connection with the "dream
psychology" standard in the age:[92]

> As the last image of that troubled heap,
> When Sense subsides, and Fancy sports in sleep,
> (Tho' past the recollection of the thought)
> Becomes the stuff of which our dream is wrought:
> Something as dim to our internal view,
> Is thus, perhaps, the cause of most we do.
> True, some are open, and to all men known;
> Others so very close, they're hid from none;
> (So Darkness strikes the sense no less than Light).

In another passage,[93] Pope combined several current tech-
nicalities of optics and vision in lines on "confused" or "in-
distinct" vision:

> Add Nature's, Custom's, Reason's, Passion's strife,
> And all Opinion's colours cast on life.
>   Yet more; the diff'rence is as great between
> The optics seeing, as the objects seen.
> All Manners take a tincture from our own,
> Or come discolour'd thro' our Passions shown.
> Or Fancy's beam enlarges, multiplies,
> Contracts, inverts, and gives ten thousand dyes.

In the third book of *An Essay on Man*, thinking back
primitivistically to the days of the Patriarchs, when Life
was simpler and truth clearer, Pope wrote (III. 229-32):

[92] We quote the passage as it appeared in the earlier version, ll.
45-53. Later Pope transposed the last three lines to another context,
in which they became ll. 110-13. On the connotations of the passage,
see *Newton Demands the Muse*, pp. 94-99.

[93] Lines 21-28. Cf. with the last couplet early lines in *The Temple
of Fame*, 132-34; see note 9 above.

The worker from the work distinct was known,
And simple Reason never sought but one:
Ere Wit oblique had broke that steddy light,
Man like his Maker, saw that all was right.

Professor Mack, in his edition of the poem,[94] quotes a
Baconian analogue to the third line. In the last couplet, his
ears catch echoes of Genesis I. 31, and the final couplet in
the first book of *An Essay on Man*:

And, spite of Pride, in erring Reason's spite,
One truth is clear, "Whatever IS, is RIGHT."

Our ears like to echo also Genesis I. 3-4, and the couplet
Pope had written in 1727:

Nature, and Nature's Laws lay hid in Night.
God said, *Let Newton be*! and all was *Light*.

Newton's interest in the "harmony" of color and sound
and the mathematical similarities he found between colors
and the chord became of great interest to poets after 1727.
Diagrams in the *Opticks* that could readily be understood
by laymen showed the proportional relationships between
the "seven Musical Tones or Intervals of the eight Sounds,"
and "seven colors, red, orange, yellow, green, blue, indigo,
violet." Again, with a diagram, he described similarities between certain color rings and the chord, and in the "Quaer-
ies" raised the question whether the harmony and discord
of colors arise from "the proportions of the Vibrations
propagated through the Fibres of the optick Nerves into
the Brain, as the harmony and discord of Sounds arise from
the proportions of the Vibrations of the Air?"[95] Norman
Ault suggests Pope's consciousness of such interrelations of
harmony in color and sound during the period of the development of his color technique,[96] though he draws no analogy with Newtonian theories: "It is perhaps also worth re-
marking of these contributions of Pope's that—for one

[94] Pp. 115-16n.   [95] *Opticks*, ed. cit., pp. 154, 212, 346.
[96] *New Light on Pope*, p. 93.

288

reader at least—after encountering several groups of them in the text, they begin to take on a curious extra-literary character; and instead of remaining a chance series of colour-notes, on being thus struck arpeggio-wise in consecutive lines, they assume a collective individuality like a chord of music."

During the 1730's color begins to disappear from Pope's poetry, only occasionally to be recaptured. Ault puts it:[97] "With social satire and moral philosophy filling his mind and requiring of colour nothing but a few sombre tints ('Sense' now taking the place of 'pure Description'), the poet to all intents and purposes shut up his old paint-box." In the four epistles of *An Essay on Man*, color is practically nonexistent. One couplet alone (II. 283-84) is devoted to color imagery: "Mean-while Opinion gilds with varying rays / Those painted clouds that beautify our days." The few color words in the poem are simple, indicating no shading, no combining: "argent fields" (I. 41); "green myriads" (I. 210); "the tainted green" (I. 214); "golden year" (III. 39); "gilded wings" (III. 55); "trees with ruddier burdens" (III. 203). There are numerous light words and phrases in the *Essay*, although these are largely conventional epithets for aspects of Nature: "burning suns" (I. 142); "glows in the stars" (I. 272); "meteor-like, flame lawless thro' the void" (II. 65); "Heav'n's blest beam" (II. 148); "light'ning's blaze" (III. 249); "deep with di'monds in the flaming mine" (IV. 10); "not dazzled with their noon-tide ray" (IV. 305); "Earth smiles around" (IV. 371). In Epistle II occur in fairly close succession passages in which we are conscious of light-dark tension:[98]

The lights and shades, whose well accorded strife
Gives all the strength and colour of our life. . . .

[97] *Ibid.*, p. 99. According to Ault's statistics (p. 100), in the *Epistles*, 1731-35, there is one color word to every 55 lines of text; in *An Essay on Man*, 1733-34, only one to every 76 lines of text.

[98] II. 121-22, 203-208, 213-14. Professor Mack in his Twickenham Edition of the *Essay* has annotated some of these lines in connection with Augustan theories of painting, others against their philosophical background.

This light and darkness in our chaos join'd,
What shall divide? The God within the mind.
Extremes in Nature equal ends produce,
In Man they join to some mysterious use;
Tho' each by turns the other's bound invade,
As, in some well-wrought picture, light and shade. . . .
If white and black blend, soften, and unite
A thousand ways, is there no black or white?

Like many poets, Pope had always been interested in light-dark imagery and used it to express various moods. Sometimes darkness was welcome as relief from excessive light, as Pope, with his poor eyesight, was only too well aware. "There is an agreeable gloominess," he wrote John Caryll in February 1713,[99] "which instead of troubling, does but refresh and ease the mind, and has an effect upon it not unlike the relief a sudden cloud sometimes gives the eye, when it has been aching and too much distended with the glaring of a summer's day." In a different mood he wrote Caryll later,[100] commenting that "half the things that employ our heads . . . are all but so many shadow images and airy prospects, which arise to us but so much the livelier and more frequent as we are more overcast with the darkness, wrapt in the night, and disturbed with the fumes of human vanity." One of the many charms of descriptive passages in *Windsor Forest* lies in its contrasts between light and shade.

Only in *Eloisa to Abelard* did Pope in youth give any suggestion of the power of darkness he was to bring to its climax in *The Dunciad*, even though the details of the early poem are largely traditional, *Il Penseroso* beginning to deepen to Gothic romance. "Ever-musing Melancholy reigns" in the "deep solitudes and awful cells," in "grots and caverns shagg'd with horrid thorns," in "lone walls" and "darksom pines." Light flickers only occasionally over the "moss-grown domes," the "awful arches." The few light-

[99] *Correspondence*, I. 172.   [100] *Ibid.*, I. 236, July 13, 1714.

figures used by Eloisa are usually associated with Abelard. When she first met him (ll. 63-64),

> Those smiling eyes, attemp'ring ev'ry ray
> Shone sweetly lambent with celestial day.

When she took the vows forever separating the lovers, "the lamps grew pale." One of the few light passages in the poem occurs in connection with Eloisa's memories of Abelard (ll. 271-76):

> When from the Censer clouds of fragrance roll,
> And swelling organs lift the rising soul;
> One thought of thee puts all the pomp to flight,
> Priests, Tapers, Temples, swim before my sight:
> In seas of flame my plunging soul is drown'd,
> While Altars blaze, and Angels tremble round.

In another light passage, Eloisa visualizes the death of Abelard (ll. 339-42):

> In trance extatic may thy pangs be drown'd,
> Bright clouds descend, and Angels watch thee round,
> From opening skies may streaming glories shine,
> And Saints embrace thee with a love like mine.

The darkness of *Eloisa and Abelard* is, however, youthfully conventional in comparison with the sublimity of darkness in the *Fourth Dunciad*. "All *general* privations are great," Edmund Burke declared,[101] "because they are all terrible: *Vacuity, Darkness, Solitude,* and *Silence.*" Burke was writing after Pope's death, but his *Sublime and Beautiful*, long regarded as the standard text on the subject, had its roots in Addison, in Akenside and other poets contemporary with Pope, possibly in the *Fourth Dunciad* itself. To Addison and Thomson and Akenside, color was associated with beauty, light with the sublime. Akenside had written:[102]

---

[101] *Philosophical Enquiry into the Origin of our Ideas of the Sublime and Beautiful* (Philadelphia, 1806), Part II, Section vii. See *Newton Demands the Muse*, pp. 123-31 for some of the ideas implied in this section.

[102] *Pleasures of Imagination* (London, 1744), I. 447-49, II. 97-99.

in th' effusive warmth
Of colours mingling with a random blaze,
Doth beauty dwell . . . .
    shall I mention, where coelestial truth
Her awful light discloses, to effulge
A more majestic pomp on beauty's frame?

As light might produce sublimity, so the effect of darkness on an observer was not infrequently like that of excessive light. "Locke, in his *Essay,* had discussed both darkness and the effect of excessive light and, moreover, had quoted a letter from Newton, in which the great scientist had commented on his own experience in observing light which caused temporary blindness and almost cost him his sight."[103] Frequently though Thomson and Akenside versified the sublimity of light and darkness, neither ever expressed the theory so succinctly as did Pope: "So Darkness strikes the sense no less than Light." As early as *Peri Bathous* he had said: "It must always be remember'd that Darkness is an essential Quality of the Profound, or if there chance to be a Glimmering, it must be as Milton expresses it, *No Light but rather Darkness visible.*"[104] It is not by chance that the overtones to the great finale of the *Fourth Dunciad* are not Newtonian but Miltonic. The Queen of Dulness had taken her presumptuous place on the royal seat as, upon his return from Chaos to Pandemonium, Satan had ascended the high throne, his "fulgent head" concealed in a cloud. So Dulness (IV. 17-18) : "mounts the Throne: her Head a Cloud conceal'd, / In broad Effulgence all below reveal'd." Milton had hymned "Chaos and old Night," words which inaugurate the fourth book (IV. 1-4) and are reiterated toward the end:

Yet, yet a moment, one dim Ray of Light
Indulge, dread Chaos, and eternal Night!

103 *Newton Demands the Muse,* p. 116.
104 *The Art of Sinking in Poetry,* ed. E.L. Steeves (New York: Columbia University Press, 1952) , p. 51.

Of darkness visible so much be lent,
As half to shew, half veil the deep Intent.

In the *Fourth Dunciad*, color, light, and darkness play a highly symbolic part. We remember at the beginning of the poem the "clouded Majesty" in which "Dulness shone," where Pope made use of still another figure—that of fog— for "imperfect vision" (I. 65-84) :

There motley Images her fancy strike,
Figures illpair'd, and Similies unlike. . . .
All these, and more, the cloud-compelling Queen
Beholds thro' fogs, that magnify the scene.
She, tinsel'd o'er in robes of varying hues,
With self-applause her wild creation views;
Sees momentary monsters rise and fall,
And with her own fools-colours gilds them all.

The very few color figures in the fourth book sound superficially like those in early poetry, as does this one (IV. 411-12) :

Did Nature's pencil ever blend such rays,
Such vary'd light in one promiscuous blaze?

Read against its context, however, the lines prove sharply satirical:

Now prostrate! dead! behold that Caroline:
No Maid cries, charming! and no Youth, divine!
And lo the wretch! whose vile, whose insect lust
Lay'd this gay daughter of the Spring in dust.

At first glance another color-light figure seems as charming as the lines on the sylphids in *The Rape of the Lock* (IV. 537-40) :

On others Int'rest her gay liv'ry flings,
Int'rest, that waves on Party-colour'd wings:
Turn'd to the Sun, she casts a thousand dyes,
And, as she turns, the colours fall or rise.

293

But here, as in the few other color passages, our ears respond to overtones, in the acoustical sense of the word, to frequencies higher than the fundamental. As Pope intended, we are chiefly conscious of the double-play on "Party-colour'd" in a political sense.

Color disappears from the *Fourth Dunciad*, and we know that after the obliteration of color will come the extinction of light, since we heard in the beginning (IV. 13-14): "Then rose the Seed of Chaos, and of Night, / To blot out Order, and extinguish Light." Color and light have striven for existence, but (IV. 627-56):

> In vain, in vain, — the all-composing Hour
> Resistless falls: the Muse obeys the Pow'r.
> She comes! she comes! the sable Throne behold
> Of *Night* Primaeval, and of *Chaos* old!
> Before her, *Fancy's* gilded clouds decay,
> And all its varying Rain-bows die away.
> *Wit* shoots in vain its momentary fires,
> The meteor drops, and in a flash expires.
> As one by one, at dread Medea's strain,
> The sick'ning stars fade off th' ethereal plain;
> As Argus' eyes by Hermes' wand opprest,
> Clos'd one by one to everlasting rest;
> Thus at her felt approach, and secret might,
> *Art* after *Art* goes out, and all is Night.

As it was in the beginning, so in the end, "The earth was without form, and void; and darkness was upon the face of the deep."

Appendix
Dr. Thomas Thompson

Dr. Thomas Thompson

wo years after Pope's death, Dr. Thompson reached both fame and infamy in a violent controversy over blood-letting provoked by the fact that one of his patients, a well-known politician, Thomas Winnington, bled to death as a result of Thompson's venesection.[1] One of the many pamphlets about the Winnington case—in spite of its anti-Thompson bias—affords a few details about his early career:[2] a cocksure man, branding many members of the medical fraternity as *"Knave, Ignorant,* and *Avaritious,"* boasting his own *"Judgment* and *Integrity,"* he declared that he had "reformed *Physick* in the *West!* and that he would now do it in the *East!"* According to Dr. William Douglas, Thompson had protested the exorbitant fees of London physicians, offering his own services at reduced rates, "and Medicines for an *old Song,"* with the result of inducing "many to hold up their Hands in Favour of the *Doctor,* till at length he had really talked himself into very good Business, and was employed in the best Families in the *Kingdom.* This so engaged the Attention of the Town in his Favour, that any Objection that was made against him, was imputed to the *Malice* of the *Physicians,* who only envy'd his Success; the Doctor having gained this Length of Rope, gave a full swing to his Practice."

So far as English literature is concerned, Thompson's "Length of Rope" was caught by three distinguished men of letters, Henry Fielding, Tobias Smollett, Samuel Johnson, and at least one lesser figure—Paul Whitehead. Dr. Johnson, in his *Life of Pope,* not unnaturally picked up the

[1] G.S. Rousseau, *Doctors and Medicine in the Novels of Tobias Smollett* (Ph.D. diss., Princeton University, microfilm, 1966), pp. 23-24, refers to many of the ephemerae in this controversy.

[2] This estimate of Thompson is quoted by Rousseau, p. 66, from William Douglas, M.D., *A Second Letter to Dr. Smelle* (London, 1746), pp. 27-28.

same rumors catalogued by Douglas:[3] "Towards the end of his life [Pope] consulted Dr. Thomson, a man who had by large promises and free censure of the common practice of physick, forced himself up into sudden reputation. Thomson declared his distemper to be a dropsy, and evacuated part of the water by tincture of jalap, but confessed that his belly did not subside." He added that "Thomson had many enemies," and—erroneously—"Pope was persuaded to dismiss him." Hawkins' *Life of Johnson* includes a lengthy passage about Thompson:[4] "This gentleman was one of the many physicians, who, in this country, have enjoyed a short-lived reputation, acquired by methods unknown to any but themselves. The earliest of his practice was among men of eminence, Mr. Pope and others; who, deceived by his confidence and a certain contempt with which he ever spoke of the rest of the profession, as being bigotted to theories and systems, looked upon him as a man of inventive genius, who had reduced the art of healing to an epitome. . . . He was an everlasting prater on politics and criticism. . . . At taverns, in coffee-houses, at the cyder cellar in Maiden-lane, he was frequently to be found holding forth on these subjects without interruption, in a tone of voice which, Mr. Garrick would say was like the buzz of an humble-bee in a hall-window."

3 Ed. cit., III. 189.
4 We first noticed this passage in a voluminous nineteenth-century anthology, *Anecdotes of Medical Men*, 3 vols. (London, 1825), III. 60-63. It was taken from *The Life of Samuel Johnson, LL.D. . . . Extended into Two Volumes, and Embellished with 150 Portraits . . .* by Sir John Hawkins, Knt., 2 vols. (London, 1787), pp. 337-39. The passage was omitted, as a digression, in Bertram H. Davis' abridged edition (New York: Macmillan, 1961). Davis includes one passing reference to Thompson in his *Johnson before Boswell* (New Haven: Yale University Press, 1960): Appendix C, p. 193, where Malone's comments on Hawkins' *Life* are reproduced. Referring to the omitted "digression" on "Lord Melcombe's protegés (among whom was Dr. Thom(p)-son)" Malone wrote: "Mentioning that Lord Melcombe [Bubb Dodington] selected his acquaintances, he gives a long character of them, & of all those who were his followers, with whom J. could have been acquainted, had he accepted the invitation, which he did not." No reference to Dr. Thompson appears in the Hill-Powell edition of Boswell's *Life*.

This is followed by the statement that Thompson enjoyed Lord Melcombe's favor, and—more important—"protection from arrests, founded on the privilege which the law grants, not only to peers, but to the lowest of their menial servants"—this in connection with a story told by James Quin, the actor, of an early meeting with Thompson just "rising into practice," who for the "want of fifty pounds" could not secure a coach to go abroad and visit his patients. Quin lent Thompson the money, which he refused to return for many months, under cover of his "protection." That Thompson, in spite of the blood-letting case, maintained his reputation for some time is implied by another statement in the Hawkins' account: "This was the man whom [Paul] Whitehead, in the simplicity of his heart, held in such estimation, that I have seen him, for hours together, listening, with his lips unclosed, to the torrents of nonsense he was pouring forth: he addressed an epistle to him, wherein he celebrates his medical and moral qualities."

From "An Epistle to Dr. Thompson" and even more from the "Life" of its author, Paul Whitehead,[5] many details about Dr. Thompson emerge. The poem was published shortly after the death of Frederick, Prince of Wales, in 1751, another moot medical case, in which Thompson was again associated with and in opposition to Mead, then Physician in Ordinary to the Royal Family. The author indicates that the verses had been written earlier and might have remained in manuscript "had not the physical Persecution carried on against the Gentleman to whom it is addressed, provoked the Publication." There follows a note: "The celebrated Dr. Thompson was one of the Physicians to Frederick, Prince of Wales, in that disorder which ended his life. Upon that occasion, the Doctor differed from all the Physicians that attended his Highness, which brought upon him their most virulent rage and indignation; for the Prince dying, the world was inclined to favour Doctor

[5] *The Poems and Miscellaneous Compositions of Paul Whitehead; with Explanatory Notes on his Writings, and His Life written by Captain Edward Thompson* (London, 1777).

Thompson's recommendations. He was an intimate Friend of Mr. P. Whitehead, and a favourite with him at the Prince's Court. He was a man of peculiar character; but learned, singular, and ingenuous."

According to Whitehead's biographer, Thompson died "about the year 1760, in his 60th year." He would therefore have been about forty-four when he attended Pope. Whitehead and Thompson seem to have been associated as Medmenham Monks at Medmen Abbey, of which Whitehead was Steward.[6] Pope would have at least heard of the "Doctor" through his own association with Frederick, Prince of Wales, in the last years of his own life; Thompson, the Prince's favorite physician, was then in the ascendancy, and it was often a royal gesture to send a court physician to an important person. It is at least conceivable that His Highness was responsible for Thompson's attendance upon Pope.

For all the biographer's defense of Thompson in the "Life" and the high praise of Whitehead in the "Epistle," it is not a pleasant picture that emerges of a doctor who must have seemed obnoxious to gentlemen like Cheselden and Mead. "Although Mr. Whitehead was neither so eccentric or slovenly as the Doctor," writes the biographer, "yet there was a mental participation that proved their souls to be congenial." The biographer continues: "Dr. Thompson was, without doubt, the most whimsical character, as a Scholar, a Wit, and a Gentleman, that I have met with; and, to tell you in small what he might be in great, he never had his shoes cleaned, but bought them at the *Yorkshire* Warehouse, wore them till his toes were through the upper leather, and then shook them off at the same place, and put on a new pair; and this he did with all his other

[6] Louis S. Jones, *The Clubs of the Georgian Rakes* (New York: Columbia University Press, 1942), pp. 122-23, discusses Whitehead and adds: "Dr. Thompson, the quack who had been court physician to Frederick, Prince of Wales, and a member of Bubb Dodington's household, may have been a member and was certainly a frequent guest."

habiliments."[7] He appends "A Recipe for Doctor Thompson," written by Whitehead, various items of which urge him to "avoid the soil" of his linen, and his "rugged ruins of garments," advise him to "forbear to haunt Cooks Shops, Hedge-Alehouses, Cyder-Cellars," and to concentrate upon visits to patients, where he may collect rather than spend money. He advises the doctor always to use a coach on his rounds, rather than to arrive (as apparently he had) at a sick Lady's chamber, bemired to the knees. Here the biographer adds a note:

> Dr. Thompson was a peculiar sloven, and in the practice of a Physician, an utter and declared enemy to Muffins, which he always forbad his patients. Being one day upon a visit to Lord Melcombe, at *Hammersmith,* with Mr. Garrick, Mr. P. Whitehead, &c. the Company was assembled at breakfast long before the Doctor appeared: just as he entered the room, in an uncouth habit, Lord Melcombe uncovered a plate of Muffins, which Thompson fixing his eyes upon, with some indignation said, "My Lord, did I not beseech your Lordship before, never to suffer a Muffin in your house?" To which his Lordship archly replied, "Doctor, I've an utter aversion to Muffins and Raggamuffins." The pleasantry of the turn, at the Doctor's expense, set the table in a roar.[8]

Tobias Smollett began his poetic career under the influence of Pope. Among his earliest works were two Juvenalian satires, *Advice* and *Reproof,* modelled on Pope's *Epilogue to the Satires,* published four years after *The Dunciad.* Like Pope, Smollett referred to many contemporaries by their real names, as in one passage in *Reproof*:[9]

[7] *The Poems of Paul Whitehead*, pp. xlviii-xlix.

[8] *Ibid.,* p. lii.

[9] G.S. Rousseau, *Tobias Smollett,* pp. 65-67, discusses Smollett's references to Thompson, among many doctors, actual, pseudonymous, or fictional, included in his works. The allusion to Mead and Thompson occurs in *Reproof: A Satire,* ll. 187-88, the Barrowby reference in ll. 195-98, in *The Works of Tobias Smollett, M.D.,* ed. John Moore, M.D. (London, J. P. Browne, 1872) , I. 310. See also G.S. Rousseau, pp. 97-101,

Condemn'd by Clark, Banks, Barrowby, and Chitty,
And all the crop-ear'd critics of the city;
While sagely neutral sits thy silent friend,
Alike averse to censure or commend.

Dr. William Barrowby was, like Thompson, a quack well known in coffee-houses and taverns, probably also Smollett's original for Dr. Wagtail in *Roderick Random*. If Dr. Richard Mead ever read *Reproof*, he must have felt wry reminiscence to find his name coupled with that of the "Dunce" who had hastened the death of the author of *The Dunciad*, as Orrery noted in Pope's last letter, and as Smollett must have heard rumored:

From Mead to Th—p–on shifts the palm at once,
A meddling, prating, blund'ring, busy dunce![10]

Of all the men of letters who mentioned Thompson in one way or another, his great admirer was Henry Fielding. The most detailed account of his relations with Thompson is that of Wilbur L. Cross in *The History of Henry Fielding*.[11] Cross first mentioned the physician in an extended discussion of the character of Thomas Winnington. Here he says of Winnington's death: "It was a notorious case of improper treatment by Dr. Thomas Thompson, who subsequently attended Fielding in a serious illness."[12] Thompson would seem to have been among Fielding's medical advisers for some time, since he attended him at least as early as 1749. Fielding characterized him in a long section of

and the same author's forthcoming article, "Smollett's Literary Indebtedness to Pope."

[10] G.S. Rousseau says (p. 65) in his note on the couplet that in the *Present State of all Nations*, Smollett declared that Mead, with Sydenham and Freind, "will always be remembered among the best writers of physic."

[11] 3 vols. (New Haven: Yale University Press, 1918), II. 72, 354, III. 2-24. See also F. Homes Dudden, *Henry Fielding: His Life, Works and Times*, 2 vols. (Oxford: Clarendon Press, 1952), particularly pp. 812-17.

[12] *Ibid.*, II. 72 ff.

Amelia. Cross writes of the alterations made in the second edition of that novel:[13]

> Most curious alterations concern Fielding's eulogies on the physicians whom he counted among his friends. During a severe illness two years before, he had been attended by Dr. Thomas Thompson, who afterwards became his chief medical adviser. Out of gratitude to this man to whom he believed he owed his life, he gave him, perhaps in lieu of a fee, a whole chapter of praise. When one of Booth's children, it is related there, was brought to the point of death by the erroneous treatment of an unnamed physician, the distracted parents summoned Dr. Thompson, who threw all the physic of his predecessors to the dogs, and by simple remedies cured the little patient in three days. Dr. Thompson's remedies also had the same marvellous effect on Sergeant Atkinson after he had been given over by several very good doctors. Happy in the restoration of her husband, Mrs. Atkinson liked to entertain her friends with a humorous account of the sergeant's physicians, always ending however, "with many vast eulogiums on him who came last."

In *Amelia* appeared also Dr. John Raney, "the most eminent surgeon in the kingdom, or perhaps in the world," who had earlier dressed the wounds of the Man of the Hill in *Tom Jones.* Others were mentioned with admiration, among them Dr. Joshua Ward, famous and infamous for his "pill and drop," satirized by Smollett in *Reproof* and in *Peregrine Pickle.*[14] Dr. Robert James was honored by a mention of his "Powder," which Professor Cross says was "destined to shorten the life of Laurence Sterne and to kill Oliver Goldsmith." Because of the protest aroused by these

[13] *Ibid.,* II. 354-56.
[14] G.S. Rousseau, *Tobias Smollett,* Appendix B, gives the "Method of preparing Antimony, for the Pill and Drop," from John Page, *Receipts for Preparing and Compounding the Principal Medicines Made Use of By the late Mr. Ward* (London, 1763), pp. 5-8.

medical vignettes, Fielding reluctantly removed most of
them from the second edition of *Amelia*.

Fielding had suffered the torments of gout and had tried
unnumbered "cures." Professor Cross says: "The gout would
put him to bed, its acute stage would pass with rest, and
he was the old Fielding again." In the autumn of 1749
he was very ill of gout accompanied by a fever. "While the
torments were upon him, he called in Dr. Thomas Thomson," says Cross,[15] and continues: "Though a general practitioner, he claimed most success with gout and smallpox,
on which he wrote treatises.[16] When Fielding's fit of the
gout had run its course, the patient attributed his recovery
not to nature, but to the remedies of Dr. Thompson or
'Dr. Thumpscull,' as Smollett called him. In sheer gratitude, not only did Fielding . . . make him physician to all
the people who fall ill in 'Amelia,' he again recommended
him to the public in 'The Covent-Garden Journal,'
wherein he is extolled for his character and for his skill.
In a suit brought by Thompson against an apothecary for
slanderous words, it is said there, a gentleman declared on
oath before the Chief Justice of England, 'that out of near
fifty persons for whom he had known the Doctor to prescribe, not one had failed while under his hands.' Fielding's
trust in the advice of this ignorant man was most unfortunate. The cure effected by the quack proved to be quite
illusory."[17]

[15] Cross remarks at this point (III. 3) that Thompson had been
physician to Frederick, Prince of Wales, and, when Fielding employed
him, was the medical adviser of the Duke of Roxborough, The Earl
of Middlesex, and other gentlemen of fashion.
[16] Unidentified by Cross these are *An Historical, Critical, and Practical Treatise of the Gout* . . . (London, 1740), and *An Enquiry into
the origin, nature, and cure of the Small-Pox. To which is added, a
prefatory address to Dr. Mead* . . . (London, 1752).
[17] Cross's references here are to *The General Advertiser*, Dec. 28,
1749 and to *The Covent-Garden Journal*, April 18, 1752. The case
referred to is mentioned in *The Political Journal of George Bubb
Dodington*, ed. Carswell and Dralle (Oxford: Clarendon Press, 1965),
p. 152, as an action of defamation brought by Thompson against
Saxon, an apothecary, on April 17, 1752. Evidence of the skill and
reputation of the physician was given by the Duke of Roxborough,

Thompson had been present at the death of Pope, but he was not to attend the deathbed of Fielding, who dismissed him, and as Cross says, "summoned the notorious Dr. Ward," whom we have already mentioned. Fielding's illness, like Pope's, was dropsical asthma, but dropsy was in the ascendant, and for this Ward treated him for some time. Fielding made a short trial of Boerhaave's milk diet, but such regimen was not for him. Then he remembered that last book that Alexander Pope read, Bishop Berkeley's treatise on tar-water, which Fielding had read earlier and kept in his library. Berkeley had learned during his residence in Rhode Island of the cures effected by tar-water and later put it to a test in Ireland. As Professor Cross says: "Berkeley never positively declared that tar-water was the universal medicine that philosophers believed to be existent somewhere in nature, but he apprehended that it might be such. His conjecture was interpreted by the public as a certain conclusion, and thousands of people— the sick and the well—began drinking tar-water."[18] Among them was Fielding, who for a time believed it beneficial. The brief remainder of Fielding's life is an account of attempts to cure dropsy and asthma. Unlike Pope, he was able to leave England and go to the Continent, but even the warmth of Portugal kept him alive only two months and a day. Like Pope before him, he suffered from asthma and dropsy; like him, too, he had been attended for a time by Dr. Thomas Thompson.

---

the Earl of Middlesex, Sir Francis Dashwood, Sir Francis Eyles, Dodington, Mr. Levison, and Mr. Drax. Thompson carried his case and the jury gave him £20 damages. "Dr. Thumpscull" does not appear in a Smollett novel; there is a character of that name in *Habbakkuk Hilding*, a pamphlet of 1752, which has been attributed to Smollett. If Smollett wrote it, he may well have had Thompson in mind, since "Habbakuk" was Fielding whom "Thumpscull" attended.

[18] III. 16.

Index

INDEX

Broxolme, Dr. Noel, 71n, 77
Bruno, Giordano, 148
Burgess, C. F., 29n
Burke, Edmund, 291
Burlington, Earl of (Richard Boyle), 44, 45
Burman, Peter, 250
Burnet, Thomas, 62, 139, 173, 214, 219n
"Burnet Controversy," 139-41
Burton, Robert, 107, 256, 265
Burton, Dr. Simon, 71-74, 77-79
Bussy, Comte de, 152n
Butler, Samuel, 252
Butt, John, 45n, 60, 63n, 178n
Button's coffee-house, 24, 25, 137, 143, 145, 146, 147, 150, 154, 155, 156, 170, 171, 179, 187
Byfield, Thomas, 165

Caesar, Julius, 181
Caius, John, 43n
Cajori, Florian, 222n
Camden, William, 163
camera obscura, 282-85
Carruthers, Robert, 77n
Caryll, John, 22, 23, 24, 26, 27, 36, 39, 41, 42n, 45, 46-50, 65, 110, 112, 135, 137, 141, 144, 145, 147, 148, 149, 155, 156, 160, 167, 177, 178n, 187, 188, 191, 197, 206, 207, 230, 243, 244, 245, 248, 272, 290
Cassini, Jacques, 135
Catullus, 104
Chalmers, Alexander, 258n
Chaucer, Geoffrey, 97, 208, 239
Cheselden, William (surgeon), v, vi, 9, 53, 58-61, 63, 64, 65n, 66, 67, 70-71, 72n, 73, 74, 76, 77, 81, 300
Cheyne, Dr. George, 55, 72
Cibber, Colley, 66, 128, 129, 231
Cicero, Marcus Tullius, 82
Clarke, Samuel, 168, 169
Clark-Kennedy, A. E., 104n, 106
Clayton, Thomas, 151
Clifford, James, viii
Clubb, Louise, 184n
Cobham, Viscount (Sir Richard Temple), 49

Codrington, Lady Elizabeth, 32
Codrington, Sir William, 32, 216
Cohen, I. Bernard, 167n, 222, 268n
Coleridge, Samuel Taylor, 86
collectors, satire on, 252-53
Collier, Katharine B., 139n
color, 233-35, 266, 269-71, 286, 289
comets, 140, 162, 164, 165, 173, 179-82, 184, 185-86, 205n, 277
Conduitt, John, 221
Congreve, William, 155n, 156
Cope, Sir Zachary, viii, 58n, 59n, 65n, 71n
Copernicus, Nicolaus, 133, 194n
"the Copernicus," 158-60, 225
Cotes, Mr., 146n
Cotes, Roger, 146, 168, 169
Courthope, Edwin, 125
Cowper, Judith, 9n, 254
Cowper, William, 7
Cox, Sir R., 178n
Cox, Lady, 32
Cromwell, Henry, 21, 23, 29n, 85, 133, 138, 139, 140, 193
Cross, Wilbur Lucius, 302-305
Cudworth, Ralph, 94
Cunningham, Peter, 259n
Curll, Edmund, 27, 54, 138

Daily Courant, 185
Dale, Mr., 146n
Daniels, Dr. Gilbert, vi
Darwin, Erasmus, 91
Darwin, Francis, 104n, 107
Dashwood, Sir Francis, 305n
David, Bertram H., 50n, 298n
David, Jean-Pierre, 16
Davie, Donald, 203n
De Beer, E. S., 96n
Defoe, Daniel, 120
Dell, Floyd, 256n
Democritus, 107
Denis, Dr. Jean, 90
Dennis, John, 214, 219n
Descartes, René, 94, 98, 100, 194, 199, 200, 205
Des Fontaines, René, 250n
Digby, Robert, 135, 201, 214, 220, 221
Dingley, William, 247

308

INDEX

INDEX